One man's marshes
the Birds of Lymington and Keyhaven

To

Squadron-Leader Norman William (Norrie) Orr (1918–2006) and Robert (Bob) Dunn (1946–2010) who both studied west Solent birds, and local marshmen, past, present and future, of whom Raymond (Foxy) Perrett (1940–1987) of Keyhaven epitomised this place.

December 28th 1821: 'The weather, which has, day after day and week after week, been most hideously abominable, this day came to such a tremendous hurricane that the whole valley could be compared to nothing but the very rage of battle. Keyhaven is no longer a village, but a sea. The tide is so tremendous that the breakers literally rage and foam against the houses, while the incessant rain is pouring in torrents and the whole population here are driven to their attics; no communication from house to house except by boats, which can scarcely live in the sea that washes our doors; and the breakers which are bursting at us, as if threatening to swallow our very houses, present a scene most awfully grand.'

January 27th 1823: 'A sudden and general thaw, with a strong wind and an incessant pour of rain. Nothing could be more novel or beautiful than the appearance of the harbour, which was one solid region of ice, with pyramids formed by the drifted snow and frozen like glass; and on the thaw setting in the whole harbour appeared like a huge floating island as it was carried off by the fall of a high spring tide; and to see this huge movable body in motion with 14 wild swans sitting upon it, as it receded and looking as if formed by nature for the only inhabitants of such a wild region, gave one more the idea of a voyage in the arctic circle than anything belonging to the shore of a habitable country.'

February 2nd 1831: 'A tremendous hurricane, with an overwhelming fall of snow and with the wind south-west. An extraordinary influx of Fieldfares, not less than 20,000 dispersed round Keyhaven and Westover.'

November 13th 1840: 'Keyhaven An awful hurricane and the most alarming flood that ever was known here. About twelve o'clock had just begun a letter to Peter, when I was obliged to throw down my pen and fly in water boots for help to save my property; had I not providentially been here, all my valuable guns, punts and gear might have been ruined. The sea banks burst and the water was soon a foot deep in all the lower rooms of the houses and such was the torrent against the doors that, had they burst open, as we every moment dreaded, our house must have been swamped.'

The Diary of Colonel Peter Hawker published in 1893

Introduction

Depending upon one's particular passions, the very names of Keyhaven and Lymington, will at once conjure-up a variety of associations in minds' eyes. To archaeologists, the past importance of this coast as a major locality for the production of salt, by combinations of seawater evaporation and brine boiling, will immediately come to mind. To dinghy, small boat and yacht enthusiasts, they will evoke memories of long, hot summer days spent afloat on The Solent and perhaps, when compounded by a diminishing breeze and rapidly ebbing spring tide, that slow and tortuous return passage into the river at the end of the day. Wildfowlers and shooting men worldwide will know of Keyhaven through the evocative writings of Colonel Peter Hawker. To the local marshmen and fishermen, Keyhaven and Lymington Rivers, sheltered as they are by the great hook of Hurst Spit and the saltmarshes, provide safe anchorages for their dinghies, punts and larger commercial fishing vessels. Yet again, to naturalists, the area has long held a reputation as a botanical and ornithological site of immense interest and importance.

Attention to the bird-life of the Keyhaven/Lymington coast is no new phenomenon. Long before bird-study for pleasure, relaxation or for scientific reasons became a popular pursuit, local marshmen were amassing knowledge of the comings and goings of waterfowl. The duck, geese and wading birds that frequented The Solent provided both a source of food and winter income, when perhaps alternative paid employment was scarce and difficult to obtain. It was therefore desirable that fishermen and agricultural workers of the west Solent hamlets and villages were acquainted, at least in some degree, with waterfowl, their habits and migrations. Wildfowling skills would have passed from father to son and fiercely independent descendants of those hardy individuals reside in the district to this day. The gunning-punt, as opposed to the shorter, higher-sided canoe, from which the fowler usually shot with a shoulder gun, was probably developed on the Hampshire coast at the turn of the nineteenth century (Marchington 1980).

The Keyhaven/Lymington shore, more by luck than judgement, escaped the industrialisation and disfigurement suffered by much of Hampshire's coastline. The first half of the nineteenth century softened the scarring of decades of intensive salt-production, but other large-scale enterprises were afoot. In the 1850s, a massive dock development, to be situated between the west bank of the Lymington River and Pennington Lake and intended to rival that of Southampton, failed through lack of finance. Other grandiose schemes, such as a railway link across Keyhaven Marshes, together with a tunnel to the Isle of Wight, as well as another for docks and quays to accommodate ocean-going liners at Keyhaven, also foundered. Advent of the railway to Lymington in 1858, the town's subsequent growing popularity as a yachting and boat building centre, however, sparked an era of growth in the maritime leisure business.

Two World Wars concentrated minds elsewhere for much of the first half of the twentieth century. Hurst Spit and the Keyhaven area, much of which was previously out-of-bounds to all but the armed services, once more became available for recreational purposes during the second half of the 1940s. At the same time, renewed development proposals were again on the agenda, but fortunately, those which involved gravel-extraction and yacht marina facilities at Keyhaven, were unsuccessful. Had they been implemented they would have destroyed not only the site of the substantial 'High Lea' eighteenth-century saltworks, but also important wildlife habitats. One has only to stand on the harbour seawall at low water and observe the many hundreds of wading birds and wildfowl that feed at close range, to comprehend the scale of destruction and loss had the marina proposal succeeded. A major ornithological site, as well as one of great amenity and much enjoyed and appreciated by countless thousands of people, would have been destroyed for all time.

Much of west Solent's coastline between Keyhaven and Lymington remained undeveloped until well into the 1950s. Fuelled by post-war prosperity, our shores became increasingly accessible during the second half of the twentieth century and vulnerable to proposals for yacht marinas, other water-based facilities and light industry. At the same time, twin needs for gravel and landfill sites exerted additional pressures on west Solent habitats and their dependent animal and plant communities. Spearheaded by one or two enlightened individuals, Hampshire County Council, whose planners were wrestling with conflicting demands of conservationists and developers, instigated a determined programme of coastal land acquisition in the early 1970s. Increasingly effective planning policy, coupled with improved international and European legislation, also afforded coastal areas much needed protection from unsympathetic development, though damage and loss occurred to adjacent non-designated land between Keyhaven and Lymington

Looking towards Hurst Castle from Keyhaven. PRD

What does the future hold for our estuaries and marshes? Already this coast is within an hour's car-drive of at least one million people and pressures on land for housing and onshore and offshore leisure facilities do not diminish. Furthermore, because of rising sea level and Cordgrass dieback, the Keyhaven/Lymington saltmarshes are undergoing coastal squeeze. Due to necessity to protect the Manor Farm domestic-waste disposal site from seawater incursion, it is imperative that the Keyhaven Marshes' seawall be maintained in the foreseeable future. Though the area Shoreline Management Plan's advocated policy is one of 'holding the line', it may prove uneconomical to maintain the entire length of the Keyhaven/Lymington sea defences in their current positions. In the wake of updated landfill restoration legislation, Manor Farm underwent much alien, ground-profile modification that rendered, for the foreseeable future, much of that area unsuited to 'managed re-alignment', a key coastal nature conservation aspiration. This, however, is not irreversible and with the possibility of a return to pre-gravel extraction landforms, Manor Farm may once again play a comprehensive role in maintaining west Hampshire coastal bird populations. One advantage of the current situation, should it be necessary to withdraw the current sea defences, would be that clay, used to line and cap waste-containing cells, would be close at hand and available as fill for new or re-aligned seawalls.

Hampshire & Isle of Wight Wildlife Trust has already commissioned Solent coastal ornithological surveys to determine possible relocation sites to accommodate feeding and roosting waders and wildfowl, as and when these become necessary. It is also imperative that prior to withdrawal of sea defence lines, comprehensive study and recording of saltworks features be undertaken. National Park Authority initiatives are already underway and archaeological excavations have taken place around remaining Lower Woodside saltworks buildings. Difficult decisions can only be taken if and when we are in receipt of adequate, up-to-date information. Such decisions will not be based solely on nature conservation requirements; the effect of increasing wave attack on coastal settlements' sea defences, with associated increasing flood risk, must also be taken into account.

Many of our most treasured landscapes are blemished. The NW Solent is no exception. Though I appreciated that difficult decisions had to be taken, the defunct Pennington Marshes' Rubbish Tip, Manor Farm's gravel extraction and landfill site and Lymington Yacht Haven are the most damaging and intrusive developments imposed upon this coastal landscape during the last five decades. Nevertheless, it is my fervent wish and hope that, not only the marshes be held in perpetuity as nature reserves, but that they are maintained as informally as possible. This will be no simple task and constant vigilance will be necessary to combat even unbelievably naive ideas, eg 'Port Pennington', a proposal to relocate the Lymington–Yarmouth Ferry terminal to Pennington Marshes' foreshore. No one wishes to see industrialisation of the area, or it closed to public access, but neither should it be allowed to deteriorate into a theme park; such facilities are available elsewhere. But already there are indications that increasingly large numbers of visitors and recreational activities are overwhelming the Site of Special Scientific Interest and wildlife is suffering. For instance, canoes and kayaks facilitate access into the shallowest creek, which now takes place at all hours of the night and day. Kite-surfing is also practised within the intertidal zone. Both cause much additional and unnecessary disturbance to the breeding birds in spring and summer and to wildfowl in autumn and winter. I say 'additional and unnecessary disturbance' as bird populations are often subject to disturbance, eg by low-flying aircraft, hunting birds-of-prey and it must be said, by birdwatchers. Similarly, large numbers of sea-anglers from as far afield as Wales, sometimes resort to overnight fishing on the important shingle banks and saltings, albeit highlighted by notice boards requesting 'no landing' during the birds' nesting season. The rocketing value of shore cottages and their sale to wealthy newcomers, often result in enlargement or replacement planning proposals, both of which have potentially devastating impacts upon the environment.

The marshes at dusk. MW

The marshes have always been held very dear and close to the hearts of local people. Not only has the area provided a livelihood for those living close-by, but also a healthy environment in which to raise their families and to spend their leisure hours. Here, they learned to swim, fish, handle boats under oar, sail or motor power, watch wildlife or walk the seawalls or 'the banks', by which they are affectionately known. The local community, as well as incomers and visitors, cherish this relatively unspoilt coast and marsh atmosphere and wish it to remain so. These are facts that all would-be managers of these marshlands would do well to acknowledge and to respect.

Though the area continues to exude an air of tranquillity, those residing close to the shore are constantly aware of nature's potential power and ultimate dominance. This was particularly evident during recently experienced extreme storm conditions during the winter of 2013/14, when the sea threatened to overwhelm Hurst Spit and the seawalls and engulf the coastal communities.

Little Tern

Sowley

Pitts Deep

Pylewell

Tanners Lane

Lisle Court

Lymington

Bulls Saltern

Pylewell Lake

Normandy
Marshes

Normandy Farm Lagoon

Eight Acre Pond

Salterns
Marshes

Salterns Lagoon

Oxey
Marshes

Moses Dock

Oxey Lagoon

Hampshire County Council
Lymington-Keyhaven Reserve

Pennington Lagoon

Pennington
Marshes

Jetty Lagoon

Butts Lagoon

Fishtail Lagoon

Keyhaven Lagoon

The Solent

Avon Water

Keyhaven
Marshes

Hampshire & Isle of Wight
Wildlife Trust Reserve

Keyhaven

Hawker's Lake

Milford
-on-Sea

Sturt Pond

Cut Bridge

Mount Lake

Hurst Castle

Hurst Spit

N

Lymington–Keyhaven from above

Looking east towards Pylewell. Normandy Farm Lagoon in foreground. GB

Looking west across Normandy Farm Lagoon to Oxey Marshes and Moses Dock. GB

Looking south-west across Moses Dock to Pennington Marshes. GB

Looking north-east across Pennington Marshes. GB

Looking south-west towards Hurst Castle and The Needles. Old Pennington Tip in foreground GB

Looking south-west. Part of the HIWWT reserve and Hawkers Lake in the foreground. GB

17

Looking west. Keyhaven - mid distance. Sturt Pond - far distance. GB

Looking east across The Lymington-Keyhaven reserves. GB

A site history

The Lymington salt industry

Salt played an important role in the lives of past communities. Other than its more obvious use in cooking and the preservation of food, which became more important as man changed from being a hunter to a farmer, other processes that included tanning of animal hides, cloth dyeing and as medicine, were also of vital importance; however, in some primitive communities, salt was considered a poison and dangerous to heath (Gouletquer 1974). For those who lived close to suitable stretches of coastline, by estuaries or the tidal reaches of rivers, seawater was an obvious source of supply. The salt-extraction process developed around the coasts of Europe where conditions proved to be favourable. In more northerly climes there was also the need for an abundant supply of fuel, which was necessary to provide heat for the final stage of salt-crystal production. The development of these processes over hundreds of years, led to a thriving industry in the Keyhaven/Lymington area, before it eventually went into decline and disappeared in the face of competition from inland salt production.

Salt making was probably practised in the Keyhaven/Lymington area long before its earliest documented reference in the Domesday Book of 1086. For instance, salt was regarded as a highly prestigious commodity during the Iron Age and evidence for Roman occupation has also been found close to the grazing marshes' boundary. Those salinae mentioned in Domesday were located at Hordle. That parish included Hurst Spit until the middle of the nineteenth century, so it was likely that they were located in the lee of the Spit, as shown on a Milford estate map dated 1720, though the area is now under the sea, off the west side of the Spit.

It is open to conjecture as to the area of marsh under salt production in the early 1600s. However, as shown on the 1811 Ordnance Survey map, it apparently encompassed much of the embanked land to which the high tides flowed. Documented evidence recorded the names of many individual salterns, eg The Pans and High Lea (Keyhaven/Keyhaven Marshes), Eight Pans or East Works, Cole's and Great Bridge, West Work and Little Bridge (Pennington Marshes), Oxey, Little Oxey, Viney's, Troy Town or Seven Pans (Oxey Marshes), Hibbert's, Great Oxey and Flatform (Oxey Marshes/Oxey Barn), Stone and Rowe (Salterns), King's Saltern (Waterford), Vienna Saltern (south of Lymington Bridge), Studley's Saltern (Walhampton) and Bulls Saltern (Lisle Court).

Edward King in *Old Times Revisited* recorded that the marshes were gradually given over to agriculture. 'The marshes were then, by degrees, more or less levelled, so as to render them useful for grazing grounds; the old houses were all removed and the ponds filled up; yet slight traces here and there exist.' It is true most salt buildings were demolished, presumably as much for their valuable building materials as other reasons and individual salterns were undoubtedly 'levelled and their ponds filled up.' Two fields extending over an area of some 16 ha at Oxey Barn (Lower Woodside) are prime examples. We know from the Lymington Tithe map of 1842 that at least four individual salterns occupied this site. Other than a series of banks in the south-west corner, close to where Troy Town saltern was situated, little evidence of those salterns remain above ground. King was probably referring specifically to salterns within the parish and thus closest to Lymington, but I cannot agree there are 'few' remains of the once flourishing salt industry between there and Keyhaven. Considerably more than 'slight traces' of the infrastructure are still to be found on the marshes.

One item of particular interest mentioned by King is that concerning the Lymington Brine Shrimp, 'first noticed by a Dr Maty about 1740.' Tubbs (1999) speculated on the source of King's information, as the first scientific description of this creature was accredited to Schlosser, who observed them in the Lymington saltpans some 15 years later. However, we now know that an unknown Persian geographer mentioned brine shrimps in 982 (Asem 2008).

There is little remaining visual evidence of salterns on Normandy Farm, but the impressive Normandy Dock, similar in scale to that of Moses Dock, which separate Oxey Marshes and Salterns, presumably also served the salterns situated on the north shore of Harper's Lake. It is possible that the present-day farm buildings, as well as 'Sandpipers', the property standing at the head of the Dock in Normandy Lane, were sites of boiling-houses and other infrastructure. A cottage that was situated south-east of the Normandy Farm buildings and featured on the Lymington Tithe Map of 1842, was possibly a former salt-worker's dwelling.

The marshes continued to be worked for salt throughout the eighteenth and into the nineteenth centuries. At the turn of the 1800s, however, the industry was in steep decline and the change to a predominately agricultural regime well under way. For hundreds of years the salterns' lands had been in the ownership of many individuals. The vagaries of weather and economic climates had gradually taken their toll and by 1845, with one exception, the industry was dead. By that time the majority of salterns were in the hands of the local St. Barbe banking family, with the Stone and Rowe works the only one still in operation; by 1865, it too had ceased production. The marshes then entered a phase of agricultural enterprise that remains an essential element of present-day management.

Upper reaches of Moses Dock with Creek Cottage and boat 'So Long' owned by Norman Rickman, former local reed-cutter. c. 2000. WW
The only remaining salt barns and Creek Cottage. GB

At its height the Lymington salt industry created a scene far removed from the relative tranquillity we now take for granted. King wrote 'Individual salterns with attendant wind pumps, boiling houses, storehouses, ancillary buildings, coal and clinker dumps, extended along the coast from Hurst Spit to Lymington and beyond. A pall of smoke emanating from dozens of furnaces hung over the coast and roads all around were black with coal-ashes from the furnaces, which had for generations been incessantly burning.

Hurst Spit and its protection

Stability of Hurst Spit is paramount to the continuation of the viability of the NW Solent settlements, including the hamlet of Keyhaven, the mudflats, seawall and grazing marshes. The Spit, of which the second youngest recurve, was formed 4500 years BP (Nicholls & Webber 1987) to 3000 years BP (West 1980) extends 3 km into the west Solent beyond the village of Milford-on-Sea. Three relic spits, aligned in a northerly direction, are encountered before the principal spread of shingle, upon which is situated Hurst Castle, the lighthouse and two cottages, is reached. The Castle's round inner keep is of Tudor origin, but much of the fortification was added during the nineteenth century. Jude James, an eminent local historian, has thoroughly researched the Spit's history (James 1986). I have drawn heavily on that scholarly work (which should be read or consulted by all those with an interest in Hurst Castle and the Spit) for much of the following résumé. His evidence shows that in addition to the Army garrison, a substantial community, which included Customs House officials and fishermen, resided at Hurst from at least the late-seventeenth century. The population was augmented in 1786 by the arrival of two newly appointed lighthouse keepers (and their families) to man the newly commissioned Hurst Light (later known as the Low Light) built just west of the Castle. National population censuses of 1841 and 1851 (but which excluded the Hurst garrison) revealed 55 and 53 residents respectively. By the time of the 1861 census, the total population of 163, the all-time maximum, included 28 children under 14, two men who operated the new telegraph station and 40 others engaged on defence construction and housed in temporary accommodation.

Earliest documents revealed that the Spit once belonged to the Manor of Hordle. In the early 1800s, the Board of Ordnance, which was responsible for Hurst Castle, contested ownership of adjacent land. The government's concern at that time was hastened by an impending sale of two buildings, the Shipwrights Arms and a herring shed, both situated close to the Castle's north walls. In the event the Board was unable to prevent the sale; the 'Arms' was sold to a Lymington man and Mr Ives, Lord of the Manor of Hordle, bought the herring store. Successive changes in ownership of Hordle Manor precipitated renewed correspondence between the two antagonists. Mr Joseph Guy, who purchased the Manor in 1810, appears to have been a co-operative man, as he later approved the positions of boundary markers around castle lands claimed by the government. However, that was not the end of the matter and a future Lord of the Manor, Mr Thomas Legh, a Cheshire businessman who became the owner in 1832, was to prove a more formidable opponent. Within a short while his solicitors were instructed to re-open the boundary issue previously approved by Mr Guy. The Board's response was leisurely to say the least. In order to amass evidence to counter Legh's impositions, it finally ordered a survey of the Spit, seven or eight years later. At this stage, Legh announced plans for substantial development at Hurst and along the Spit. These included the manufacture of asphalt, for which a large building, later to become the New Inn, was constructed on the east side of the Camber.
He also planned a coal depot on the Spit, a tram road to Milford, Keyhaven and Hordle and cottages for summer letting. Protracted claims and counter-claims between Legh and the Crown were to follow. Finally, at Winchester Assizes in 1840, a jury upheld Legh's assertions that he owned Hurst Spit and land up to, but excluding, that upon which the Castle stood. It was also ruled that agreement on the positions of boundary markers, previously approved by Mr Guy, was of no relevance to the case. Fortunately, other enterprises dreamed up by Legh, which necessitated acquisition of Crown mud-lands between Hurst and the mainland, also came to nothing. Legh finally relented on the boundary issue and by 1845 had agreed the sale of 35 acres of land that included five buildings and three gardens adjacent to the Castle, to the Board of Ordnance.

Hurst Castle continued to be considered of great military significance throughout the nineteenth century. Ongoing improvements and updating of armaments culminated in the building of the Castle's massive east and west wings between 1861 and 1870 and garrisoned in April 1871 with 57 officers and men. The Castle continued to be manned throughout the late 1800s, with 131 officers and men in 1891, but which fell to 61 in 1901. Only a small force then remained on station during the 1914–18 and 1939/45 World Wars and until 1956. In spite of a rapidly declining civilian population and closure in 1905 of Hurst's schoolroom, amid controversy concerning ill treatment of a pupil, Jude James was still able to portray a vivid account of life on the Spit in the early 1900s. The children then attended Milford school that necessitated a daily journey by rowing boat to Keyhaven and a mile-long walk to Manor Road. When late, the Hurst spokesman would explain this was due to 'headwind and tide sir.'

During the nineteenth century, many buildings were situated to the north of Hurst Castle. These were: barracks inside a mud battery (part of which survives outside the west wing of the Castle), coastguard buildings, two low lights, an electric telegraph station, the Shipwrights Arms, a storehouse, a block of married quarters, the New Inn, later serving as officers' quarters, the Round House (also known as Crusoe's Cottage), two cottages within the High Light boundary, the original High Light, two additional cottages north of the Light, a group of coastguard cottages with adjacent boathouse and the Castle Inn and lodging house. Other than the High Light with its attendant cottage and the Castle custodian's dwelling, the only buildings left standing outside the Castle walls in the mid-1980s were the very dilapidated coastguard cottages and the ruins of the Castle Inn, all of which were demolished by Hampshire County Council in 1984.

Hurst Castle Sailing Club's race starting-box was erected on the north point of Hurst in the late 1940s. Standing for more than sixty years, it was destroyed by storm-force winds in January 2014. Also dating from the 1940s, an adjacent semi-circular concrete base is all that remains of the 'Half Boat', donated by Bill Adams of Keyhaven following destruction of the original hut during the Second World War. Originally a ship's lifeboat, which was sawn across the beam, it was erected on end and cemented into the shingle for use as a wet-weather shelter for Hurst Castle Sailing Club's officers. Fitted with an internal thwart, it also doubled as protection during inclement weather for a generation of sea-anglers and birdwatchers, before its destruction by vandals in 1968. At that time the shingle spit extended no more than fifty metres beyond the starting-box. Today it is several hundreds of metres in length and threatens to close-off Keyhaven River mouth, should not New Forest District Council periodically dredge away the shingle accumulation, to provide material to strengthen vulnerable spots elsewhere on the Spit.

Hurst Spit was traditionally maintained by longshore drift, the easterly movement of sediment washed away from cliffs to the west of Milford; many references indicated that the Spit was vulnerable to wave attack over a very long period. As early as 1608 it was deemed necessary to strengthen the beach in front of the Castle, when '300 tons of timber was required to reinforce the beach with piles and groyning work' (James 1986). The savage storm of 26 November 1703 that resulted in the destruction of most of England's windmills and so graphically described by Daniel Defoe in 1705, was considered to have had a dramatic effect on Hurst Spit (West 1980) and major defence works to the south of the Castle were carried out in 1710. Furthermore, Dr K F Sawyer (1982) recorded that of a total of 16 salterns, ten in the vicinity of the Spit and Keyhaven/Pennington Marshes, went out of production between 1779 and 1789. He concluded that the sea overwhelmed them, following breaching of the Spit during savage storm conditions.

Hawker documents a number of very severe gales during the first half of the nineteenth century, eg those of 28 December 1821, 2 February 1831, 29 November 1836 and during 13–18 November 1840. Only the storm of 1836 appeared to have breached the Spit, but Hawker, commenting on that of 18 November 1840, wrote 'so furious was the sea last night that it came over the beach and spray flew to the top of the lighthouse.' He didn't have a great deal to say of the hurricane and storm-surge of November 1824, as he was seriously ill for much of that month and absent from Keyhaven. However, he mentioned the event as he received information that 'his house at Keyhaven was inundated by another tremendous flood; the chimney had fallen through the roof by the late tremendous gale; the house and everything round completely inundated and severely damaged.' The famous geologist, Sir Charles Lyell, then living in the New Forest, wrote, sic: 'Hurst-Castle Bank – The entrance of the channel called the Solent is becoming broader by the waste of cliffs in Colwell Bay; ... it is crossed for more than

Hurst Lighthouse and kidney vetch. PRD

23

two thirds by the shingle bank of Hurst Castle, which is about seventy yards wide and twelve feet high ...' He continued 'Storm of Nov 1824 – In the great storm of November 1824 this bank of shingle was moved bodily forward for forty yards towards the north-east; and certain piles which served to mark the boundaries of two manors were found after the storm, on the opposite side of the bar. At the same time many acres of pasture-land were covered by shingle, on the farm at Westover, near Lymington' (Lyell 1835).

It was recognised in the early nineteenth century that the lighthouse, which was erected to the west of the Castle in 1786, was also under threat of encroachment from the sea. Accordingly, Trinity House authorised construction of a breakwater in 1809, though 'it is not clear from the surviving documents whether the construction of this groyning was actually executed' (James 1986).

There was more recent concern for the stability of the Castle, where the sea was gradually eroding shingle from the base of its west wall, but the Spit, though over-topped, was not breached until 1954. Consequently, a substantial groyning scheme was undertaken around the west side of the Castle and to the base of the Spit in the early 1960s. Stacks of massive wooden piles and revetment timber planking that were stored for a while at Cut Bridge, provided shelter from westerly storms, for the small group of friends, who regularly watched the area in those days. The new groynes, however, were badly damaged during subsequent gales, particularly those of January 1962. Rock armouring was installed at Milford-on-Sea in 1965/66, but the Spit was breached southwards of the Milford works on several occasions between 1973 and 1983 (Mackintosh 1984).

Subsequently, the viability of the entire Spit was of great concern. The principal causes for the deterioration were considered to be extensive shingle-trapping schemes that were initiated over many decades by authorities west of the Spit, compounded by sea-level rise and increasing wave attack. Increasing degradation culminated in further severe damage in February 1979, October 1987 and December 1989. During hurricane-force winds in October 1987 the Spit was again rolled back, in places by as much as 60 m, the crest flattened throughout its entire length and the bank breached in several places. Additionally, the storm of late 1989 severely damaged the Keyhaven/Lymington seawall in a dozen places and resulted in flooding of the coastal marshes and adjacent properties, with several feet of salt water. This was exacerbated by fresh water back-up that accumulated behind the outfall closure-flaps during high-tide periods. In 1990, New Forest District Council initiated major beach replenishment, which coupled with additional seaward rock revetment with thousands of tons of Norwegian granite blocks, succeeded in stabilising the Spit. Effects of storm damage and subsequent re-nourishment, however, resulted in Spit re-alignment. In the 1960s, much of the beach was convex on its seaward side; it is now almost straight or even concave in places.

Dual effects of continuing sea-level rise and wave attack on the Spit and neighbouring saltmarshes were subjects of detailed research, headed for many years by Professor Andrew Bradbury of New Forest District Council. Unfortunately, the downside of stabilisation was an increasing artificial look and feel to the Spit and loss of wildness and remoteness, accelerated by increasing numbers of visitors, on foot and by boat.

Keyhaven

Keyhaven is reputed to mean 'harbour where cows are shipped.' Garrow described it as 'a small detached village, the tenements are chiefly occupied by labourers and poor fishermen whose dependency solely rests upon the families around. There are, however, several genteel residences, which are retired and most pleasantly situated; among which is Auberry House, Sir James Gardiner, Bart.; Keyhaven Cottage, Colonel Hawker, Salt Grass, C. Gordon. Esq.; and Vidley Van, Mr B. Hicks. Here is a small salmon fishery, the property of the last gentleman and a long extent of fine rich pasture, on which some good cattle are raised.'

At that time the Keyhaven shoreline was somewhat different from that of today. Drawings, from which the 1810 Ordnance Survey map was produced, depicted the high-tide mark following a line close to

Saltgrass Lane. The harbour, therefore, was smaller and less sheltered than now. It is unclear when the outer wall was built. Hawker made no mention of it, but it featured on a map of 1867, so was presumably constructed between 1853 and 1867? Interestingly, an area of shingle on Iley Point and well shown on a 1924 aerial photograph, was identified by my wife as possibly a relic spit.

Prior to the 1920s, Keyhaven was known to few of the sailing fraternity. Bill Adams, the boatyard owner, founded the Keyhaven Yacht Club in 1928. The Club's original tin-constructed clubhouse was situated on the east bank of the harbour, adjacent to what is now Iley Point House. It was upgraded to a timbered building in 1935, dismantled in 1949 and re-assembled on its present site on the harbour's west bank. Meanwhile, Hurst Castle Sailing Club was formed in 1938; its Keyhaven premises, constructed in 1949, were recently demolished and rebuilt.

Other than Bill Adam's boatyard, the few properties on the east side of Keyhaven Harbour consisted of a bungalow (now replaced by Iley Point House), Faraway, Gorselands, also known as Gorsepatch (Tazeena Firth pers. comm.) and Saltmarsh and Lyndon (two bungalows dating from the mid-1930s); the hamlet remained relatively unscathed until well after the Second World War. Mary Trehearne's description of the area opposite The Gun Inn illustrated the informality of the village in the 1950s, ie 'The construction of a car-park alongside the two yacht clubs finally sealed in a marshy lake of rubbish, an informal tip where Water Rails took cover in the sedges among rusty bicycle wheels and old tin cans.'

But changes were afoot and Harewood House, still in a ruined state in the late 1950s, together with its large garden, was re-developed and renamed Harewood Green. Flat-roofed and of incongruous appearance at close range, the properties, nonetheless, sit comfortably in the landscape and are relatively inconspicuous at greater distances.

The grazing marshes

Early seawalls were probably primarily constructed within and across salt marshes as defence against rising sea-levels, but those on the west Solent were more likely to have been constructed for salt production and agriculture (Tubbs 1999). Modern maps show that the line of the Keyhaven/Lymington seawall has not altered to any great extent since the 1700s. Exceptions were major reclamation works at Normandy Farm in about 1830, re-alignment south of Saltgrass Lane and to a section eastwards of Pennington Marshes' Butts, following storm-damage in the early 1930s.

Garrow referred to drainage of the marshes. 'Over Keyhaven Bridge is a footway intersecting the salt marshes, which eventually leads to Pennington and Woodside; but the latter are so encumbered with disused salt pans and so many pits and dykes present themselves in almost every direction of them, that it affords a tedious walk by day and is a dangerous course to pursue at night. Lately however, Mr Dennet has drained a great part of this marsh contiguous to Keyhaven, at very great expense; it now forms a part of his farm. It now affords, at seasons, a dry and sweet pasture for sheep, horses etc and will, it is to be hoped, in the course of time, repay him for the pains he has taken to redeem it from the general waste. On Cole's Saltern, better known by the name of Eight Pans, is a large waste piece of ground covered with furze, whereon are an abundance of rabbits; it is the property of Charles St. Barbe, Esq.'

Thus, we have evidence that at the turn of the nineteenth century, Pennington Marshes already resembled the present-day scene. Hawker made no reference to the defunct salterns inside the seawalls, though when obliged to leave his gunning-punt at Pennington/Oxey Marshes during inclement weather, his accounts of night marches to Keyhaven accord well with Garrow's description of the terrain.

Lymington Golf Club was formed in 1893. Its 'links' on Oxey Marshes were apparently completely covered with Marsh Samphire until 1916. On Sunday 5 November of that year, a great storm swept away much of the embankment leaving behind muddy silt. Grass gradually replaced the Samphire before being invaded by a Kentish perennial clover. The resulting sward, after being cut and rolled, was later exploited for bowling-green turfs (Jones 1930). Much of the sward on Pennington/Oxey Marshes remained in a similar condition for many years and I recall that turf cutting still took place there during the mid–late 1950s. Little evidence of the golf links now remain, though a group of concrete blocks immediately west of the Oxey Marsh access track, possibly formed a support-base for the club's premises.

It can be seen from early maps that in the early 1800s, Normandy was about only half the area of today's Farm; its outer seawall followed the line of the present-day prominent scrub-belt. The outer section was reclaimed at the beginning of the industrial revolution in about 1830, during a period of farming prosperity (Tubbs 1999). Present-day agricultural buildings in the centre of the grazed meadows almost certainly date from the nineteenth century, though some bricks are possibly of an earlier age.

Percy Jones also alluded to the Lymington salt industry. He wrote 'in 1871 there were still two salterns standing and two windmills; but the latter were demolished in 1873.' He presumably referred to buildings and windmills that stood at the head of Moses Dock. Salterns estate that included Salterns house and Maiden and Creek Cottages, was in the ownership of the Ouvry family from the late 1800s. With the exception of Maiden and Creek Cottages, Major James Anthony (Tony) Hibbert MC MBE, a Second World War veteran of Dunkirk and Arnhem, became the new owner in 1957 and rebuilt the house in a bungalow style. He developed an oyster fishery, which necessitated deepening Eight Acre Pond, drag-lining away old salterns banks, installing sluices and culverts and modifying Saltern's pools and lagoons; he also founded the Salterns Sailing Club.

Creek Cottage, Salterns Marshes. PRD

A C G Crawford, of Ordnance Survey, who took a series of fine aerial photographs of the marshes in the early 1920s, was a pioneer of that archaeological technique. They are particularly interesting in that they show the area before development of Iley Point. The Marsh Road, a simple, un-surfaced track in those days, deviated onto Manor Farm, then rejoined its current line, immediately west of the defunct Pennington Marshes rubbish tip. A significant slice of that area to the north of the track was presumably under salt production during the industry's heyday. Second World War aerial photographs by both British and German Air Forces, a large selection of which can be viewed at Swindon's National Monument Record office, are as valuable and interesting as those taken by Crawford.

Modified from salt production to a predominately agricultural regime, the grazing marshes remained a single intact parcel of low-lying land until well into the 1950s. At that time Lymington Borough Council was obliged to acquire much of Pennington Marshes to enable disposal of the area's domestic waste. Other than anecdotal evidence, there appears to be little information on early agricultural practices, but it was reputed that Keyhaven/Oxey Marshes, then owned by New Forest commoner George Harris, were often grazed by 'hundreds' of horses and cattle: Saltern's marshes were grazed until about 1960 (Tony Hibbert pers. comm.). Rabbits also inhibited the growth of marsh vegetation until myxamotosis, introduced into Britain in the early 1950s, decimated their populations. Interestingly, I recorded not a single Rabbit (only Hares) on Normandy Farm during 1973–2001. More recently, Roe Deer became a regular sight on the marshes and in fields bordering the shore.

Twentieth-century shellfish ponds, on the site of possible nineteenth-century fish or salt ponds. Salterns Marsh. PRD

Some lagoons situated immediately landwards of the seawall have undergone considerable change in character since the mid-1990s. Due probably to a combination of factors, some of which were outside man's control, those between Iley Point and the Pennington Marshes sewage outfall were most affected. During the latter half of the twentieth century, water levels and salinities greatly fluctuated; in spells of drought, they became highly saline and virtually non-existent. Conversely, since the mid-1990s, they have exhibited relatively low salinity, high and stable water levels. Accordingly, the vegetation has considerably altered, eg an edging of short Cordgrass (*Spartina*) on the Butts lagoon during the 1960s/1970s, developed into a Common Reed (*Phragmites*) and rush-dominated marsh. A combination of factors contributed, eg up-dated Manor Farm landfill regulations that resulted in discharge of greater volumes of freshwater onto the marshes, probable groundwater interruption, the seawall rebuild that prevented seawater ingress into the lagoons and rising sea-levels that resulted in accumulations of mud, shingle and debris against the outer flaps on water outflows. Net results were positive for birds but negative for the rare animals and plants, for which The Solent and Isle of Wight Special Area of Conservation (SAC) was designated. However, a thorough survey of the coastal lagoons between Keyhaven and Lisle Court (Bamber & Robbins 2010) concluded that Keyhaven Lagoon had, to some extent, recovered its previous saline status.

A sense of remoteness on the marshes was probably at an optimum at the turn of the twentieth century. The salt industry had been long dead, most of the buildings had been removed and nature had healed much of the scarring. However, Pennington Marshes' rifle butts, though probably in use during 1914–1918, presumably dated from an earlier age. Also, during 1940–1945, the marshes became sites for gun emplacements, bomb decoys and other infrastructure.

Aubrey, Carrington, Vidle Van and Manor Farms

As with much of Hampshire's farmland, Aubrey, Vidle Van, Carrington and Lower Pennington's Manor Farm, were made over to more productive regimes during and following the Second World War. The net result was loss of a substantial acreage of pasture and low-lying rough grazings, which was detrimental to wildlife populations. Also, in the early 1960s, a formerly wet area on Vidle Van Farm was subject to a major drainage scheme. A small brick building that housed the pumping unit remains, but the field on the west side of the River, now known among birdwatchers as 'Avon Water flood', became a first-class site for breeding, passage and wintering waterfowl. However, birdwatchers should be aware that this privately owned area is out-of-bounds, though much is viewable from the road skirting the north end of Keyhaven harbour.

Pressures on land immediately north of Pennington Marshes also increased. A relatively small area of land abutting Lower Pennington Lane, changed hands in the 1990s. A planning application to allow re-development of a small bungalow that formerly housed a farm-worker was approved. A large property and ancillary outbuildings soon materialised, followed by enlargement of an adjacent, low-key, caravan site. Within a decade, an out-of-character and over-illuminated complex that included additional seasonal caravanning and camping facilities overwhelmed a formerly tranquil area. Remaining pasture, however, though subject to increased disturbance, remains an important waterfowl feeding and roosting site, particularly during wet conditions.

The seawall rebuild

Discussion and planning of the seawall rebuild were controversial and protracted affairs. They occupied much time at meetings of the Lymington Coastal Area Advisory and Management Panels, set up in the 1970s to oversee the marshes' management and chaired from the forum's inauguration by County Councillor Alan Rice. Southern Water's original concept was to re-align the new wall on a line immediately inland of the brackish lagoons, remove the old wall and return the lagoon area to the intertidal. This proposal was totally unacceptable on conservation grounds and it was finally agreed that the re-build should follow the line of the existing sea defences. The loss of the small, historical, Oxey Marshes' salt-dock was regrettable, but large granite blocks situated on top of the rebuilt seawall indicate its position and shape. Issues, eg contractors' offices, materials' storage, heavy machinery access routes and a host of others, were less contentious and depots were established on the west field of Normandy Farm and on the site of the old Pennington Marshes Rubbish Tip. Differences of opinion, such as the merit of armouring certain sections of seawall, ie around Iley Point, did arise. However, Southern Water accepted the land was of sufficient height and agreed to forgo sea defence re-construction at that point. Scheduled to commence in late December 1989, work was postponed for a month, following marsh flooding during severe storm conditions at that time. Two decades later it is difficult to comprehend the scene during seawall re-construction. Over the four-year period during 1990–94, the marshes resembled one vast building site, but time and nature were great healers. Constructed with perforated concrete blocks, the face of the new seawall quickly vegetated. The Normandy Farm lagoon, created to provide fill for the wall and flooded with salt-water in early November 1990, proved an irresistible attraction to feeding, roosting and breeding wildfowl, waders and other wetland birds. It also developed into a major British site for salt and brackish-water animals and plants, but proposed additional borrow-pits on Oxey and Pennington Marshes were unacceptable to the conservation authorities. Though original sections remained inside Moses and Maiden Docks, many mourned the loss of the old seawall. With the exception of two locations, at Saltgrass Lane and Oxey Marshes, where slumping occurred, subsequent storm damage at only one or two other spots was proof that the new wall was well-designed and constructed.

That such a large-scale project was completed with little permanent damage to the Reserve was due in no small measure to Mr Colin Seago, the project's senior site-engineer. It was his final major enterprise before retirement; no one was more helpful and co-operative throughout the duration of the contract.

An ornithological history

Watchers and publications

Though Francis Willoughby (1635–1672) visited Hurst Spit in 1667 (see Habitats), David Garrow's short account of local birds in his *History of Lymington and its Immediate Vicinity* (1825) was one of the first of such lists to appear in print. Wise's *The New Forest: Its History and Scenery*, first published in 1865, contained many references to the ornithology of the west Hampshire coast, but those were predominately for Christchurch, now of course, in Dorset.

Much early natural history writing came from the pens of clergymen or the hunting and shooting fraternity. Most of our early knowledge of NW Solent birds stems from one such writer, Colonel Peter Hawker (1786–1853). Written from the standpoint of an obsessive game shooter and punt-gunner, his diaries during 1802–1853 recorded his shooting exploits and other facets of his life, such as his military career and his passion for travel, music and the arts. Though often vague on even approximate numbers of wildfowl present at a particular time, the diaries affords an invaluable insight into wintering waterfowl then frequenting the west Solent. Towards the end of the century, Sir Ralph Payne-Gallwey, himself a noted wildfowler and game shot, was sufficiently far-sighted to edit the diaries, which were published in two volumes in 1893. Hawker had already written *Instructions to Young Sportsmen in All that Relates to Guns and Shooting* and this work, which first appeared in 1814, also contained references to Keyhaven's birds. The originals consisted of small, pocketsize notebooks (John Bishop pers. comm.) which together with Sir Ralph Payne-Gallwey's edited version have an interesting history. Mr Eric Parker, editor of *The Field* during 1931–1937, highlighted anomalies between the two versions of the diaries. He was puzzled by the fact that Payne-Gallwey's text suggested that Hawker shot mostly alone. Parker's researches led to the discovery of the originals' typescript copy, from which Payne-Gallwey had worked, as well as the printers' proofs, which were then still in the ownership of Hawker's great-grandson, Ryves Hawker. Parker concluded that Payne-Gallwey's edited version often attributed a whole day's game shooting bag to Hawker's gun, whereas the original entry for the same day often indicated the presence of companions. Further investigation suggested that most of the originals, thought to have been lost, had been acquired by Mr David Wagstaff and then by Yale University in 1945 (Sedgwick *et al* 1970). Whatever the truth of the matter, the diaries portrayed a vivid account of Hawker's life, including his long association with Keyhaven.

Hawker's country seat, Longparish House, situated on the west bank of Hampshire's River Test, was inherited from his father. Hawker retired from active military service in 1813, following a severe thigh wound received in 1809 at the Battle of Talavera. Many of his early coastal wildfowling forays took place in Poole Harbour in Dorset, but he later found Keyhaven, first visited in 1814, much more to his liking, despite the fact that his first season (the latter half of winter 1814–1815) was nothing short of a disaster. Dr Harris (1914) wrote 'the sport was bad, the weather atrocious and the number of those who were also wishing to have some shots, which he [Hawker] called the "levee en masse of blackguards', so irritated him that he was constrained to leave in a months time." Hawker observed that it was lucky that he and his wife 'escaped without loss of their limbs', as the place where they stayed 'was as damp as a church and scarcely fit to shelter a Newfoundland dog.'

Whatever his initial impressions of Keyhaven, Hawker was associated with the hamlet for almost 40 years, during which he spent much of each winter in the village. He initially stayed in rented accommodation, eg Aubrey House in December 1815, before purchasing and rebuilding Mr Lee's cottage, which he named Wigeon Cottage and then Keyhaven Cottage. The house was re-named 'Hawker's Cottage' in the early 1950s.

Hawker's Cottage. EJW

Hawker was described by many, perhaps with justification, as a 'butcher'; the grand totals of those game birds, wildfowl and other birds he killed, were certainly on a scale unacceptable by present-day standards. However, in his favour, though he did not suffer fools gladly, he comes across as a kindly employer who thought highly of family servants. Hawker's wildfowling was conducted mostly from gunning punts. His most famous puntsman, James Reade of the Isle of Purbeck, was employed at Keyhaven from 1821. On 27 January of that year Hawker wrote: 'My man Charles, whom I sent to Poole for the unrivalled James Reade, the Mozart of all the wild-fowl men, returned this evening with this illustrious gunner and his punt in my boat cart.' According to Hawker, Reade retired 'to the other side of Lymington' some 30 years later. Following Hawker's death, his widow, Mrs Helen Hawker, continued to reside at Keyhaven. In her will she bequeathed the house, much of its contents and land around Keyhaven and Milford to Lucy Saunders of Milford, who was in the Hawkers' employ at Keyhaven from the age of 13, initially as maid and then as housekeeper.

There appear to be few other readily available nineteenth-century Keyhaven/Lymington ornithological observations, other than of three Bitterns near Lymington during the winter of 1848/49 and submitted to the *Zoologist*. E G B Meade-Waldo's list of New Forest birds in the *Victoria County History* specified little of significance for the Keyhaven/Lymington coast. A milestone in Hampshire's ornithological history was the publication of the first county avifauna, *The Birds of Hampshire and the Isle of Wight* in 1905. The authors, The Revd John E Kelsall MA and Philip W Munn, drew together an immense amount of data that included much of Colonel Hawker's information. Kelsall was born at Fareham in 1864 and served as New Milton's rector from 1897 until 1924. Together with Richard Edward Coles, he also produced *The Birds of Milford*, to which the 1913 Volume 1 No. 6 issue of Milford-on-Sea Record Society's occasional magazine was entirely devoted. Kelsall previously lived in the parish and Coles, who had known Milford since 1883, was at one time a tenant of Keyhaven Cottage, the property owned by Colonel and Mrs Hawker some four decades earlier.

Dave Wooldridge, EJW and Len Mummery seawatching in poor weather in the shelter of a stack of revetment timber, on the inside of Hurst Spit at Cut Bridge, September 1960. RB

The advent of World War I curtailed much ornithological observation, but by the 1920s, birdwatchers were again visiting the Keyhaven/Lymington coast. R E Moreau, who worked at the Edward Grey Institute at Oxford University during 1947–1966 and became editor of *Ibis* from 1946 until 1960, spent a few days on the Lymington marshes in September 1922. Here he recorded migrating passerines, as well as a group of Kestrels (see Systematic Accounts). Another was Bruce Campbell who, as a 14-year-old and together with his father and a family friend, visited the area on two occasions during April 1926. He went on to work at the BTO, at the BBC's Natural History Unit in Bristol and on a part-time basis, on the staff of *The Countryman*. It was a further 40 years before Campbell's next visit, in mid-April 1969. With Rosemary Jackson, he 'actually saw fewer redshanks than spotted redshanks, but eleven kinds of wader altogether, including two pairs of oystercatchers which first bred on the Hampshire mainland in 1934. We saw three Little Terns, also now nesting in the area and my first for Hampshire. So I did not feel that change had been for the worse.'

Observers during the 1930s/1940s included S D Barfoot, G Brasnett, L P Day, F H Haines, Miss P E G Harding, C M Kelsall, G Marples, Miss C Popham, B J and Mrs M Ringrose, Dr K B Rooke, K D Smith, Capt. J Stares, R Watkin and J B Watson. Among those not born in Hampshire, but with long associations with Keyhaven were Norman Orr and Edwin Cohen. Norman was closely involved with New Forest birds for more than six decades. He continued to visit the area during periods of leave of absence from the RAF, a particular interest being the Little Tern breeding population. On retirement to Highcliffe in 1958, he resumed his tern studies and through the county Naturalists' Trust (now Hampshire & Isle of Wight Wildlife Trust), of which he was its first Chairman, became involved in tern conservation. I co-operated with him on that project during 1966–2001; he died in 2006 (Bright 2006, Wiseman *et al* 2007). Edwin Cohen, from Cheshire, settled at nearby Sway in 1940. For 30 years (he died in 1970) Keyhaven was a favourite stamping ground where, dressed in shorts throughout the year, he became a familiar figure along the seawalls.

In December 1991 I received a most interesting letter from Michael Harrison of Oldwinford in the West Midlands. In October of that year I met Michael, his brother and Bob Hayward of New Milton, at Keyhaven. I had known Bob for many years, but was unaware he and his friends were schoolboy birdwatching companions on the marshes in the 1940s. I can do no better than quote from Michael's letter.

'I said that I would look through my diaries of those times to see if there was anything in them that you might find interesting from an ornithological historical viewpoint. Since then, I have managed, over several days, to read them through from start to finish, something incidentally that I have never done before. It was a fascinating and at times a chastening experience. The diaries run more or less continuously from 8 January 1944 to the end of 1949 (when National Service intervened) and in more sporadic fashion thereafter to early 1952.

The west side of Hurst Castle with Bill Truckle.
Showing the profile of the beach prior to major groyne work 1960. RB

Perhaps I should set the scene at January 1944 when it all began. At that time we were three inexperienced but madly enthusiastic beginners, 12 years old and having the most rudimentary field guides — *Sanders Bird Book for the Pocket*. I saw a copy of this venerable tome on a friend's bookshelf only a few weeks ago and I know Bob still has his original copy and *The Pocket Book of British Birds*, with the classic illustrations, by T. A. Coward. Poor fare by modern standards but they served us well enough at the time. More restricting was the lack of binoculars, these in wartime were an unheard-of luxury and we only managed to get hold of 'bins' in late 1946 or 1947 (the diary is not very clear on this). Being youngsters, we were very competitive among ourselves as to what we saw and the early years are laced with streaky identifications which, with hindsight, were plainly wrong or at best most unlikely.

Group at Hurst Castle from right-left Bill Truckle, Gedge Westerhoff (both standing), Len Mummery (note Barr and Stroud binoculars), Don Westerhoff, Dave Wooldridge & EJW. West side Hurst Castle 1960. RB

The best/worst example of this was an entry for a day in February 1946 when we flushed a 'jack snipe', which towered away from us into the distance, a dead give-away if ever there was one! Most of these though were just hasty judgements. In looking through the diaries now, I have eliminated all (I hope) of these and have still been left with a fascinating half-forgotten picture of what it was like in the 'old days. In putting together this compilation of old memories, I have included anything I have found interesting from anywhere in the New Forest and surrounding area as well as records from the Keyhaven Marshes themselves. In fact, many of the differences between birdwatching then and now arose among the non-marshes birds. Perhaps the Keyhaven Marshes have not changed very much since the 1940's.

There is a new large marina of course with its attendant traffic up and down river and birdwatchers are more numerous than in the early days. Probably, most of the birds seen are much the same such as Redshanks, Curlews and Godwits; there is no real indication in the diaries of any great changes here.

Same group, returning to Milford. 1960. RB

St Catherine's Point, the group's pig-sty camp of the 1950s/1960s. RB

33

Nonetheless, some things do stand out, most noticeably for me the great winter of 1947 when very cold weather was compounded by miners' strikes and severe coal shortages. We could go down to the marshes that winter and pick Fieldfares and Redwings out of the hedgerows, too weak and starved to fly away. What is really an eye-opener, though, is that we began birdwatching six months before D-Day – 6 June 1944 – and The Solent was stuffed full from shore to shore with ships of all kinds. We were at a Scout Forestry Camp in the Forest when war actually ended but none of these momentous events are recorded in the diaries! Clearly, these were birdwatching diaries and nothing else was going to get in the way.'

The early 1950s were 'probably the most critical few years of the century for the progress of Hampshire ornithology' (Leach & Pratt in BoH). With full employment and increased leisure time, many southern folk, emulating the example set by their pre-war, north-country rambler counterparts, were turning to countryside pursuits, ornithology among them, for stimulation and relaxation. Subsequently the Keyhaven/Lymington coast became increasingly popular among birdwatchers and as a result the area has since figured noticeably in Hampshire Bird Reports and county avifaunas. Another active and very competent observer was John Boys, who initially visited the marshes in 1948 and was a regular watcher there until 1972. Later, he compiled a *Check List of the Birds of Dorset* (1974) and with Colonel E D V Prendergast, co-authored *The Birds of Dorset* (1983). Early 1950s observers included Mike Adams of Yarmouth, Isle of Wight, whose discovery of breeding Firecrests in the New Forest in 1961 (Adams 1966) was a significant contribution not only to Hampshire, but also to British ornithology. Other watchers at that time included Mr and Mrs J Goodhart, A C S Holtom, Oliver Hook, Frank Pearce, R A Sharland (finder of Hampshire's first Lesser Yellowlegs at Pennington Marshes in 1953) and E G Riddick who lived in Milford-on-Sea, as well as members of the New Forest Ornithological Club (NFOC) eg Gordon Wooldridge, Alan Moody, Graham Bundy and Gerald Kinsey.

An alleged, amusing anecdote involved the latter observer. In the early 1950s, following a time-consuming and tedious journey from Southampton, he arrived at Hurst Spit on a calm, winter morning to find the sea, unusually, dotted with waterfowl. Hastily pulling his binocular case from his rucksack, he was horrified to find it full of toy soldiers. Apparently the culprit was a young brother and it was rumoured that Kinsey spent the rest of the morning, throwing them – toy soldiers, not young brothers – into the sea.

Bev Snellgrove and the Pearce-Smith twins hailed from Lymington. As well as contributing to the marshes' ornithology, they were among the first to watch Hampshire's first breeding Little Ringed Plovers at a Sway gravel pit in 1952. To those familiar with the area, Bev can at once be recognised

Roger Brown in the Half Boat, Hurst North Point 1960. BT

Peter LeBrocq mid-1950s - note duffle coat and the LeBrocqular, his 'religion'. DFB

as a local when he refers to Creek Cottage, the property standing at the head of Moses Dock, as 'Nicholsons'. Captain Nicholson, a well-known sailing enthusiast, was the Creek Cottage tenant, prior to the arrival of the Hill family in the early 1950s. Bev is also one of the few birdwatchers still around who remember Salterns Eight-Acre Pond prior to the removal of internal banks that divided the Pond into three separate units.

Sea-watching in Hampshire is no recent phenomenon. Inspired by that great Sussex ornithologist, Peter Alder of Brighton, senior members of the Portsmouth Group, among them David Billett, Graham Rees and Bryan Renyard, were recording sea-bird movement off the east Hampshire coast during the early 1950s. Extending their spheres of activity to the New Forest coast and together with John Bowers, Bill Truckle and others, they were soon monitoring tern and wader migration from various NW Solent watch points between Hurst Spit and Lepe's Stone Point. Similarly, NFOC members watched The Solent's western approaches from Headon Warren on the Isle of Wight. Dave Wooldridge, an Eastleigh man and Jim Williams of Southampton, were recording seabirds at Keyhaven during the second half of the 1950s. They were among Hampshire's most active and competent sea-watchers at that time and together with D Poole, added Sooty Tern to the Keyhaven and Hampshire list in June 1961. Dave also recorded Hampshire mainland's first Cory's Shearwater off Hurst Spit in May 1982 and discovered Hampshire's first breeding Roseate Terns. He 'retired' to his maternal Isle of Wight roots, following his marriage to Jenni Norris, whose parents managed Niton's village grocery store. Jim moved to Orkney, where he met and married local girl Ruth (née Foster) and where they continue to reside and where principal interests include the islands' breeding birds. Earlier in that decade D W H Brown found breeding Sandwich Terns at Keyhaven, though, unsurprisingly, the west Solent tern colonies were targeted by egg-collectors.

Following my National Service and while indulging in six weeks paid demobilisation-leave, I met by chance, Dave Wooldridge (demobbed only three months earlier), Len Mummery and Don and Gerald Westerhoff, at Portland Bill in September 1959. This heralded our era of regular watching in the Keyhaven area, thus supplementing observations by Edwin Cohen, John Boys, Bev Snellgrove and others. Around this time we met Peter Hobby of Milford-on-Sea. Wildly enthusiastic about birds and everything else to do with Hurst Spit and Keyhaven, his father, also Peter, was the last of Hurst's full-time light keepers. Retiring in 1987, he was awarded the British Empire Medal in recognition of 37 years service with Trinity House. Dave, Len, Don and Gerald also shared a great affinity with Bishop's Dyke in the New Forest, where they spent a great deal of their early ornithological years, sleeping rough, particularly during long winter nights, in a weatherproof shelter built from the forest's

Bill Truckle on Hurst Spit, with Braodhurst Clarkson 'scope - no tripod! Spring 1961. RB

EJW at Salterns slipway in Aug 1982. NO

Bill Truckle with Grey Phalarope in tow. Hurst Spit autumn 1960. RB

natural materials. Together with Jim Williams, they were also among the first to implement post-war counts and estimations of west Solent's breeding gulls and terns (carried out using rowing dinghies hired from Bill Adams of Keyhaven) as were John Everett and Roy Dennis, later synonymous with Fair Isle Bird Observatory and conservation of Scotland's Ospreys.

Among others who also regularly watched Keyhaven at that time was Roger Brown of Lee-on-the-Solent. I first met him at Titchfield Haven during the mid-1950s and together with Graham Rees, John Bowers, Bill Truckle and others we also spent much of our time on the Isle of Wight (particularly at St Catherine's Point, Newtown and Needles/Alum Bay) and in the New Forest.

Without private transport and living some distance from Keyhaven, we camped in the vicinity from Friday evening until as late as possible on Sunday. We usually slept under the stars, but inclement-weather bivouac sites included a small, easterly facing, derelict and door-less brick building, situated immediately west of the then-named Marine Café and sheltered spots around Hurst Castle and the marshes. Occasionally we were given permission to sleep in the lighthouse cottage. This proved a little unnerving for some as one of the rooms had a reputation of being haunted, so the usual procedure was to sleep on the kitchen floor behind locked doors. However, accepting that 'the better part of valour is discretion', we were often to be found sleeping outside in the garden on following mornings.

Our binoculars were many and varied. My first prism binocular was an unimpressive 8×25, but I soon upgraded to a Kershaw 12×40, a glass popular with Sussex birdwatchers in the mid-1950s; it was in constant use for many years before its replacement with a Barr & Stroud 10×42. Dave Wooldridge initially used a Ross 9×35 and Len Mummery a Barr & Stroud 10×50, which remains in use by him to this day. In his book *The Gyr Falcon Adventure*, Stanley Cerely so graphically illustrated birdwatchers' reliance on and attachment to their binoculars, when he wrote 'The language of bird men who lose these by mis-adventure compares with that of bargees, when provoked. Or so I am told.' Much of our gear, particularly during the early years, was bulky and heavy; standard kit was usually an ex-army combat jacket or a Blacks of Greenock anorak and we usually opted for Dunlop Hood Bullseye wellingtons. In winter, we donned as many woollen jerseys as required, beneath our outer jacket, but Peter LeBrocq, owner of the 'Lebrocqular', wore an ex-Navy duffle coat. Waterproof kit consisted of PVC jackets and over-trousers, though Peter relied on an ex-service gas-cape, onto which he applied French chalk to prevent deterioration. It made little sense, living in soft, mid-south England, to indulge in ultra-expensive, extreme weather clothing (not that we were able to afford it) that was more suited to Cairngorm winters or Polar expeditions.

Bob Dunn, Mike Stewart, Chris Fox, Susan Wood and Owen and Tricia Haisell appeared on the Keyhaven scene in the late 1960s/1970s. Bob's family moved from Aston in the West Midlands, to Southbourne near Bournemouth, where they owned and managed a greengrocery business. Bob and Mike originally watched at Stanpit and Hengistbury Head, though Bob switched allegiance to Keyhaven following his parents' retirement to Milford-on-Sea. Chris Fox lived at Broomsquires, a large cliff-top property, now long demolished and replaced by intrusive and characterless 'retirement' flats. According to Garrow, a broomsquire was a person who made heather besom brooms, as opposed to those manufactured from birch twigs. I met Chris on Hurst Spit on 17 April 1967. Fortunately he had chosen a day of southerly winds and rain for his sea-watching baptism and notched-up four new bird species within an hour or two. He never looked back and became a Keyhaven regular until qualification as a schoolteacher necessitated a move to West Sussex. Susan Wood, another schoolteacher, also lived in Milford-on-Sea, where none other than J R R Tolkien sometimes visited, as he and Susan's stepfather, Chris Wiseman (no relation) were friends since their schooldays. Owen Haisell, who originated from Leigh on the Essex coast (so no newcomer to Brent Goose haunts) and his wife Tricia, moved to the area in 1967, then into Lymington in the early 1970s. Among his ornithological interests was the BTO Common Bird Census, which we jointly carried out at Normandy Farm and Salterns during 1976–2000. Barry Duffin of Gosport was a frequent weekend visitor from the mid-1960s, partaking of sterling voluntary work with wardening the Keyhaven tern and gull colonies. Following acquisition of Titchfield Haven by Hampshire County Council in 1972, Barry became The Haven's first full-time warden. Retiring in April 2012 he was awarded the MBE in 2007 for outstanding ornithological achievement. Diana (Jones) Westerhoff also assisted with tern wardening at Keyhaven. Now retired, she worked for Natural England in the New Forest, where she was employed principally on habitat management policy. Captain John Nevitt MC (formerly of the Parachute Regiment) and his wife Ruth previously lived on the Wirral. They became very fond of the area and settled at Keyhaven where they spent much of their time birdwatching on the marshes. Leslie and Beryl Masters also found Keyhaven very much to their liking as it was 'such a friendly place', unlike a previous bird haunt they had known where, by all accounts, the local watchers were a little aloof, to say the least; the Masters' ashes were scattered on the marshes.

Three observers who became close buddies and often together in the field were Herbert Girdlestone, Sid Webb and Tom Brice. I gleaned nothing of Mr Girdlestone's background, but knew Tom Brice as a staunch 1950s Titchfield Haven watcher, reputedly the first to suggest that the small mysterious warbler (it became the first acceptable British record of the species) singing from dense reedbeds at The Haven in early March 1961 was a Cetti's. Sid Webb, a retired Wiltshire gamekeeper, was a tough individual and among the first to be recruited into the SAS Regiment during the Second World War. He was a great walker and usually notched-up at least 70 miles a week in the New Forest and along the Keyhaven/Oxey seawall; sadly none of that trio are now with us.

Fledgling 1960s/70s observers from Southampton/Eastleigh included Philip Agland, John Cantello, George Green, Phil Gregory, Graham McIntyre and Barry Stewart. Others, who visited, or regularly watched the area from, or around that period, included Brian and Rosemary Cooke, Pete and Mike Combridge, Geoffrey Field, David Gittins, Roger Harris, John (Fawley) Jones, Robin Saunders, David Peart, Ted Purkiss (a native of the Chilterns), Gerald and Ann Smart and Mike Terry, all of whom contributed to NW Solent's ornithological record.

A tremendous upsurge in the number of birders visiting the area from the late 1980s/ 1990s included, among others, Martin Cooper, Graham Giddens, Steve Keen, Tony Locke, Marc Moody, Tim Parminter,

Russell Wynn and Marcus Ward. Hampshire hog, Marc (Moody) from Brockenhurst, a committed 'pen and paper man', specialised in sea birds from his earliest days and this aspect of birdwatching continues to occupy much of his time. He added much to our understanding of sea-bird movement into and through Christchurch Bay and carried out a comprehensive study of Gannets in the vicinity of the Needles and Shingles (unpublished MS). Following a chequered career that included a spell as an East Anglian RSPB warden, Tim Parminter settled in Hampshire and adopted the Keyhaven–Lymington coast in 1989.

Titchfield Haven bridge in March 1961 (Cetti's Warbler Twitch).
From l - r Jim Williams, Dave Wooldridge, Bill Truckle, Martin Terry, Shaun White, Dave Billett, EJW, Bill Barton, Dave Price aka 'The Hanging Heap', Jock McGregor and Alan Searle. RB Dave Price affectionately known as 'The Hanging Heap', because of his habit of festooning the outside of his rucksack with items of kit, on one occasion even a loaf (no packaging) was tied to his pack with a piece of string'

The birdwatching philosophy of the 1950/1960s Keyhaven 'old guard' was embodied in Rudyard Kipling's poem 'A Song in Storm', ie 'The game is more than the player of the game and the ship is more than the crew!' Similarly, in James Fisher's words, we favoured 'atmosphere to achievement' (Fisher 1951). It is reassuring to know that at least one or two of the more recent recruits have a similar outlook. Those of us at Keyhaven prior to the 1990s' observer-boom may not have set-alight the twitchers' domains, but I beg leave to doubt if many had more fun or enjoyed their birdwatching so much.

Nonetheless, numerous watchers, numbering a dozen or two in the mid-1950s, to more than six hundred by 2012, have contributed countless hours observing west Solent birds. They also made the very considerable effort, particularly before the advent of personal computers, to assemble their records, on which a book such as this heavily relies, for submission to Hampshire's data-gathering bodies. It was impossible to list all observers of Keyhaven/Lymington birds, but from HOS files, I have extracted the names of those known to have submitted records during 1993–2012; they are listed elsewhere in this book

I acknowledge their massive, combined contribution and offer my sincerest apologies for errors or omissions, for which I accept sole responsibility.

A Conservation History

The NW Solent

Kelsall and Coles highlighted specific concerns regarding threats to the NW Solent's bird populations in 1913. They drew attention to Cordgrass encroachment over wildfowl feeding grounds, as well as to other effects on waterfowl, should a proposed massive dock development at Keyhaven, materialise. Local people also stressed the significance of the marshes as a wildlife haven in 1930, when a proposal was advanced to upgrade the track, known locally as the Marsh Road or Ancient Highway. Designed 'to aid development of the coastal corridor between Keyhaven and Lymington', this plan, fortunately, came to nothing.

During 1939–45, a 'Conference on Nature Preservation in War Reconstruction', generated a memorandum in March 1943, which in turn contributed to Command Paper 7122 in 1947, when the participating British Ecological Society promoted Hurst Castle and Keyhaven as a National Habitat Reserve (NHR). The 1947 conference entitled 'Conservation of Nature in England and Wales' and chaired by Sir Julian Huxley, became the foundation of our modern conservation system. Command Paper 7122 identified the entire New Forest as a Conservation Area and a Scientific Area (SA 19), within which 900 acres at Hurst and Keyhaven became a proposed Nature Reserve (NR29). The citation quoted areas of shingle and salt marsh as being of interest for plants, insects and birds. Meanwhile members of the Lymington Naturalists' Society, stimulated by a talk by Peter Day on the birds recorded on the marshes during the severe winter of 1946–47, called for the area to be recognised as a bird sanctuary. However, formal recognition of the area's wildlife importance was not achieved until 1961 (see below).

Conservation initiatives

Foremost among NW Solent conservation actions were SSSI declarations by the Nature Conservancy Council (NCC) now Natural England (NE), practical measures adopted by Hampshire Naturalists' Trust in the 1960s and coastal-land acquisition by Hampshire County Council during 1973–2008. Those initiatives occurred against a background of increasing concern for the future of Hampshire's remaining prime wetland habitats.

Natural England then Nature Conservancy Council

The NW Solent marshes and mudflats between Hurst Spit and Colgrims were finally notified as a Site of Special Scientific Interest in 1961 and known as the Hurst Castle/Lymington River Estuary SSSI. The Conservancy's fight to maintain and to increase protection of The Solent's habitats and wildlife was led by Colin Tubbs, who became their senior Hampshire and Isle of Wight officer.

Hampshire and Isle of Wight Wildlife Trust

The Hampshire & Isle of Wight's Naturalists' Trust, later the Wildlife Trust, was formed in 1960. Within a year or two, the organisation became involved in tern conservation at Keyhaven. On Norman Orr's instigation, they secured an agreement to erect seasonal temporary fencing to delineate a Little Tern breeding site on Hurst Spit in 1962, followed by a lease from Lymington Borough Council of Keyhaven saltmarshes in 1964. However, wardening took place only on a weekend voluntary basis and the project was only partially successful until the appointment of a full-time seasonal warden in June 1966. By that time, the few pairs of Little Terns breeding on the Spit were becoming increasingly vulnerable to disturbance from increasing numbers of visitors. Fortunately, small colonies, documented from at least the 1940s, remained on the shingle and shell ridges fronting the saltmarshes, where large colonies of Black-headed Gulls together with Ringed Plovers, Redshanks, Oystercatchers and Mallards,were also nesting. Trust officers continued to be very active during the 1970s and offered much support for the County Council's land-acquisition policy.

Hampshire County Council

Further conservation opportunities arose in the early 1970s when Normandy Farm came onto the market. Following its purchase of Titchfield Haven in 1972, Hampshire County Council acquired the Farm at auction in May 1973, followed by Salterns and the Eight Acre Pond in the autumn of that year. It was at that time that the County Council appointed a permanent full-time warden. Such was the spirit of co-operation between conservation bodies, HCC's warden was also allowed to apportion such time as deemed necessary, particularly during the spring and summer months, to continue to oversee the Trust's saltmarsh reserve.

A particularly critical period for NW Solent conservation arose in the late 1970s. With the owners of Pennington and Oxey Marshes already in possession of a valid gravel-extraction approval, the threat of large-scale grazing marsh loss became imminent. Their permission was conditional on that gravel being shipped away by sea; removal by lorry, via the narrow and built-up Lower Pennington Lane, was prohibited. Fortunately, the sea-removal route proved to be unviable. New proposals that included an extraction road from Pennington Marshes onto and through Manor Farm to join the A337 at Efford, met with stout opposition, one reason being that this would sever a public right-of-way. Archaeologists, such as local champion Arthur Lloyd, also voiced opposition to gravel extraction and highlighted the fact that this would destroy remaining prominent salt-industry features.

It was then proposed that Hampshire County Council, with financial assistance from the Countryside Commission, would purchase Pennington/Oxey Marshes. Compensatory gravel-extraction permission was approved for a larger area of Manor Farm, where small-scale aggregate removal was already in progress. Though unpopular in some quarters, there was overwhelming support for the County Council scheme, especially as there were no guarantees that gravel would not be removed from the marshes in the future, nor an undertaking the resulting gravel pits would later be turned over to nature conservation interests.

The County Council was also able to purchase Keyhaven Marshes in 1984, administered at that time by the George Harris Trust. This included the area for which the initial gravel extraction proposal had been refused some thirty years earlier. In the same year, old coastguard cottages on Hurst's North Point that, despite the owner's interim renovation attempts, were in an extremely poor state of repair, again fell into disuse. Amid rumour of the possibility of inappropriate re-development, such as a holiday camp, Hampshire County Council acquired the site and took the decision to demolish the derelict buildings and bury resulting rubble and debris in nearby un-vegetated shingle. Finally an area of rough pasture and scrubland on Iley Point in the ownership of Miss Fortesque, a long-time Keyhaven resident, was put-up for sale in 2008. Hampshire County Council again stepped in and purchased this last link in the grazing-marsh chain between Lymington and Keyhaven.

Much was due to the tenacity of a few enlightened and far-sighted individuals, such as County Councillor David Pumfrett. Their foresight and HCC land-acquisition policy cannot be praised highly enough. At that time, the cost of buying the freehold of the land seemed far beyond reach. For instance Salterns and Normandy Farm, purchased at auction for a combined sum in excess of £400,000, was the most expensive nature conservation acquisition ever made by a local authority, the price inflated by 'hope-value of the locality for marine and other development' (Tubbs 1999).

Manor Farm (Lower Pennington)

Gravel extraction at Manor Farm commenced in the late 1950s. Though small-scale at first, it became a major excavation and domestic waste infill site and was active over a period of more than 50 years; final stages of reinstatement work, in the south-east segment of the farm, continued into late 2014. Among the initial Manor Farm 'dilute and disperse' zones was a 25 ha parcel of land on the west side between the Avon Water and Iley Lane. Following excavation, it was infilled with domestic waste and restored to grassland to approximately original ground levels: it developed into a fine site for grazing waterfowl, particularly Dark-bellied Brent Geese and Wigeon. Inevitably it became known as the Goose Field, but its potential was threatened in the early 1990s by a seemingly innocuous application for a Woodland Grant, to plant-up the area with blocks of trees. Fortunately Hampshire County Council was able to make representation during the Forestry Authority's consultation process and the application was refused: the site was included in the Site of Scientific Interest and the Special Protection Area for Birds in the mid-1990s. At the same time, a former eighteenth-century saltern adjacent to Saltgrass Lane and in the ownership of Edgar's' Farms was also included within the protective designations.

Sturt Pond

From the late 1950s the vicinity of Sturt Pond, Hurst Spit and Mount Lake became subject to increasing disturbance by growing numbers of visitors. In spite of this, the site remained excellent for birds, due in no small measure to efforts of local people, particularly Keith Metcalf, who was Clerk to Milford-on-Sea Parish Council. Together with the support of local councillors, he was instrumental in ensuring the area be designated and managed as a Local Nature Reserve. The owners of the adjacent Carrington Caravan Site were also supportive of nature conservation aspirations and welcome the flocks of Dark-bellied Brent Geese, which annually graze on their fields between October and March.

Habitat loss

The destruction of four areas of prime habitat totalling c.28 ha of land and intertidal between the late 1950s and 2007, was a significant loss to nature conservation. In chronological order these were: 8 ha of grazing marsh (domestic refuse-tipping in the late 1950s), 10 ha of mudflat in Harper's Lake (Lymington Yacht Haven in 1968), the 2 ha Iley Lane Lake (inert waste infill in c.1995) and Manor Farm's 8 ha SSSI-standard SINC field (gravel extraction in 2007).

Pennington Marshes RT

Approval for Lymington Borough Council's domestic refuse tip application for Pennington Marshes in the late 1950s was a major blow to Hampshire coastal conservation. Lower Pennington Lane was previously metalled only as far as the most southerly house, but the tip project necessitated upgrading the access as far as the tip entrance. No gravel extraction took place and waste was tipped directly onto the marsh floor. It was originally envisaged that waste be tipped to within tens of metres of the seawall between Pennington Butts and the sewer outfall. Officially, the area was solely for domestic waste, but it was rumoured that more-toxic material found its way into the site. The marshes were relatively remote in those days and though protected by a two-metre high wire fence and a locked gate, those proved no deterrent to determined nocturnal fly-tippers. In an attempt to combat unlawful use of the site, a public amenities element was installed, though downsides were increased traffic on the narrow approach road and a constant pall of smoke from continuous rubbish burning. Opposition by the Nature Conservancy to continued large-scale tipping finally secured an agreement to close operations there and to relocate them to nearby Manor Farm. Though high-quality grazing marsh, as well as significant salt-industry features were destroyed, the net result was retention of a much larger area of marsh inside Pennington Marshes' seawall, in addition to the area that included the 'Shoveler Pools', to the east of the access track: both areas developed into superb wildfowl and wader habitats.

Harper's Lake–Lymington Yacht Haven

This was a particularly contentious affair when originally mooted in the early 1960s. Planning permission was initially refused on grounds of, among others, landscape issues, though a follow-up submission later in the decade was, surprisingly, given the go-ahead. The scheme resulted in the loss of about 10 ha of prime mudflat and saltmarsh of Harper's Lake, but unlike the Berthon Lymington Marina, was particularly intrusive into the landscape when viewed from both Keyhaven in the west and from the shore to the east of Lymington River. It originally accommodated about 250 boats, but the Yacht Haven complex now provides berths for 500 craft and up-to-date onshore facilities, eg those for yacht maintenance and winter storage.

Iley Lane Lake

Following the demise of a small permanent pump that was installed to drain a low-lying area in the northern half of Manor Farm, a fine water body known as Iley Lane Lake was created in the early 1990s.

It rapidly developed, if only for a few years, into a fine habitat for breeding, migrant and wintering birds. Planning conditions pertaining at that time rendered the authorities powerless to act and in spite of concerted endeavours by local ornithologists to reverse the decision, it was infilled with inert waste. Two smaller water bodies that replaced the original lake, though not without bird interest, have much less ornithological significance.

The SINC field (Site of Importance for Nature Conservation)

Mr (Bill) Bailey acquired the 600-acre Manor Farm in 1944. Though farmed to up-to-date standards under his watch, much of the farm retained a very rural atmosphere with retention of many fine features such as hedgerows, copses, ponds, profusions of primroses and bluebells in the spring of the year, as well as many resident badgers. An area of low-lying rough grazing land adjoining the Ancient Highway was also retained throughout Mr Bailey's ownership. Though of the necessary quality, an oversight, which omitted this parcel from the Site of Scientific Interest designation in the early 1960s, ultimately sealed its fate. It was later classified by the County Council as a Site of Importance for Nature Conservation (SINC) and thereafter was known as the SINC field. A vigorous campaign by local people, however, failed to save it (though not before a thorough archaeological evaluation took place) and it was lost to gravel extraction in 2007. Much thought and expense were lavished on compensatory and reinstatement measures, which included the inclusion of ponds and a lake specifically designed to attract breeding, migratory and wintering wetland bird species. In my view, however, in no way did those measures compensate for the loss of previous habitats and aesthetic appeal.

Milford-on-Sea and Woodside (Lymington)

Though the grazing marshes were of major conservation concern during the 1970s–1990s, it was distressing to witness the loss, albeit for housing and recreation, of small pastures on the northern perimeter of Sturt Pond and at Woodside (Lymington), both of which previously supported feeding and roosting waders, eg Ruffs and Redshanks.

A summary of the history of site designations

Sites of Special Scientific Interest

The procedure by which land is recognised as being of importance for nature conservation was established through the National Parks and Access to the Countryside Act 1949. Such sites were to be notified as Sites of Special Scientific Interest. A substantial proportion of the NW Solent coast was notified as the Hurst Castle and Lymington River Estuary SSSI in 1961, a designation that was updated in 1979 and then re-notified under the 1981 Act, in 1987 and again in 1995.

Rock Samphire

Ramsar Sites

The Convention on Wetlands of International Importance especially as Waterfowl Habitat (Ramsar Convention or Wetlands Convention) was adopted in Ramsar, Iran, in February 1971 and came into force in December 1975. The United Kingdom was one of the first countries in the world to ratify the convention. The Ramsar Convention provides a way to assess the relative importance of a site in a world context. Whilst the convention 'especially' deals with waterfowl habitat, it is inclusive in identifying the importance of a much wider range of habitats and species. In October 1998, The Solent and Southampton Water was designated as a Ramsar site.

Sites of Importance for Nature Conservation (SINC)

Local government can designate land as being of importance for nature conservation, as part of their planning functions. The statutory basis of SINC designation rests in the powers delegated to local government, although the designation itself is non statutory in its effect. In the NW Solent, there are a number of SINCs designated on conventionally farmed fields and amenity grasslands, used by estuary birds as roosts and feeding grounds. As such, the SINCs are an integral part of the functioning of the ecosystems for which the SSSIs have been notified and Natura 2000 sites, classified.

Section 41 of the Natural Environment and Rural Communities Act 2006, sets out a list of species and habitats, which are priorities for conservation. This Act reflects the commitments entered into by the UK Government when ratifying the United Nations Biodiversity Convention of 1992. The process of identifying SINCs contributes to the United Kingdom's response to the Biodiversity Convention.

Natura 2000 sites

Following the accession of the United Kingdom to the European Community in 1973, sites have been assessed for their relative importance in a European context. In 1979 Member States adopted the Directive 79/409/EEC on the conservation of wild birds. One of the provisions of the Directive was to establish protected areas, called Special Protection Areas (SPAs).

The Solent and Southampton Water SPA, which included the SSSIs of the western Solent, was classified in 1998.

In 1992, Member States adopted Directive 92/43/EEC on the conservation of natural habitats and of wild fauna and flora. A provision of the Directive was to establish protected areas called Special Areas of Conservation (SACs). In 2005 two SACs were designated in the Western Solent: these were The Solent Maritime SAC, together with The Solent and Isle of Wight Lagoons SAC. The combined boundaries are similar to the SPA. The separate lagoon SAC reflects the priority status given to coastal lagoons.

Together, Special Protection Areas and Special Areas of Conservation are called Natura 2000 sites.

Local Nature Reserves

Local Nature Reserves can be designated by local government under the National Parks and Access to the Countryside Act of 2006, which amended the provisions of the 1949 Act. In 1990 the grazing marshes protected by the seawall to the west of Lymington, were declared a Local Nature Reserve and four years later so were the intertidal marshes of the Boldre Foreshore.

The New Forest

Two different statutory processes, the New Forest Acts and legislation relating to National Parks, have set the statutory boundaries of the New Forest. The documented history of the boundaries of the New Forest, as an area subject to Forest law, runs back to the twelfth century. The boundary of the modern Forest can be dated from the New Forest Act 1877 and the New Forest Act 1964. Whilst the whole of the coast of the north-western Solent fell within the 'large bounds' of the medieval Royal Forest, by 1964 the functioning of the Forest to the west of the Lymington River was much reduced. In contrast, the Boldre Foreshore to the east of the river remains open to grazing by New Forest commoners' cattle and ponies. The definition of the boundary, or the perambulation, of the New Forest defined under the 1964 Act, includes the Boldre Foreshore as within the Forest and subject to the Verderers' bylaws.

The New Forest was first formally proposed as a candidate for national park status by John Dower in the 1945 report to the minister of Town and Country Planning on National Parks in England and Wales (Cmd 6628). The map accompanying that report confirms it was the intention to include the NW Solent into the National Park. The New Forest was not included in the proposed list of National Parks to be progressed, in the subsequent report of 1947 by Sir Arthur Hobhouse.

The New Forest was designated a national park in 2005 under the provisions of the Environment Act 1995. The New Forest National Park includes the coastal marshes but not all the settlements or farmland of the NW Solent.

Little Robin

Hurst. Biting Stonecrop, Sea Campion and Little Robin in the foreground. PRD

The Habitats

Hurst Spit and vegetated shingle

The earliest biological records that give insights into the habitats of the NW Solent date from the seventeenth century. Hurst Spit was clearly a place of interest, as botanical records exist from John Parkinson (1567–1650), John Goodyer (1592–1664) and John Ray (1627–1705).

Parkinson was herbalist to King Charles 1. He visited the Spit sometime before 1640, when he recorded Tree Mallow 'about the cottages neere Hurst Castle.' Tree Malllow *Lavatera arborea* is a short-lived perennial plant, which is salt-tolerant and thrives in the enhanced nutrient levels of bird colonies. The plant may have been of interest to him with its reputed qualities as a poultice for the treatment of sprains.

It is unclear whether John Goodyer actually visited Hurst Spit. Goodyer was a prolific botanical recorder whilst working as an agent for the Mapledurham Estate in East Hampshire. Goodyer was certainly active in south Hampshire and there are precise botanical records from him for elsewhere on The Solent coast. In 1656 Goodyer recorded Golden Samphire *Crithmum maritimum* from Hurst Castle, indicating the origin of the record being by way of a relation of John Meader, a grocer from Downham Market and a source of botanical intelligence. Golden Samphire is another perennial plant of stony shores and saltmarshes.

Golden Samphire

Golden Samphire was recorded again in 1667, when John Ray visited the spit along with his friend Francis Willoughby. John Ray also re-recorded Parkinson's Tree Mallow. Willoughby was an accomplished naturalist in his own right, with expertise in both fish and birds. Unfortunately, whether the records made by Willoughby from this visit survive, is not known.

These three early records indicate a habitat of a shingle spit, vegetated by perennial plants. From the nineteenth century onwards, there are a great many more records. Hurst Spit remains an exceptionally rich area of vegetated shingle and supports annual and well as perennial plant communities. Golden Samphire remains in abundance in the upper saltmarsh transitions, as does Sea Wormwood *Seriphidium maritimum*, with Sea Kale *Crambe maritima* and Yellow Horned Poppy *Glaucium flavum* on the higher ridges of the shingle. A highlight is the presence of the annual Little Robin *Geranium purpureum* subspecies *forsteri*. The world distribution of this sub-species is limited to The Solent and neighbouring West Sussex coast.

The habitats of Hurst Spit support an equally rich invertebrate fauna. Golden Samphire is the habitat of the rare picture-winged fly *Myopites eximius*. The lichen-rich turf of the older parts of the spit supports a strong population of the day-flying Dew Moth *Setina irrorella*. The rather unremarkable stands of Ribwort Plantain *Plantago lanceolata* in the more mature stands have in recent years supported one of the few mainland populations of the Glanville Fritillary butterfly *Melitaea cinxia*.

Hurst Spit is the largest area of vegetated shingle in the NW Solent, but this habitat also occurs elsewhere along the coast. There are extensive areas of shingle at Sowley, but in recent years the rate at which this area has been reworked by the tides has precluded formation of stable vegetation. The small area of stable beach at Sowley is open to grazing by New Forest livestock, but is otherwise little disturbed. This vegetated shingle supports exceptionally rich coastal grassland, with species, such as Heath Pearlwort *Sagina subulata* and Subterranean Clover *Trifolium subterraneum*, with freshwater flushes through the shingle supporting a small population of Hampshire Purslane *Ludwigia palustris*.

A local variant of vegetated shingles are the cheniers, which form on the seaward face of the saltmarshes. These are comprises of a mixture of shingle and shell. The cheniers can remain stable long enough to become vegetated, but the communities which form tend to be simple and dominated by species such as the more common Knotgrasses *Polygonum spp* and Goosefoots *Atriplex spp* and *Chenodopium spp.*

The inter-tidal zone

The intertidal zone is characterised by exposed intertidal sediments, with algal mats and a rich infauna, together with the contrasting saltmarshes dominated by flowering plants. Over time, these habitats change in their extent. The major saltmarsh expansion of the nineteenth and early twentieth century is currently in reverse, with expanses of sediment shore being exposed, as saltmarsh receeds. Both suites of habitats are of exceptional importance to nature conservation, as is their ability to retain the ability for dynamic responses to changing environmental conditions.

The sediment shore is locally vegetated by Eelgrass *Zostera spp*. Eelgrass is a flowering plant, which can bloom entirely submerged in saltwater. Along the coastline of the Lymington River estuary, Eelgrass beds can be found in the lower reaches of the intertidal and into the sub-tidal. Eelgrass beds are the richest of all intertidal habitats for marine animals. The fauna is dominated numerically by mudsnails and marine worms, with abundant cockles, winkles and crustaceans such as shrimps and crabs. The foliage of the Eelgrass provides cover for fish nurseries, as well as habitat for seahorses.

The intertidal sediments of the NW Solent tend to be soft mud with grades into muddy sand on more exposed shores. These sediments are highly productive in marine animals, with the tiny crustacean *Coronophium volutator* recorded at densities of up to 14000 per m² between Lymington and Hurst Spit. It is this extraordinary productivity which supports the birdlife of the estuary.

Hurst Spit and salt marsh. RC

The succession of communities in the saltmarshes within the intertidal to the west of the Lymington River, are truncated through the construction of the seawalls and simplified through the absence of grazing. The saltmarshes here are characterised by Sea Purslane *Halimione portulacoides* dominated communities, with other species of the 'middle marsh', including Sea Lavender *Limonium vulgare* and the saltmarsh grass *Spartina anglica*. In more sheltered creeks there are stands of perennial Tasselweeds *Ruppia spp*, together with annual glassworts *Salicornia spp*. The invertebrate fauna reflects the truncation of habitats. Where upper saltmarsh persists, such as in the shelter of Hurst Spit, the specialist hoverfly *Platycheirus marginatus* may be found.

The main marsh may not support specialist species, but the seasonal abundance of the fly *Scathophaga litorea* undoubtedly contributes to the food supply of birds and fish. Transitions to freshwater marsh are limited to the heavily modified banks of Sturt Pond, where the Danes Stream reaches the estuary. The Avon Water is a much larger river, reaching the estuary at Keyhaven. Tide gates prevent the flow of saltwater into the potential tidal reaches of the Avon Water. In recent years the closure of the pumps draining the river into the estuary, has enabled the formation of one of the largest reedbeds and freshwater swamps on the south coast.

To the east of the Lymington River, free-ranging ponies and cattle suppress the dominance of Sea Purslane, to produce a shorter, more botanically diverse marsh. The absence of seawalls enables localised expressions of upper saltmarsh transitions with freshwater marshes. At Pylewell, a flight-pond on the very upper limits of the saltmarsh remains open to Forest livestock with its grazed banks supporting Brackish Water-crowfoot *Ranunculus baudotii* and Fennel Pondweed *Potamogeton pectinatus*. The transitions at Sowley Marshes are far more complex, with the tidal element and salinity of the marsh undergoing numerous and sometimes contradictory changes. Brackish and freshwater marsh transitions with the saltmarsh, support a wide range of species, including Divided Sedge *Carex divisa*, with Chaffweed *Anagallis minima* locally sufficiently dominant to form lawns, as well as a myriad of hybrids on Marsh Orchids *Dactylorhiza spp*. The very rare hoverfly *Sphaerophoria loewi* has recently been recorded from these marshes. The transitional and dynamic nature of the habitats at Sowley Marshes is without parallel on The Solent coast.

The grazing marshes and lagoons

Between Lymington and Hurst Spit, the landward side of the saltmarshes is embanked behind a seawall. The marshes have a complex history, having developed on sites of nineteenth-century saltworks. Early editions of Ordnance Survey illustrated most of the land as being under use. Whilst the seawalls truncate the landward succession of the intertidal marshes, they artificially extend the transitions of the upper and freshwater marshes.

Late summer grazing on Normandy Farm. PRD

A range of habitats are present behind the sea walls, ranging from the stands of a Red Fescue–Thrift community, usually associated with coastal heathlands, to a series of brackish and freshwater marshes, as well as seasonally parched acid grasslands. Characteristic species of these brackish and freshwater transitions are the rushes *Juncus gerardii* and *J. maritimus*, Bulbous Foxtail *Alopecurus bulbosus* and its hybrids, together with Dotted Sedge *Carex punctata* and Divided Sedge *C. divisa*. The freshwater elements include swamps of spike rushes *Eleocharis palustris* and its hybrids and localised stands of Royal Fern *Osmuda regalis*, a species usually associated with bogs. The invertebrate fauna is equally diverse, including the striking large and persistent cleg *Haematopa grandis*, together with the Muscid

'Hairy Canary' Fly *Phaonia jaroschewskii*, a species better known from the peatlands at the head of the Humber Estuary.

The grazing marshes lack the hypersaline habitats of some other Solent marshes. Historically, the brine industry located on these marshes artificially generated extensive areas of this habitat. It was here the Brine Shrimp *Artemia salina* was recorded from the 1740s, through to the nineteenth century. The shrimp attracted a great deal of attention from naturalists, not least Charles Darwin, for its ability to thrive in a most extreme environment. With the closure of the saltworks, the species is now extinct in Britain. Other lagoons within the seawalls support an exceptional fauna and flora, including the algae Foxtail Stonewort *Lamprothamnium papulosum*, Tassleweeds *Ruppia spp*, the Insensible Lagoon Shrimp *Gammarus insensibilis* and Starlet Sea Anemone *Nematostella vectensis*.

Grazing on Oxey Marshes. PRD

The farmland

The farmland within this stretch of coast is at first sight unremarkable. Arable holdings are still present, which continue to support national rarities, such as the annual Quaking Grass *Briza minor* and the Nit Grass *Gastridium ventricosum*. The permanent grasslands reflect cattle farming and equestrianism, both uses managing the grassland at conventional intensity. Semi-natural grasslands are very rare and are associated with the wettest sites and amenity grassland. Where access to New Forest livestock persists such as at Tanners Lane, there are characteristic New Forest grasslands with species such as Chamomile *Chamaemelum nobile*. Regrettably, it was in Tanners Lane a chance accident destroyed the last Hampshire plants of Field Eryngo *Eryngium campestre*. Amongst the brine-soaked ancient Oaks, the scrub along this coast reflects the slightly base-enriched soils of the Headon Beds, with an abundance of species, such as Wild Madder *Rubia peregrina* and Burnett Rose *Rosa pimpinellifolia*.

Sea-lavender

Lymington–Keyhaven
Nature Reserves

'Men that undertake only one district are much more likely to advance natural knowledge than those that grasp at more than they can possibly be acquainted with; every kingdom, every province should have its own monographer.'

Gilbert White, 8 October 1770

The Lymington–Keyhaven shore is one of a number of nature reserves established on The Solent since the early 1960s. Unlike some very close to heavily populated areas and in spite of increasing numbers of visitors, the area retains a predominately rural atmosphere. For many, its special appeal lies in its relative informality, wide skies and extensive views both eastwards and westwards, northwards to the hinterland and southwards to the to the ever-changing backcloth of the Isle of Wight's renowned downs, chalk sea-cliffs and its red and white Needles Lighthouse.

Sunset over Normandy Farm Lagoon. MW

The region embraced by this publication is located on the central south coast of England in the county of Hampshire. The area is predominately rural; the historic town of Lymington is the only built-up area of significance abutting the coast. Large conurbations are not too distant, with the NW Solent shore lying midway between Southampton and Bournemouth, with combined populations in excess of 400,000 people. The recording area is limited to that part of the west Solent designated as the Hurst Castle/Lymington River Estuary Site of Special Scientific Interest, together with adjacent farmland that is also used by the SSSI's breeding, feeding and roosting bird populations.

As the gull flies, the area under consideration extends about 10 km from Milford-on-Sea in the west to Colgrims to the east. The recording area boundary is defined as follows: Hurst Castle and Spit to where the B3058 road converges with Milford Beach, northwards to its junction with the A337, then eastwards to Lymington's Avenue Road, Bridge Road, Undershore and South Baddesley Roads to East End Green, eastwards along Sowley Lane to Sandpits Lane, then south to Colgrims shore. The southern boundary follows the spring-tide low-water mark westwards from Colgrims to Hurst Castle, but the recording area also includes the waters of The Solent between Colgrims and Hurst Spit and that area of Christchurch Bay that includes the Brambles and Dolphin offshore shingle banks and out to The Needles (see map p.14).

Snow at Cut Bridge. RC

The area is situated predominately within the parishes of Milford-on-Sea, Lymington & Pennington, Boldre and Beaulieu. The recording area encompasses about 2,000 ha that include 750 ha of saltmarsh and mudflat and 200 ha of fresh and brackish grazing marshes, together with associated brackish lagoons immediately behind the sea defences. Other habitats include Hurst Spit, a prominent shingle ridge which protects the western end of The Solent, scattered mobile shell and shingle spreads (cheniers) along the saltmarsh outer fringe, Keyhaven's Avon Water with its associated reedbeds and adjacent wet meadows, agricultural land and small woods and copses and Sowley Marshes.

Sandwich Tern and Mediterranean Gull colony. MW

Those marshes were under the influence of a tidal regime for more than 50 years, following severe south-westerly storms, which breached a protective seawall in the early 1950s, though recently there were indications that an accreting shingle ridge fronting the marsh was inhibiting freshwater run-off. Half the recording area is protected by national and international nature conservation designations and lies within The Solent and Southampton Water Special Protection Area for Birds (SPA), as well as the New Forest National Park created in 2005. The SPA embraces 5,500 ha, of which the Hurst Castle/Lymington River Estuary Site of Special Scientific Interest (SSSI) component is 1,100 ha in extent. The close-by privately owned Sowley Pond is a Site of Special Scientific Interest in its own right. The 48 ha so designated, of which the water area is about 16.5 ha, also includes sections of fringing woodland to safeguard the solitude of the Pond and a long-established heronry. I have not attempted to document the Pond's considerable ornithological interest, but it should be noted that wildfowl flight between there and the NW Solent intertidal.

The Solent estuaries support large populations of waders, wildfowl and other wetland species, often at greater densities than on similar sites elsewhere in Britain. For example, over a five-year period during 1991/92 to 1995/96, The Solent and Southampton Water SPA supported an annual average of 54,000 waterfowl, of which the Hurst Castle/Lymington River Estuary's contribution was regularly in the order of 15,000–16,000 birds. Additionally, the Keyhaven/Lymington coast is unsurpassed in Hampshire for its sheer variety of species and several, such as the Dark-bellied Brent Goose and Black-tailed Godwit, are often present in numbers of international or national importance, though such large concentrations are relatively recent phenomena. Available evidence indicate that populations of over-wintering ducks, geese, waders and other waterbirds, although subject to periodic fluctuations, often beyond man's control, eg catastrophic migration disasters, were much reduced on the west Solent between 1900 and 1950, before becoming more numerous during the second half of the twentieth century. Tubbs (1992) analysed the diaries of wildfowler William Mudge, an amateur punt gunner who operated in Southampton Water and the Beaulieu Estuary during 1897–1952. Tubbs deduced that wildfowl and wader numbers were depressed, due in part to excessive hunting kill, during years before and between the 1914–18 and 1939–45 Wars, followed by recovery during and following those periods. Further increases followed the Bird Protection Act 1954, by which time there was less necessity to kill birds for food or to supplement incomes to the same degree. Furthermore, recent sympathetic habitat management, aided by grazing by New Forest commoners' stock, an annual rush-mowing regime and a rotational system of scrub control, resulted in a progressively increasing use of the Keyhaven/Normandy Farm grazing marshes by wildfowl and waders.

Black-headed Gull colony. MW

The Keyhaven/Lymington intertidal, much of which is leased to the Hampshire & Isle of Wight Wildlife Trust, together with Hampshire County Council's marshes, form one of those Solent estuaries particularly well known for the richness of their bird life. The most characteristic breeding bird of the saltmarshes is the Black-headed Gull. The gull breeding population dates from the early twentieth century when the saltmarsh was in an early stage of development. Though also present during winter months, one of the first indications that spring has arrived, may occur on an early March morning when the gulls, very vocal at this time of year, may be observed flying around and over prospective breeding sites. Several tern species, such as Little and Common Terns, also breed on the Reserve. It was the perilous plight of the Little Tern breeding population that prompted the Hampshire & Isle of Wight Wildlife Trust to set up a Little Tern conservation project and to oversee establishment of the saltmarsh reserve, in 1962. At that time, a major, pre-war Little Tern colony on Hurst Spit, had become depleted owing to constant disturbance by increasing numbers of visitors walking the beach. The terns eventually moved onto shell and shingle spits fronting the saltmarshes, where they joined relic groups already utilising those sites. Other species breeding on the saltmarshes include Mute Swans, Canada Geese, Mallards, Oystercatchers, Ringed Plovers, Redshanks, one or two pairs of Common Gulls, Great Black-backed Gulls, Lesser Black-backed Gulls, and a few Meadow Pipits and Reed Buntings.

A flurry of Wigeon. RC

The grazing marshes come into their own during the spring and autumn migrations and in the winter months. Regular spring migrants include ducks, such as Garganey, and waders, such as Ringed Plovers, Dunlins and Bar-tailed Godwits, which migrate from Africa and southern Europe to breed in Scandinavia, Siberia and other northern lands. Autumn migrants regularly include Redshanks, Dunlins and Whimbrels from Iceland, Spotted Redshanks, Greenshanks, and Ruffs from Fenno-Scandia and Curlew Sandpipers, Grey Plovers and Little Stints from north Russia. There are more birds on the Reserve during winter, when principal species include Dark-bellied Brent Geese, Wigeon, Teal, Pintail, Shoveler, Lapwings and Golden Plovers. Species, such as Great Crested and Slavonian Grebes, diving duck, such as Eiders and Red-breasted Mergansers, are often encountered in offshore waters. The saltmarshes offer high-tide wader roost sites, but when over-topped by spring tides, they resort to the lagoons, grazing marshes and fields, inside the seawalls.

The marshes are well served by public footpaths and are viewable from the seawall between Lymington and Keyhaven. The area is conveniently accessed from Keyhaven where there is an adequate all-year pay & display car-parking facility opposite the Gun Inn. From there, an alternative walk is eastwards

Remains of a section of Pennington Marshes seawall, east of The Butts, abandoned in mid-1930s following storm damage . MW

along the Marsh Road, an ancient track-way bordering the north side of the marshes that served the salterns situated between Keyhaven and Lymington. Parking facilities, accessed from Milford-on-Sea, are also available at New Lane, from where one can walk along Hurst Spit to Hurst Castle. Alternatively there is a frequent ferry service between Keyhaven and Hurst Castle. A convenient car park is also situated at Bath Road (Lymington) at the east end of the marshes, from where the coastal footpath runs westwards, around the seawall to the Yacht Haven and Normandy Farm. Because of its informality and rural setting, notice boards and other signage are restricted to a minimum, but visitors are requested to behave responsibly when on this extremely important nature reserve and to keep dogs under control at all times. Unauthorised vehicles are not permitted on the footpaths or track-ways.

Hampshire County Council personnel are responsible for the day-to-day management of the Reserves and can be contacted, via the site manager, at Town Hall, Avenue Road, Lymington, Hampshire, SO41 9ZG.

54

Ornithological recording at Lymington–Keyhaven

Selborne parish alone can and has exhibited at times more than half the birds that are ever seen in all Sweden; the former has produced more than one hundred and twenty species, the latter only two hundred and twenty-one. Let me add also that it has shown near half the species that were ever known in Great Britain.

Gilbert White, 2 September 1774

Introduction

The evolution of ornithological recording in Hampshire was very fully discussed by Richard A Leach and Norman H Pratt in *Birds of Hampshire* (1993). They recounted how the Hampshire Field Club 'was the only countywide organisation contributing to Hampshire ornithology prior to the formation of the separate Ornithological Section in 1954.' The HFC, formed in 1885, maintained a Natural History Section from its earliest days and appointed subject secretaries, Kelsall and Munn, authors of the first Hampshire avifauna of 1905, being the first in 1922. An Ornithological section of HFC was formed in 1954, followed by a completely independent Hampshire Ornithological Society, in 1978.

The Northwest Solent

The aim of this publication is to portray, in one volume, as much available information as possible of those bird species recorded on the NW Solent from the early nineteenth century and up to 2012, though a few records to 2015 are also included, as are one or two references to earlier material.

By any standards, the NW Solent comprises an impressive array of bird habitats. Hence, up to the end of 2015, of a Hampshire total of 377 species, at least 318 (including sub-species) within the NW Solent recording area were accepted as reliably documented. Of those, at least 112 have bred or have attempted breeding and a further five probably did so. At least 38 species and subspecies are considered to be 'firsts' for Hampshire, including those that became so, following subsequent county boundary changes. A few records, eg a Madeiran Petrel *Oceanodroma castro*, found dead on Milford-on-Sea beach on 19 November 1911 (K&M) and a Red-breasted Flycatcher *Ficedula parva* at Oxey Marshes on 2 October 1968, have been omitted from the current list. Following review by relevant Records Committees, they were deemed inadequately documented and therefore no longer acceptable, but in connection with the former species, see Munn (1912) and Combridge & Wiseman (2009.)

For the period 1959–2001, I drew heavily on personal records and those of Roger Brown, Pete and Mike Combridge, Bob Dunn, Roger Harris, Peter Hobby, Chris Fox, Owen Haisell, Len Mummery, David Peart, Mike Stewart, Bev Snellgrove, Phil Toye, Colin and Jenni Tubbs, Gerald and Don Westerhoff, Jim Williams, Dave Wooldridge and Susan Wood. For pre-1959 data and post-*Birds of Hampshire* (1993) material, I was increasingly reliant on information published in *Hampshire Bird Reports* and Hampshire Ornithological Society's digitised database, to which I was kindly allowed access.

The Tetrad Atlas breeding bird survey (Atlas Survey)

A survey of Hampshire's breeding birds during 1986–1991 was organised by a Steering Committee, under the auspices of the Hampshire Ornithological Society. The Committee consisted of seven members that included Peter Puckering who acted as survey co-ordinator. He did a superb job; collating data in those pre-computer days was no mean task. The adopted methodology was that used for *The Atlas of Breeding Birds of Britain and Ireland* (Sharrock 1976). The aim of the Hampshire Atlas was to map bird distribution on a 2×2 km grid, placing breeding evidence in one of three categories (confirmed, probable or possible), though note that in the following species accounts I often refer to breeding as considered likely. Ninety percent of tetrad SZ28V (Sturt Pond) was within the recording area and six tetrads, all part intertidal and wholly within the NW Solent area were: SZ39A (Keyhaven), SZ39B (Lower Pennington), SZ39G (Pennington Marshes), SZ39H (Waterford), SZ39M (Lisle Court) and SZ39S (Pitts Deep).

The Wetland Bird Survey (WeBS)

The long tradition of systematic wildfowl counting dated from the late 1940s and was initially under the guidance of the Wildfowl Inquiry Committee of the British Section of the International Council for Bird Preservation, based at the British Natural History Museum. The survey was extended in the winter of 1951/52, but organisation of the National Wildfowl counts (NWC) passed to Sir Peter Scott's Wildfowl Trust, now the Wildfowl and Wetlands Trust (WWT), in 1954. Wader species were included in 1969, on commencement of the Birds of Estuaries Enquiry (BoEE). Currently known as the Wetland Bird Survey (WeBS) and set-up to monitor non-breeding waterfowl in Britain, it is jointly organised by the British Trust for Ornithology (BTO), Royal Society for the Protection of Birds (RSPB) and Joint Nature Conservation Committee (JNCC), in association with the Wildfowl and Wetlands Trust. The aims of the survey are to identify population sizes, determine trends in numbers and distribution and identify important waterfowl sites.

NW Solent observers contributed monthly wildfowl and wader counts to the above scheme since its inception, though wildfowl counts were carried out from 1965. Counts were originally conducted for the Hurst Spit/Lymington River coast, but were later extended to embrace the whole of the Hurst Castle/Lymington River Estuary Site of Scientific Interest. Ornithologists who contributed to the waterfowl counts, included Bob Dunn, Chris Fox, Owen Haisell, Bev Snellgrove, Susan Wood and Ed Wiseman. Others involved at different times during the 1970s/1980s included Mike and Pete Combridge, Barry Duffin, Roger Harris, John Jones, Diana Lockton, Diana Westerhoff and Wendy Wiseman, and in the 1990s, June Irvine (Pitts Deep) and Robin Saunders and Steve Lancaster (Lymington River–Tanners Lane). I particularly record Robin's Pylewell contribution (carried out until August 2004) as he was not allocated a BTO online 'user name' so is not listed as the observer for the above period, on the BTO WeBS Pylewell database.

Latterly, the WeBS team comprised Pete Durnell and Adrian Clark (professional HCC staff), Owen Haisell, Peter Hobby, Tim Parminter, Marcus Ward and Ed Wiseman, who continues to act as organiser and co-ordinator.

Waterbirds at low tide

The WeBS core counts were supplemented by Low Tide counts, which were introduced at a limited number of British estuaries during the winter of 1992/93. The aim is to record, every five years, the low-water distribution of feeding and roosting wildfowl, waders and other water birds, within individual estuaries. NW Solent observers contributed to the scheme since its concept. For recording purposes, the NW Solent intertidal zone is divided into 18 count sectors and limited counting was also undertaken on a further six sectors across the grazing marshes and other inland areas. For the purposes of this survey, birds within each sector are counted once a month at low tide (defined as a period of two hours each side of dead low water) during November–February inclusive. Ed Wiseman carried out the counts during the winters of 1992/93, 1997/98, 2004/05, 2008/09 and 2010/11, but during 2012/13 Adrian Clark, Peter Durnell, Owen Haisell Peter Hobby and Marcus Ward, also participated.

Waders feeding in Mount Lake. RC

The Common Bird Census (CBC), the Breeding Bird Survey (BBS) and local surveys

Common Bird Censuses were carried out on Normandy Farm during 1976–2000 and at Salterns during 1976–1999. Owen Haisell did much of the Salterns work and Ed Wiseman censused Normandy Farm. Until it was officially discontinued, Peter Hobby monitored the breeding birds of Hurst Spit as a 'special' BTO plot for a few years. CBC methodology followed that set out by the BTO, which necessitated at least ten visits, carried out at regular intervals some seven to ten days apart, on pre-determined plots during late March–late June. All birds (contacts) seen or heard were plotted onto large-scale maps. At the conclusion of each season all registrations for each species were plotted onto separate species maps and sent to the BTO for professional analysis. NW Solent maps are archived at BTO headquarters at The Nunnery, Thetford, Norfolk.

In 1996, I supplemented the Normandy Farm and Salterns CBC with a Keyhaven Marshes Breeding Bird Survey (BBS) plot. Simpler and much less time-consuming than the CBC, this entailed two spring visits to a 1 km square, where a pre-determined route was divided into 200-metre sectors and all categories of 25, 25–100 and more than 100 m, were plotted on each side of each sector. Six 200-metre sectors along the Keyhaven seawall between Iley Point and the eastern end of Keyhaven lagoon were walked on two occasions each season; the survey remained ongoing in 2016. Meanwhile, Pete Hobby and Marc Moody continued detailed annual surveys of the breeding birds of Hurst Spit and the saltmarshes between Mount Lake and Keyhaven River and eastwards to Pennington Marshes Butts.

Systematic accounts of the birds of Lymington–Keyhaven

Winter gathering on Pennington Marshes

The following abbreviations are used:

Atlas Survey	Hampshire Ornithological Society Tetrad Atlas Breeding Bird Survey, 1986–1991
BBS	Breeding Bird Survey
BOU	British Ornithologists' Union
BOURC	British Ornithologists' Union Records Committee
BST	British summer time
BTO	British Trust for Ornithology
CBC	Common Birds Census
DEFRA	Department for Environment, Food and RuralAffairs
HBR	Hampshire Bird Report
HOS	Hampshire Ornithological Society
HWT	Hampshire & Isle of Wight Wildlife Trust
IOC	International Ornithological Committee
JNCC	Joint Nature Conservation Committee
RBBP	Rare Breeding Birds Panel
RSPB	Royal Society for the Protection of Birds
SAC	Special Area of Conservation
SPA	Special Protection Area for Birds
SSSI	Site of Special Scientific Interest
WeBS	Wetland Bird Survey
WWT	Wildfowl & Wetlands Trust

Authors and publications

References to authors and publication dates of books and papers are of paramount importance and their use unavoidable, but in the following species accounts, dates are omitted whenever possible. Where a publication is the work of a single author, only the surname is given; when the work of two authors, only surnames' initials are given; if three or more, the surname of the first is given, followed by *et al* (abbreviation of Latin *et alii*, meaning 'and other persons').

Books

History of Lymington and its Immediate Vicinity by David William Garrow 1825 **(Garrow)**
*The Diary of Colonel Peter Hawke*r by Sir Ralph Payne-Gallwey Bart. 1893 **(Payne-Gallwey)**
The New Forest: Its History and Scenery by J R Wise 1895 **(Wise)**
The Birds of Hampshire and the Isle of Wight by Rev. J E Kelsall & P W Munn 1905 **(K&M)**
The Birds of Milford by Kelsall & Coles 1913 **(K&C)**
A Geographical Biography of British Ornithology by W H Mullins, H Kirke Swann & Rev. F C R
 Jourdain 1920 **(Mullins *et al*)**
British Game by Brian Vesey-Fitzgerald 1946 **(Vesey-Fitzgerald)**
Wildfowl in Hampshire by J H Taverner 1962 **(Taverner)**
Birds of Hampshire and the Isle of Wight by Edwin Cohen 1963 **(Cohen)**
A Revised List of Hampshire and Isle of Wight Birds by Edwin Cohen & J H Taverner 1972 **(C&T)**
Birds of Hampshire (1993) edited by J M Clark & J A Eyre **(BoH)**
The New Atlas of Breeding Birds in Britain and Ireland: 1988–91 by Gibbons, D W, Reid, J W &
 Chapman, R A 1993 **(Gibbons *et al*)**

Journals

Papers and Proceedings of the Hampshire Field Club and Archaeological Society (Proc.) from
 1932–1946, the *South Eastern Bird Report* (1934–1946) successive *Hampshire Bird Report*s
 to 2015 and the journal *British Birds*.

Status Terms

The current NW Solent status of each species is assessed upon the following simple, broad categories

Rare   Twenty records or fewer and unlikely to be encountered

Scarce   Possibly encountered in optimum seasons

Common Likely to be encountered in optimum seasons

Nomenclature and species sequence

Scientific nomenclature and species' names and sequence follow the British Ornithologists' Union's (BOU) most recently published checklist of British birds (2013), but note that alternative names (shown in brackets) though not used in this publication, are adopted by the International Ornithological Committee (IOC) eg Bewick's Swan (Tundra Swan) Arctic Skua (Parasitic Jaeger) and Magpie (Eurasian Magpie). Brief accounts of species' current NW Solent status, together with global summer and winter distribution of those that do not breed here or have small or tiny British populations then follow. Where applicable, the species accounts open with those by Kelsall & Coles (*The Birds of Milford*, 1913) that with one or two exceptions, eg White-tailed Eagle, are reproduced in their entire, original format.

Many accounts are then divided into two seemingly randomly selected periods, ie up to 1992 and post-BoH, the reason being that 1992 was the cut-off date for information that appeared in *Birds of Hampshire* (1993). However, note that some data in that work, eg five-year averages of autumn/winter wader and wildfowl maxima, spanned the period 1955–1990. For the purposes of this publication, post-BoH data, unless dated otherwise, refer specifically to the period 1993–2012. Peak weekly periods of migrations of some species, eg summer residents and migratory waders, were assessed by summing available daily counts of individual species, thus giving 'bird-day' totals. NW Solent bird-ringing data were not researched in detail, but I have included a few selected recoveries of birds ringed or recovered in the vicinity, For those species routinely monitored by the Wetland Bird Survey (WeBS) the means of five-year maxima during 2007/08–2011/12 for Great Britain, Hampshire and NW Solent respectively, are given. Information in this work may differ from that in *A Checklist of the Birds of Keyhaven–Lymington and Milford-on-Sea* (2014); where it does so, it corrects or updates that publication.

I hope readers will take the trouble to copy me details of errors or inaccuracies, for which I accept sole responsibility.

Gannet & Great Skua

Species Accounts

Shoveler

Mute Swan *Cygnus olor*
Common, a resident, passage migrant and winter visitor
'Resident, in a more or less domesticated condition and a highly characteristic bird of our coast' (K&C).

During the CBC, single territories were occupied at Normandy Farm in 1994 and 1996–2000 and at Salterns in 1987–1994 and 1999. During the Atlas Survey, breeding was confirmed at Sturt Pond, Keyhaven, Pennington Marshes and Lisle Court.

Since at least the early 1950s, Sturt Pond emerged as a site favoured by Mute Swans and where, in severely cold weather, up to 75 were present on 29 December 1953, 90 in early January 1954 and the all-time Pond's maximum of 120 on 6 January 1979. The average of annual winter-maxima, west of Lymington River (Sturt Pond included) during 1970/71–1989/1990, was about 50.

Post-BoH, Mute Swans nested specifically at Sturt Pond, Avon Water flood, Manor Farm, Keyhaven and Pennington Marshes, Salterns Eight Acre Pond, Normandy Farm lagoon, Lymington River (between the railway bridge and Bridge Road) Elmer's Court, Bulls Saltern (Lisle Court) and Sowley Marshes. Despite increasing vulnerability to high spring-tides, one or two pairs also attempted nesting on saltmarshes west of Keyhaven River in most years. Up to c.12 pairs was the upper limit of the annual NW Solent breeding population.

Winter-maxima during 1990/91–2011/12 also averaged about 50 and peaks usually occurred in November/December, sometimes in January (four occasions) or February (three occasions) with a NW Solent day-maximum of 124 on 17 November 2012. Numbers usually declined during March, though at least 58 remained on 11 March 2011. Sturt Pond and the immediate vicinity of Mount Lake and Keyhaven continued to harbour the majority of Mute Swans, particularly in autumn and winter, though with stabilising water levels, significant numbers were latterly attracted to Keyhaven/Pennington Marshes' lagoons.

Bewick's Swan *Cygnus columbianus*
Scarce, a winter visitor; breeds in W Siberia
Though not recognised as a distinct species until 1830, Hawker did not appear to have encountered this bird. He was very well acquainted with Whooper Swans and routinely measured and weighed those he killed. A smaller and much lighter individual would have immediately attracted his attention and a mention in his Diary, but he made no reference to such wild swans.

Paralleling establishment of wintering herds in other southern English counties and in Cambridgeshire, during the 1960s, Bewick's Swans increased in Hampshire, where they wintered mostly in the Avon valley. The first record for Keyhaven appeared to be an adult during 17–30 December 1967. A further 105 individuals during 1968–1992 included day-maxima of 11 that flew north at Pennington Marshes on 1 January 1979 and 12 at Sowley on 3 January 1982. All occurred during 27 October (in 1984 and 1985)–1 March (in 1991) in October (8), November (18), December (5), January (68), February (3) and March (3). A flock of 14, in flight over Lymington on 9 January 1986, was possibly outside the recording area.

Post-BoH, a significant decline in the Hampshire wintering population was reflected on the NW Solent, where only 37 individuals, but which included a day-maximum of 15 (12 adults) at Pennington Marshes on 17 January 1993, were recorded. All were reported during 26 November (in 1995)–15 February (in 1996) in November (1), December (4), January (30) and February (2) though none were after 1997.

Whooper Swan *Cygnus cygnus*
Scarce, a winter visitor; breeds in Iceland and from Fenno-Scandinavia to eastern Siberia
'A rare winter migrant, only occurring in severe weather. Hawker bagged thirty-eight in fifty years' (K&C).
Hawker considered the Whooper Swan a punt-gunner's ultimate prize. He recorded a total of about 90–100 at Keyhaven between January 1823 and January 1845, of which at least 40 occurred on 25 January 1838. Few are on

in February 1991 (3,335) in January 1992 (4,800, an all-time high, of which 4,500 grazed on grass on the Manor Farm Goose Field and which represented roughly 3.5 per cent of the British wintering population of almost 138,000 at that time) in January 1993 (3,446) and in January 1995 (3,546). Winter-maxima were reported in December (4 seasons), January (13 seasons) and February (5 seasons). Numbers declined during March, the peak day-maximum being 2,150 in 1993. Three-figure April counts were attained in 12 years with a day-maximum of 623 in 2006. Few remained into May, the most being just 15 that flew west at Hurst Spit on 2 May 1994 and 15 at Pennington/Oxey Marshes on 13 May 2006. Stragglers during June–August were presumably mostly sick or injured individuals.

First autumn arrivals were usually during the second half of September, though some in early September were also deemed genuine first returns. A count of 197 in September 1996 was the only three-figure count for that month; otherwise few September counts attained double-figures. October maxima exceeded 1,000 only in 1993 (1,145) in 1999 (at least 1,100, of which 1,000 were west of Lymington River) and in 2012 (1,050 that included 850 west of Lymington River). Unsurprisingly, all occurred during years when large numbers of juveniles were present.

The dusk-flights of Brents to their intertidal nocturnal roosting grounds became anticipated features of 1980s/90s, NW Solent winters. Enjoyed not only by birdwatchers, but also by interested locals and other onlookers, three or four thousand Brents in full cry over Keyhaven Harbour were never-to-be-forgotten sights and sounds.

Previously undetected behaviour during the winter of 2005/06, involved small numbers that crossed Hurst Narrows from Keyhaven to the Isle of Wight, with corresponding returns later in the day; one such count was of about 100 on 8 February 2007.

Spring passage at Hurst Spit took place during mid-March– mid-April, but sometimes in May and once on 2 June 2002 (a singleton that flew east). A grand total of 2,370 that flew east included 525 in 2000 during 1–30 April and a day-maximum of 208 on 1st.

Autumn migration sometimes occurred in September but more often in October, eg 75 flew west on 23 September 2000 and 187 flew east on 24 October 2012. Mid-winter movements were also detected at Hurst Spit and included 340 that flew east on 28 January 2011.

Those wintering to the east of Lymington River often flew towards the Beaulieu Estuary, but returned at dusk to roost in the Pylewell intertidal.

Age-counts carried out during 1991/92–2011/2012, revealed significant fluctuations in numbers of juveniles. The average of about 16 per cent (a little above the calculated minimum reproductive success rate considered necessary to maintain the global population) ranged between none in 2000/01 and 53 per cent in 1991/92. Factors that contributed to the significant and rapid growth of the British population included increased legal protection under the 1954 Protection of Birds Act, which reduced hunting mortality, as well as a series of very successful breeding seasons. Also, adaptation to inland grazing on grass and autumn-sown cereals during the 1970s/1980s (first recorded at Keyhaven in 1982/83) enabled geese to remain in optimum physical condition throughout the winter. Five-year averages of British, Hampshire and NW Solent WeBS maxima during 2007/08–2011/12 were 82,633, 13,793 and 2,000 respectively.

Light-bellied Brent Goose *Branta bernicla hrota*

Scarce, but increasing spring/autumn passage migrant and winter visitor and occasionally in summer; breeds in Franz Josef Land, Svalbard, Greenland and north-east Canada and winters in Denmark, north-east England, Ireland and US Atlantic coast from Maine to Georgia

Three Brent shot by Hawker on 30 January 1823 appeared to be of this race and probably the first for Hampshire. Though he had handled fewer than 250 Brents at that time, he described them as 'the finest I ever saw and almost white in the breast'; nowhere else in the Diaries does he mention Brents with such striking white under-parts. Otherwise, the first authenticated record of *hrota* on the NW Solent was of 20 at Keyhaven on 3 March 1929; another was at Keyhaven, together with nine Dark-bellied Brents, on 2 March 1952. During 1969–1992, at least 19 individuals were recorded in January (4), February (2), March (10) and December (3). All were singletons, other than five at Pennington Marshes on 5 March 1971, five, of which three were juveniles, at Pylewell on 28 March 1980 and two adults at Pitts Deep on 8 February 1981.

Post-BoH (1993–2015) it was more frequently detected. At least 180 occurred during 8 July (in 2012)–14 May (also in 2012) in July (1), August (1, an injured individual), September (21), October (22), November (11), December (4),

January (18), February (24), March (2), April (60) and May (16). Among the more notable records were 11 on 1 April 1994, 16 that flew east on 20 April 1999 and 31 that flew west on 18 April 2012 (all at Hurst Spit) and ten at Normandy Farm on 14 May 2012.

In autumn, nine flew east at Hurst Spit on 16 September 2008 and ten were in Mount Lake on 3 October 1999. An adult female in the vicinity of Sturt Pond during 26 January–28 February 2009, was colour-ringed in south-west Iceland in May 2005 and wintered at Strangford Lough (Northern Ireland) in 2005/06. It was reported in Iceland in the springs of 2006 and 2007 and was recorded in Dublin Bay during 8–11 November 2008. This provided evidence that at least some birds recorded in Hampshire were from the Canadian/Greenland, rather than the Svalbard population.

Black Brant *Branta bernicla nigricans*
Rare, an autumn, winter and spring visitor; breeds in arctic coasts of western N America and E Siberia and winters both coasts of N Pacific

Post-BoH (1993–2015) two in late 2001 (an adult female from 25 November and an adult male from 16 December) represented the first for the NW Solent; they were part of a record influx into southern and eastern England, at that time. Both remained in the Hurst/Lymington area into March 2002, the male until 24th and the female until 29th. Another was at Sturt Pond on 7 October 2002 and though difficult to be precise, it was considered that at least a further 11 individuals that included up to three during 25 October 2009–12 April 2010, occurred during 2003–2013. Other than one first-winter/summer in the Sturt Pond/Mount Lake area on 6th and 12 April 2010, all those aged were adult.

The Hampshire total to 2015 was 31 individuals.

Red-breasted Goose *Branta ruficollis*
Rare, an autumn and winter visitor; breeds in W Siberia and winters, locally, as far west as the Black Sea

At least ten records involved a minimum of five individuals, of which at least two, assigned to the 'escapes from captivity' category, occurred on 26 May and 6 June 1994 and on 2nd and 23 September 1995, and during 14–24 February 2011; the latter bore a small, red leg-ring. Individuals considered to be of wild origin were: a first-winter during 11 January–31 March 1997 and an adult at Keyhaven during 26–31 January 2007, at Keyhaven–Normandy Farm during 31 October 2008–6 February 2009 and with ten Brent Geese on 5 October 2010, possibly referred to one individual. Finally, another at Keyhaven/Pennington Marshes on 25/26 February 2012 and at Hurst Spit–Keyhaven on 24 October 2012, moved to Langstone Harbour where it remained from 25 October into 2013. It returned to Langstone Harbour on 27 September 2013, was at Sturt Pond/Pennington Marshes during 10 October–24 November 2013 and again in early January 2014: in between times it frequented the Beaulieu Estuary and Shalfleet/Newtown (Isle of Wight) during 30 November–20 December 2012.

The Hampshire total to 2015 was ten individuals.

Egyptian Goose *Alopochen aegyptiacus*
Rare, a feral visitor; its native range is Africa

At least 18 records involved about 42 individuals; one at Pennington Marshes on 13 August 1971 was deemed the first modern-day county record (also see K&M).

Post-BoH, one was at Pennington Marshes on 18 October 1994. The remainder, all singletons at Keyhaven/Pennington Marshes unless otherwise stated, occurred on 5 September 1995, 26 October 2003, 30 April/1 May 2004, 14th and 30 August, 18th and 25 September, in 2005, 3/4 April 2006, 5 April 2007, 7 January and 21 September 2009, during 31 January–20 February 2010, 14–16 April and 15 October, in 2011, four that flew east at Keyhaven on 17 June 2000, 14 that flew east at Hurst Spit on 21 October 2012 and nine that flew east over Hurst Spit then landed at Keyhaven, on 25 October 2014.

Ruddy Shelduck *Tadorna ferruginea*
Rare, most were probably escapes from captivity; its native range is S Europe, Africa and Asia

This handsome shelduck has long been popular in captivity (Delacour & Scott 1954–64) so it was not surprising that the validity of many of the British records was discussed, eg by Saunders (1899), Rogers (1982) and Vinicombe & Harrop (1999). Only those that occurred in 1892 as part of an influx, detected as far west as Greenland, are currently accepted as referring to wild individuals (Harrop 2002).

K&M were well aware of the circumstances surrounding the 1892 immigrants. Of three reported that year, one was shot in August 'by Mr. Vores of Lymington, in the neighbourhood of that town' and was 'still in his possession.' The next were two at Hurst Spit on 3 April 1977 and five that flew west at Pennington Marshes on 29 August 1988. **Post-BoH**, 13 individuals, which included three that flew west off Hurst Spit and reported later at Weymouth (Dorset) on 26 September 2009, were recorded during 24 July (in 2007)–11 April (in 1997) in July (1), August (2), September (3), October (1), November (2), December (1), January (1 that showed signs of pinioning), February (1) and April (1).

Shelduck *Tadorna tadorna*
Common, a resident, spring/autumn passage migrant and winter visitor

'A resident, nesting in several places in the neighbourhood but chiefly to be seen at Keyhaven in small flocks in winter. We are glad to think that this handsome species is increasing in numbers and hope it may continue to do so without molestation, being a great ornament to our estuaries and of no value whatever as food' (K&C).
Garrow recorded that 'a few flocks of Burrow Duck' frequented our coast 'in rigorous weather.' Wise made no reference to this bird wintering on the New Forest coast during the first half of the nineteenth century, but K&M noted that Hawker killed 37 in fifty years, adding 'it was not much more common then than now.'
Estuaries are the preferred habitat of breeding Shelduck in Britain and as such, other than the Eider, are unique among British breeding ducks in that the majority are confined to maritime counties. Wise did not mention Shelduck in his list of breeding species of the New Forest and adjoining coastline, though 40 years later K&M reported that nests had been found at Keyhaven and in the salterns towards Lymington. Post-1945, Taverner cited a crèche of 11 with two adults on 30 May 1947, though it is unclear if Shelduck nested regularly on the NW Solent at that time. During 1961–1989, at least 127 broods were recorded, with season-maxima of ten broods in 1968 and 15 broods, between Keyhaven and Sowley, in 1975. During the Atlas Survey, when breeding was confirmed in 25 Hampshire coastal tetrads, six successful pairs between Lymington River and Colgrims was one of the largest concentrations reported in any one year. First broods usually appeared during mid-May–mid-June, somewhat earlier than the second or third week of June as reported by Cohen.
Summarising Hampshire Shelduck populations, Taverner cited the NW Solent's usual annual-maxima as 100–500, but the first documented estimate in excess of his upper limit, was 540 on 28 December 1969. Cohen noted that 'it is now very common along the coast in winter.' C&T were more forthcoming, but Hampshire Bird Reports and BoH give a clearer understanding of its NW Solent status. Shelduck usually returned in October, sometimes as late as December, eg a group of 15 that flew west over Hurst Spit and into Poole Bay on 6 December 1955 coincided with small parties at sea off Eastbourne (East Sussex) and a significant influx to Langstone Harbour. Winter peaks occurred usually in January, sometimes in February or in early spring, eg March. Annual winter-maxima during 1960–1990 averaged about 400, with a day-peak of 1,100 during cold weather, of which 400 were in Oxey Lake and 700 at Keyhaven, on 5 January 1979.
An easterly spring movement at Hurst Spit included 183 during 10 April–10 May 1976, 164 during 19 April–21 May 1978, 13 on 13 June 1985 and a day-maximum of 80 that flew east on 25 April 1973.
Post-BoH, Shelduck continued to breed throughout the NW Solent, on the grazing marshes, on farmland and within and around Hurst Castle; a total of at least 81 pairs that included a season-maximum of 15 pairs in 1999, were recorded on territory or with broods, during 1990–2012.
Significant decreases occurred in Hampshire Shelduck populations during that period. Mid-winter (January) counts on the NW Solent declined from 404 in 1993, to 94 in 2005, to 83 in 2009 and to 76 in 2010, but recovered to 190 in 2011. Otherwise, monthly-maxima during February–December were 333 (in 1994), 250 (in 2011), 250 (in 1998), 127 (in 2006), 130 (at Pylewell in 2004), 51 (in 2007), 33 (in 2010), 54 (in 2012), 60 (in 1993) 122 (in 2010) and 256 (in 1993) respectively. Prior to the late 1980s, flocks of 100–200 were often reported east of the Lymington River, but during 1993–2012, other than 65 in December 2010, populations barely attained 40–50.
At least 99 that included 53 during 8 April (in 1997)–25 May (in 1999) flew east at Hurst Spit in April (42) and May (57). Also, easterly movements of birds possibly en route to moulting grounds in the Netherlands, were noted in July and included 65 at Milford-on-Sea on 11th in 1996, 14 at Normandy Farm on 4th in 1999 and 20 at Milford-on-Sea on 8th, also in 1999. In autumn, 33 flew east at Milford-on-Sea on 19 September 1999.
A principal concentration in the vicinity of Keyhaven habitually flight between the grazing marshes' lagoons and

creeks and spreaders around Hawker's and Telegraph Lakes. The previously much-favoured haunt of Oxey Lake was often devoid of Shelduck in later years, but more likely then encountered on the adjacent Normandy Farm lagoon.

A Hampshire-bred bird that was ringed at Southampton Docks in June 1978 was found dead at Hurst Castle in January 1987 (BoH).

Five-year averages of British, Hampshire and NW Solent WeBS maxima during 2007/08–2011/12 were 51,275, 1,296 and 219 respectively.

Mandarin Duck *Aix galericulata*
Scarce, an autumn, winter and spring visitor, but probably more frequent than records suggest; its native range is E Asia

Mandarins were introduced into England from Asia in the eighteenth century, nowadays breeding not uncommonly in many parts of Hampshire, including the woodlands of the New Forest. Two, shot near Lymington in 1957 (Taverner) were the first reported on the NW Solent.

Post-BoH, a male was at Keyhaven on 30 November 1996 and a further 19 individuals to 2003, included a pair at Salterns on 11 May 2000. Other than up to four at Lower Pennington on 27 October 2012, a majority since 2004 were reported east of Lymington River where the day-maximum was nine on 20 November 2005. Those at Pylewell, an area highly suitable to the species, hinted that it was probably more frequent there than the few records indicate: it certainly became more numerous in winter on nearby Sowley Pond, from where they flight at dusk to nocturnal feeding areas.

Wigeon *Anas penelope*
Common, a winter visitor and spring/autumn passage-migrant and occasionally in summer

'Regular winter migrant, the most common of our wildfowl' (K&C).

Garrow observed that Wigeon appeared 'about October; they keep out at sea by day; and make great flights over our shores by night, to their feeding haunts.' Though much information can be gleaned from Hawker's accounts, we are unable to speculate fully on the annual pattern of Wigeon occurrences at Keyhaven at that time. First arrival dates were not always documented, as Hawker did not usually visit Keyhaven until later in the year. Writing of his arrival on 13 November 1832, however, he commented 'the greatest number of wildfowl killed by any gunner this season that I have heard of was three Wigeon. Quite marvellous when in former years I have known hundreds killed in October.' A large influx also occurred in early October 1840, 'the greatest October flight ever known.' Due no doubt to high disturbance levels, Wigeon were not continually present at Keyhaven throughout the winter; Hawker would often be out night after night and not hear or see one bird. It was possible that Wigeon resorted to Christchurch Bay and thus remained undetected, but that was unlikely for any length of time. We know little of the extent of inland feeding by NW Solent Wigeon in Hawker's era, though some 2,000 on the sea 'under Barton cliffs' in February 1845 were said to fly at night to Christchurch's rivers. Other than the Brent Goose, this species was Hawker's principal quarry. Of a total bag of 2,211, all but a handful were obtained at Keyhaven, where his most prolific winters were 1828/29 and 1837/38 during which he killed 433 and 220 respectively. His estimate of 1,000 at Keyhaven on the night of 5/6 January 1816 appears to be the first documented four-figure number for the area. However, he had recorded 'prodigious flights' there on 2 January 1815 and other significant estimates included 2,000 on 5 February 1838 and 1,500 on 8 January 1850.

During the nineteenth century, Wigeon fed principally on Eelgrass *Zostera sp.* in the intertidal and flew to the waters of The Solent, or out to sea, when shooting pressure became too severe. K&C lamented the encroachment of Cordgrass (*Spartina*) into the Lymington–Keyhaven estuary, as it was detrimental to Eelgrass, observing that 'the character of the feeding grounds has much altered owing to the rapid increase of a rice or cord grass and this probably accounts for the disappearance of many birds.' They were, however, able to report that in favourable seasons, Wigeon frequented the harbour (by which they meant the entire area inside Hurst Spit) in considerable numbers, adding that large flocks spent the day with other ducks on the open sea and came into the harbour at dusk. Taverner noted this species was occasionally encountered in large numbers on the open sea, close to the Hurst Castle tide-race, particularly when disturbed by game shooting on adjacent coastal estates. C&T cited a post-Second World War maximum of just 500 between Hurst Spit and Pennington Marshes, stating that this species, as with Teal, was usually to be found in the creeks amid the *Spartina* or on exposed mud flats.

There was no adequately documented breeding record for Hampshire, but sick or injured birds occasionally summered at coastal sites, or inland, eg at Blashford Lakes. Summering was recorded on the NW Solent during 1966–1992, eg up to four, in July 1969. Also, single males were reported at Tanners Lane on 23 June 1977 (presumably the same as one at Lepe the previous day) and at Hurst Spit on 11 June 1978.

Wigeon greatly increased in Hampshire from the mid-1950s, at both coastal and inland sites, ie the Avon Valley, particularly when in flood. Further increases occurred on the NW Solent in the late 1980s, especially during spells of cold weather. The average of winter-maxima during 1972/73–1989/90, but which excluded an isolated cold-weather-count of some 2,000 between Hurst Spit and Pylewell on 2 January 1979, was around 680, split evenly between both banks of the Lymington River. During that period, a flock of 500 that grazed by day on Oxey Barn fields on 8 January 1979 was unprecedented; prior to the 1980s Wigeon were rarely encountered inside the seawalls during daylight hours. At that time, autumn and winter wildfowl habitually flighted onto the grazing marshes only at dusk and returned to the saltings at dawn. Only exceptionally were wildfowl induced to vacate the intertidal earlier in the day, eg when rapidly rising tides coincided with stormy conditions.

Returning autumn migrants usually arrived in August, but though the first significant autumn influxes occurred in September, few post-war counts in that month exceeded 100; an exception was 162 that flew west off Pennington Marshes on 21 September 1980. Cold-weather movements also sometimes occurred when one of the most significant, during 10–13 January 1987, involved 923 that flew west through The Solent and 1,000 on Keyhaven/Pennington Marshes, on 11th.

Post-BoH, very few diurnal spring migrants were reported moving through The Solent. Of 64 individuals during 2001–2012, the day-maximum was 23, that flew east on 2 April 2004 and 25, that also flew east, on three dates during 1–27 April 2005. The wintering population remained into late March/early April, but the latest significant count of 153 on 1 April 2006, possibly included passage migrants. May records included up to 30, on 19th in 2012 and summering individuals, reported in at least 13 seasons during 1993–2012 included a maximum of three on 28 July 2009.

During the mid-1990S and coinciding with high, stable water levels and decreasing salinities, large numbers of Wigeon fed during the hours of darkness, on a profuse growth of Tasselweed *Ruppia sp.* on Keyhaven Marshes' lagoon, eg up to 300 during September 1994, up to 600 during September 1995 and October 1997 and up to 750 during October 1998. Autumn passage was also pronounced east of Lymington River, where significant counts included 900 on 31 October 1996 and at least 1,600 at Pylewell on 20 October 2012. Autumn and early winter movements were detected off Hurst Spit, where at least 187 flew east and 30 flew west, during 10 September–11 November, in 1999 and about 200, most of which flew east, during 12 September–13 October, in 2005.

The annual NW Solent wintering maxima during 1990/91–2011/12 averaged about 1,360, with a day-peak of c.1,730 west of Lymington River in January 2010; unusually, a flock of 600 was on the sea off Hurst Spit on 15 January 2000.

Other than Teal, this species was the most numerous NW Solent wintering duck and became a regular sight on the grazing marshes and lagoons. Principal winter feeding areas were flooded meadows on Vidle Van Farm, Keyhaven–Oxey Marshes and Normandy Farm. East of the Lymington River, Wigeon favoured the Pylewell creeks and Sowley shore.

Five-year averages of British, Hampshire and NW Solent WeBS maxima during 2007/08–2011/12, were 361,907, 8,655 and 1,675 respectively.

American Wigeon *Anas americana*
Rare, a spring vagrant; breeds N America and winters south to Panama
One record: a drake at Tanners Lane on 13 March 1994 was the seventh county record.
The Hampshire total to 2015 was nine individuals.

Gadwall *Anas strepera*
Common, has bred, a winter visitor and spring/autumn passage migrant
This species was rather rare and localised in Britain in the nineteenth century (Holloway 1996). It was unsurprising, therefore, that K&M noted that the Gadwall had been 'unknown to Hawker' and described it as a 'scarce winter visitor' to Hampshire, an assessment that remained true until the 1970s. Breeding was confirmed on the NW

Solent in 1993 and 2009, when fledged young were seen in August and June respectively, though other individuals reported in late spring hinted at additional breeding attempts.

The first report for the NW Solent was one in Pylewell Lake on 9 December 1945, but no more were reported until five were at Keyhaven on four dates in 1971. They remained irregular visitors during the following two decades; the largest count involved just eight in February 1987. Between 1976 and 1989, Gadwalls occurred in small numbers on spring passage off Hurst Spit during 22 April (in 1976)–11 May (in 1980); a majority occurred during 2–11 May. Though regular visitors to nearby Sowley Pond, Gadwalls were fewer and of a more erratic nature, east of Lymington River, where five, of which a male remained until 18 April, lingered on Bulls Saltern (Lisle Court) during 7–12 April 1973. At Pylewell, records occurred in 1979 (seven on 19 August) and 1982 (three on 5 June and ten on 29 August).

Post-BoH, the annual wintering population to the west of Lymington River increased to an average of about 48; the first three-figure counts were in 2000, in January (107) and February (140) the largest of all. Another of this magnitude was 120 at Pylewell in February 2012. NW Solent peaks usually occurred in December/January, but also in November (twice) and in February (five occasions). Wintering birds remained into March, the largest count being 89 on 10th, in 1996. Those present in April/May, eg up to 35 in 2006 and 23 in 2015 respectively, were presumably passage-migrants. Gadwalls remained scarce during June–August (maximum of 26 in August 2013) but numbers increased in September/October, eg 30 and 63 in 2013 respectively.

Gadwalls were found mostly on lagoons on Keyhaven Marshes' Fishtail, Pennington Marshes, Manor Farm and flooded land on Vidle Van Farm; prior to its demise, Iley Lane Lake was also a favoured site. East of Lymington River, they occurred mostly in Pylewell Park and on Sowley Marshes, but also resorted, particularly during cold weather, to the intertidal.

The Gadwall's British breeding stock, largely sedentary with about 1,710 pairs during 2006–2009, probably stemmed entirely from nineteenth-century escapes and releases. Since the 1960s, the British wintering population also increased steeply (Musgrove *et al* 2013).

Five-year averages of British, Hampshire and NW Solent WeBS maxima during 2007/08–2011/12 were 21,301, 1,844 and 88 respectively.

Teal *Anas crecca*
Common, has bred, a spring/autumn passage-migrant and winter visitor

'Regular winter visitor. Hawker's bag of 135 was doubtless chiefly made at Longparish' (K&C).

Of those shot by Hawker, relatively few were killed at Keyhaven, where most of his coastal Teal were obtained during the winters of 1840/41 (14) and 1844/45 (10). He specifically mentioned their presence on 5 December 1844, when he wrote 'I should have had a beautiful shot at a little mixture of Teal and Wigeon, with 3 Pintails but a rascally boy with a popgun and a yawl rowed them up out of downright spite.'

Breeding was proved on the NW Solent in 1953, when of three nests on Pennington Marshes, one was successful and the others failed when a grass cutter killed the sitting females. A female and five ducklings were reported on 28 June 2013 and a female with small ducklings in 2015 and though no young were seen, one territory was occupied on Normandy Farm in 1983. Additionally, a male was present at Keyhaven/Pennington Marshes during 25 May–20 July, in 1968 and other records hinting at breeding attempts, included a pair in late May 1995 and individuals in June in at least 12 seasons during 1975–2012.

Outside the breeding seasons during 1945–1960, Taverner cited a peak count of 400 and remarked that the Cordgrass edges along the Keyhaven/Pennington shore were favoured sites for wintering Teal. The first documented four-figure count for the NW Solent was about 1,000 at Keyhaven on 22 November 1975. Considerably more information was available to C&T, by which time NW Solent annual winter-maxima during 1972/73–1989/90 averaged about 1,000, with a day-peak of c.2,300 in December 1981. These data seem at odds with those given in BoH. The Lymington–Sowley mid-winter-maxima in that work included those on Sowley Pond, but most Teal on the Pond at that time did not necessarily flight to The Solent coast, but resorted to nocturnal feeding on the Sowley Estate's inland flight-ponds and other New Forest wetlands.

Other than insignificant, but noticeable, influxes to the brackish lagoons during early–mid-February and in July/August and occasionally in September, Teal were rarely encountered inside the seawalls during daylight hours prior to the mid-1980s. It was unclear whether those late winter increases were responses to cessation of wildfowling above the high-water mark, to changes in lagoon salinity, or to spring-passage. Throughout the autumn/winter, Teal remained in the saltings during daylight hours, but habitually flew onto the grazing marshes at dusk. Considerable numbers often arrived from east of the Lymington River, but returned during the following morning. During the 1950s/1960s, Teal tended to resort to The Solent or the open sea during periods of excessive disturbance, eg 400 were in Hurst Narrows on 21 December 1955. The highest numbers normally occurred in November/December, but sometimes, particularly when cold weather prevailed, in the New Year, eg at least 2,000 were present between Hurst Spit/Pylewell during the first week of January 1979.

Post-BoH, corresponding values during 1990/91–2011/12, boosted by day-maxima of 3,000 in 2010/11 and 2,000 in 2011/12, to an average of about 1,800, were indicative of further increases. Many Teal departed during March, but the population often remained in the low to mid-hundreds; exceptionally 700 were reported west of Lymington River in March 2007, 2008 and 2013 and a little over 1,000 in March 2014. Fewer were recorded in April; the maximum was 318 in 2003.

Sightings increased during July, though counts rarely attained double-figures. The first significant autumn influxes occurred in August when numbers sometimes rose rapidly to three figures, eg to 153 in 1994, 138 in 1999 and 190 in 2010. Further arrivals occurred in September when day-counts of 400–500 or more were frequently attained, with 767 in 2014. During October, the population was often in the high hundreds, with a day-peak of 1,762 in October 2015.

Teal often migrated with other wildfowl off Hurst Spit where, during late March–mid-May, the day-maximum was 135 that flew east on 1 April 2003. Fewer were recorded off Hurst Spit in autumn, but 14 flew east on 30 August 2001. Relatively few were recorded off the Spit during winter, but 54 were on the water off Milford-on-Sea on 10 November 2001.

The NW Solent Teal population was centred on Keyhaven–Lymington River, where they frequented the saltings, grazing marshes, open water in the Avon Water reedbed, flooded meadows on Vidle Van Farm and on Normandy Farm lagoon; significant numbers also occurred on Sowley Marshes. They often congregated close to the seawalls where fresh water entered the intertidal; at one favoured spot several hundreds could be found at first light, adjacent to public footpaths. Reserve designation, habitat improvement and measures to reduce disturbance, resulted in increasing numbers of Teal, particularly on the grazing marshes during daylight, even close to rights-of-way.

On 15 January 1968, a female that had been ringed at Sanderho Decoy, Denmark, on 18 December 1967, was found dead in the Lymington River Estuary by local marshman, R E Mathias. One ringed at Sowley on 22 December 1986 and shot 813 km to the south, in Pyrenees-Atlantique, France on 12 January 1987, was presumably forced there by severe cold weather at the time.

Five-year averages of British, Hampshire and NW Solent WeBS maxima during 2007/08–2011/12 were 155,212, 5,567 and 1,918 respectively.

Green-winged Teal *Anas carolinensis*
Rare, a winter vagrant; breeds N America and winters in South America
One record: a male frequented Keyhaven Marshes' Fishtail lagoon during 26 February–12 April 2013.
The Hampshire total to 2015 was 23 individuals.

Mallard *Anas platyrhynchos*
Common, a resident, spring/autumn passage migrant and winter visitor
'A resident, largely increased in winter. We gather that Hawker's bag of 441 was chiefly made at his place on the Test' (K&C).

At first sight, the status of this species, once known as the Wild Duck — the name Mallard originally referred only to the male (Kear 1990) — had changed little on the NW Solent since K&C's day, but their reference to Hawker's bag implied it had become a commoner winter visitor since his time.

Though few specific breeding season data were available, Mallards bred commonly throughout the area. The CBC indicated an increase, during which up to seven and 15 territories were on Normandy Farm and Salterns respectively, following creation of the Farm's salt-water lagoon in 1990. They were very tolerant of humans and were not above being hand-fed by the public at sites such as Lymington Quay, a trait that made them a highly successful species. Those released by wildfowling clubs to provide early season quarry, tended to remain close to release areas. Prior to 1993, the Keyhaven/Lymington coast, in a county context, was an unimportant wintering site.

Pintail, Teal, Shoveler & Lapwing. Normandy Farm Lagoon

Taverner's data summary during 1945–60 indicated a population of 50–100; a November count of 215, which remained a site record to 1972, was 'unusual and probably the result of disturbance.' Mallards were noticeably fewer on the intertidal east of Lymington River, where counts exceeded 50 in only four winters during 1970–89, with a day-maximum of 150 in November 1989. It should be noted, however, that Mallard habitually flight onto stubble at dusk during late summer/autumn, but those that presumably did so within the recording area, were unrecorded.

Post-BoH, at least 254 counts in excess of 100, of which no fewer than 88 were of 200 or more, included day-maxima of 550 on 4 November 1994 and 583 on 14 February 1999. This trend, the reasons for which were obscure, ran counter to a long-term, national decline (Austin *et al* 2008). The British Mallard population was supplemented in winter by birds from the Low Countries, Fenno-Scandia and central and Eastern Europe (Wernham *et al* 2002). Five-year averages of British, Hampshire and NW Solent WeBS maxima during 2007/08–2011/12 were 129,649, 4,063 and 360 respectively.

Pintail *Anas acuta*

Common, has bred. A spring/autumn passage migrant and declining winter visitor; sometimes occurred in summer

'An occasional winter visitor. Hawker killed thirty-nine in fifty years, while Coles shot a duck from marsh-land close to Hurst Castle on 11 January 1892' (K&C).

Most of Hawker's bag involved singletons, but on 24 February 1845 'eight were shot out of a bunch of ten'; K&M cited no other NW Solent records.

The Hurst/Pennington area was of little significance in a county context for Pintail during 1945–60, but increases during 1970/71–1989/90, resulted in an average of winter-maxima of about 30, with a peak of c.100 in January 1982 and an isolated late winter/early spring-count of 32 at Tanners Lane on 4 March 1978.

At Hurst Spit, two flew west on 26 April 1978, two flew east on 3rd and 4 April 1987 and 11 flew east during 4/5 May 1989. Autumn passage there included five on 13 August 1962 and 11 that flew west on 21 September 1980 (cf Wigeon). Additional selected records at Keyhaven/Pennington Marshes included ten that flew east on 18 August 1971, three that flew west on 21 July 1979, 15 that flew west on 25 October 1987, an unprecedented 160 that flew east in mild weather on 28 December 1989 and 43 that flew east on 15 January 1991.

Post-BoH, further increases in Hampshire's Pintail population were mirrored on the NW Solent where, during 1993/94–2011/12, winter-maxima averaged about 320, with a massive day-peak of at least 752 on 28 February 2006. Wintering Pintail usually vacated the area during March, though substantial counts, eg 228 on 13th in 2005 and at least 300 in March 2013, possibly included passage migrants. Relatively few remained into April, but 62 on 5th in 2008 were notable in a county context. Otherwise, four occurred in May 1996 and 2011 and summering, involving a male and female during 2 April–27 July 1994 and a singleton in 2001, culminated in confirmed breeding in 2014, the first such record for Hampshire when, following reports of a male and female during April–June, two juveniles were reported on 14 June.

The Pintail became commoner on spring passage into and through the west Solent. About 200 during 1993–2012, of which at least 145 occurred in March (day-maximum of 27 on 7th in 2001) were reported during 1 March (in 2000)–12 May (in 2008).

Pintails were frequently reported in autumn, particularly during September/October, when monthly day-maxima on the marshes included up to 11 in August 2002, 77 in September 2002 and 204 in October 2012. Diurnal migration through The Solent during 25 August (in 1999)–31 October (in 1996) included at least 183 that flew west, of which 109 occurred during 27–31 October, in 1996 with a day-maximum of 88 on 31 October and about 192 that flew east, with a day-maximum, also of 88, on 25 September 2001. Exceptional numbers were recorded during December 2002, when 259 flew east (at least 150 were initially resting on the sea) on 17th and 281 on 27th; they were possibly displaced from the Avon Valley. Cold-weather movements also occurred, eg 76 flew east at Hurst Castle on 3 January 2010 and seven flew east, the following day.

Pintails were relatively scarce on the intertidal to the east of Lymington River, where the maximum day-count was 40 in March 1996. They apparently became more frequent from 2004/05 and averaged about 100 during the following eight winters. Tidal flights between Pylewell saltings and Sowley, eg 66 on 5 November 2006, were occasionally recorded.

Other than Wigeon and Teal, the Pintail was often the most numerous wintering duck on the NW Solent, on occasions outnumbering the Mallard. Favoured areas included winter flooding on Pennington Marshes, flooded meadows alongside the Avon Water, the intertidal zone in the vicinity of Keyhaven River and Hurst Camber and the Pylewell/Tanners Lane creeks and saltmarshes.

Five-year averages of British, Hampshire and NW Solent WeBS maxima during 2007/08–2011/12 were 19,839, 774 and 408 respectively.

Garganey *Anas querquedula*
Scarce, has bred, a spring and autumn passage migrant

That K&C did not encounter this attractive species at Keyhaven was unsurprising, as pre-1900, fewer than ten pairs bred annually in Britain. The Garganey was a summer visitor where its breeding stronghold, albeit in rather small numbers, was in eastern England; the British summer population was estimated at about 83 pairs in 2012 (Holling 2014). It nested only occasionally in Hampshire.

A pair was reported in Pylewell Park on 7 April 1946, but probably due to a paucity of observers, Taverner noted that the Garganey was an irregular visitor to Keyhaven/Pennington Marshes. There was no indication in Hampshire's ornithological literature that the NW Solent was a favoured haunt until C&T, unaware of 13, that included ten males, on flooded pasture at Keyhaven on 22 March 1954, instanced 11 on marshland at Pennington Marshes on 22 March 1966 as the county's record count. The Garganey then became a regular spring passage migrant on the NW Solent. The earliest were single pairs at Salterns Eight Acre Pond on 6 March 1977 and on Keyhaven/Pennington Marshes during 10–14 March 1981. The Garganey occurred at Hurst Spit on spring passage, sometimes accompanying other wildfowl species, such as Eiders, Common Scoters and Velvet Scoters; during 1970–1992 at least 16 migrated eastwards, the latest date being on 31 May, in 1978.

There were few Hampshire autumn records prior to 1955, but counts at Keyhaven/Pennington Marshes during 1966–1992 included 15 on 7 August 1967 and eight on 10 August 1986; the latest was a singleton at Keyhaven during 23 September–8 October 1983.

Post-BoH, breeding was confirmed when a female with 12 ducklings was observed on 13 June 1993 and possibly occurred during 2007–2015 when females with fledged juveniles were recorded on several occasions.

Those recorded at the Spit totalled 34 during 31 March (in 2001)–25 May (in 2007) in March (2), April (22) and May (10) with a day-maximum of nine, of which five were males that flew east on 6 April 2002. Just six autumn reports at the Spit were two that flew north on 27 August 1995, a female or juvenile that flew east with Common Scoters on 4 August 2001, one that flew west on 9 August 2001, one that flew onto Sturt Pond from the west on 13 July 2003, one in Hurst Narrows, with 11 Common Scoters, on 3 November 2004, the latest for the NW Solent and one that flew east on 11 September 2015.

Blue-winged Teal *Anas discors*
Rare, late spring vagrant; breeds N America and winters South America

One record: a drake on Keyhaven/Pennington Marshes during 30 May–28 June 1972 was the first for the county. The Hampshire total to 2015 was five individuals.

Shoveler *Anas clypeata*
Common, has bred, a spring/autumn passage migrant and winter visitor

'Rare winter migrant, having occurred several times in the neighbourhood' (K&C).

Breeding was confirmed on the NW Solent on at least three occasions, ie in June 1993 (female & seven ducklings) June 1999 (female and eight ducklings) and May 2010 (female and ducklings). Up to five individuals that hinted at further breeding attempts were reported in June in at least nine additional seasons during 1962–2012. At least 872 pairs currently breed in Britain (Holling 2014).

The Hampshire wintering population increased greatly post-K&M, though six decades later Taverner, instancing a maximum of 80 at Keyhaven during the early 1947 cold spell, concluded it was an irregular visitor on the NW Solent. C&T were unable to add additional NW Solent information, but its status was fully portrayed in BoH, when the average wintering population during 1970/71–1989/90 was c.30 and the day-maximum was 50 in December 1981; its winter presence was consistently associated with cold weather.

Shovelers were also regularly reported on easterly spring passage through The Solent, particularly at Hurst Spit where an all-time day-maximum was 65 on 31 March 1990. The species was infrequently observed at sea at other seasons, though was recorded in Hurst Narrows as long ago as December 1955.

Usually encountered on the grazing marshes and lagoons west of Lymington River, peak numbers normally occurred in January/February. Iley Lane Lake, together with Keyhaven/Pennington Marshes, were favoured early 1990s haunts, where, in the 1970s, one particular area was named 'Shoveler Pools', on account of attracting significant numbers of dusk-flighting individuals. An autumn record of note was of ten that flew south over Pennington Marshes on 20 August 1991.

Shovelers sometimes resorted to the intertidal, particularly Oxey Lake and east of the Lymington River, where small numbers, typically fewer than 20, often associated with other wildfowl.

Post-BoH, Shovelers became more numerous, so much so that they became a familiar sight on the grazing marshes. The first three-figure count of at least 100, occurred on 7 February 1993 and the average winter-maximum increased to about 120, with day-peaks of about 200 in November 2000 and 211 in December 2014. The wintering population usually declined sharply during March, but in the year 2000, numbers increased from 70 in February to 100 in March, presumably due to spring transients and 121 were reported in March 2014. Migrants also probably augmented April counts, eg 55 in April 2006 and the few May occurrences on the marshes.

They were often reported off Hurst Spit, where at least 542 that flew east during 7 March (in 2001)–14 May (in 2009) included day-maxima of 45 on 24 April 2001 and on 10 April 2009.

Though rarely attaining double-figures, first autumn returns were in July, but they became more frequent during August–October, when monthly peaks were 23 and 39 in 2000 and 79 in 2015 respectively. At Hurst Spit, 40 that flew east on three dates during 17 July (in 2007)–27 October (in 1996) included a day-maximum of 16 on 16 October 1999; also, 12 flew west on 11 August 1999 and on 13 July 2009.

One ringed in The Netherlands in August 1967, was found dead at Keyhaven (464 km west–south-west) in January 1969 (BoH).

Five-year averages of British, Hampshire and NW Solent WeBS maxima during 2007/08–2011/12 were 12,496, 741 and 155 respectively.

Red-crested Pochard *Netta rufina*
Rare, a winter vagrant; small UK feral population, but its native range is S Europe/Asia

Two records: an adult male on Salterns Eight Acre Pond on 12 February 1990 and a pair on 10 November 2001. Though the provenance was uncertain, all three were possibly of wild origin. The pair in 2001 fed with other ducks on Pennington Marshes' Jetty lagoon and appeared after the first hard frost of the autumn; they were wary and showed no signs of captivity.

Pochard *Aythya ferina*
Common, a spring/autumn passage migrant and winter visitor

'Winter migrant, appearing in most years' (K&C).

In the early nineteenth century, Pochards were scarce visitors to the NW Solent, witnessed by the fact that the indefatigable Colonel Hawker, who shot just 17, wrote in 1831 'the Dunbird at Keyhaven is a rara avis.' They were probably commoner during the latter half of that century as, according to Wise, they were known on the New Forest coast by the local names of 'red-head' and 'ker'. K&M, writing of Hampshire as a whole, remarked 'At the present time it seems to be an increasing species and is found in equal numbers on the coast and on our inland waters.' They also stated that Pochard had 'nested regularly in the New Forest district since the year 1880' though it must be added that Cohen gave the first Hampshire breeding record as 1950, while BoH suggests the first nesting was in 1935. Rather curiously, given the implication that Pochard were not unusual on the NW Solent at the end of the nineteenth century, Taverner categorised them as 'irregular or not recorded' at Keyhaven, which suggests this diving duck was scarcer on this coast than in K&C's day. Pochards continued to be reported irregularly in small numbers until the winter of 1973/74 when during November–January, a regular evening flight took place onto Salterns Eight Acre Pond. In that three-month period, counts regularly exceeded 100 and peaked at 160 on 13th and 17 November 1973. Regular flights also occurred during October–December in 1974 and 1975, though none exceeded 50. Those involved arrived from an easterly direction and it was thought they spent the daylight hours on Fawley Reservoir. Dusk flights onto the Pond subsequently became erratic; 21 on 29 October 1982 was the earliest in autumn and the maximum was just 40 on 22 January 1986. At that time significant intertidal cold-weather-counts included 35 at Pennington Marshes on 22 November 1977, 43 in Oxey Lake on 6 January 1979 and 30 at Keyhaven on 12 January 1985.

Pochards were occasionally reported moving east in spring at Hurst Spit, though the largest such movement was just 11 on 10 May 1980 (reported as 11 May in HBR). In winter, 16 flew west off Pennington Marshes on 7 November 1981 and 18 flew west there on 19 December 1981.

Post-BoH, the flooded gravel pit known as Iley Lane Lake, proved attractive to Pochard during 1992–1994, with a day-maximum of 79 on 4 December 1993. Elsewhere throughout the recording area, post-1995, Pochard numbers were unremarkable in a county context. The spring-maximum was eight on 17 March 1996, but the majority were reported at Normandy Farm lagoon in winter, where the day-maximum was 36 on 13 November 2004. Few occurred during June–October, but up to three were at Normandy Farm during 12–15 June 2008 and 13 on Sturt Pond/Mount Lake on 28 October 2002. The Pochard was seldom reported east of the Lymington River, (the largest count being 22 in Sowley Marshes on 22 January 2012) though others were probably undetected at the latter site where there were regular records during May/June 2015.

A few sometimes moved along the coast in spring, autumn and winter. With the exception of eight that flew west at Tanners Lane on 2 November 2004, most occurred off Hurst Spit where in 2013, easterly-moving singletons occurred on 17 February, 24 March and 8 April, with three on 7 May, seven flew east on 31 August 2003, five flew west on 11 October 2006, nine flew east in cold weather on 1 January 2009 and three were on the sea on 10 January 2010. Five-year averages of British and Hampshire (where it is a declining winter visitor) WeBS maxima during 2007/08–2011/12 were 21,917 and 445 respectively; the NW Solent's contribution was negligible.

Ring-necked Duck *Aythya collaris*
Rare, a winter vagrant; breeds in N America and winters C America/Caribbean
One record: a first-winter female arrived at Keyhaven on 8 November 1996. It was seen to 'drop out of the sky' onto saltmarsh beside a tidal creek where, apparently exhausted, it rested for over two hours before it flew onto Keyhaven Marshes' lagoon; it was the sixth record and first female for the county.

The Hampshire total to 2015 was ten individuals.

Tufted Duck *Aythya fuligula*
Common, has bred, a spring/autumn passage migrant and winter visitor
'Regular winter migrant, now nesting at several spots in Hampshire. Hawker's bag of twenty-seven was chiefly obtained on the Test, but Coles has seen the bird occasionally in the Harbour at Keyhaven' (K&C).

This species was rather rare in the first half of the nineteenth century. Hawker shot just 11 at Keyhaven, of which seven were between 1841/42 and 1844/45.

K&M reported that it was a winter visitor in small numbers in Hampshire and a few pairs nested. The earliest British breeding records date from 1849 (Holloway 1996) but the first recorded breeding in Hampshire was in 1890 where, following creation of much suitable habitat by the gravel-extraction industry, it became a common resident. During the Atlas Survey, breeding was considered likely at Pitts Deep.

Few data of significance were evident for the NW Solent until a massive flock of some 800 was recorded (presumably on saltwater) 'near Lymington' in early 1940 (Vesey-Fitzgerald 1946). The winter of 1939/40 was at the time one of the three most severe winters recorded in the twentieth century, with many bird species killed or displaced by the cold, the others being 1916/17 and 1928/29 (Ticehurst 1940). With this in mind, Vesey-Fitzgerald's report, though remarkable and pre-dating by 48 years the county's next highest count of 705 in the Avon Valley in November 1988, becomes explicable and in my view, acceptable. Taverner categorised this species as 'irregular or not seen at all' in the area and noted a group of 14 in Keyhaven harbour, during cold weather on 1 February 1954. Tufted Ducks were increasingly reported during the 1960s, mostly in winter, though the largest group was only 29 that flew south over Keyhaven was on 12 August 1968. An increase in reports during the 1970s included 30 in flight at Pennington Marshes on 21 November 1975, a figure not exceeded until 40 were off Hurst Castle, in cold weather, on 13 January 1985 and 49 on Iley Lane Lake on 29 October 1992.

A few were recorded moving eastwards at Hurst Spit in spring, eg in 1989 when two occurred on 5 May and four on 4 June.

Post-BoH, breeding was proved in 1993 when a female with eight ducklings was seen at Iley Lane Lake in July and two broods were raised there in 1994. Nesting also took place at Keyhaven, Salterns and Normandy Farm, where a total of up to four territories were occupied in 1999.

The increase in reports was due, at least in part, to suitable habitat on offer at Iley Lane Lake during the early part of the decade. Here, double-figure flocks that included a day-maximum of 56 on 24 October 1993, were regularly recorded. The lake was infilled in the mid-1990s, but the two smaller replacements proved much less attractive to wildfowl. Tufted Ducks then resorted to the grazing marshes' lagoons, where the day-maximum was 72 on 18 December 2010. This species was scarcer east of the Lymington River, with peaks of 20 in Sowley Marshes on 30 September 2012 and 31 on 21 March and 32 on 28 November, in 2015.

At Hurst Spit, Tufted Ducks were mostly recorded on spring passage. At least 84 that flew east during 4 March (in 2000)–17 May (in 2011 and 2004) included 46 during 22 April–17 May 2004, of which the day-maximum was eight on 21 April.

Autumn migration there was confined to one that flew east on 2 August 1993, eight in 2000, ie singletons on 21 and 22 August, three on 25 August and 16 October and one on 24 July 2005. In winter, four, seen earlier that day at Hengistbury Head (Dorset) flew east on 14 February 2004.

Five-year averages of British and Hampshire WeBS maxima during 2007/08–2011/12 were 59,790 and 1,557 respectively; the NW Solent contribution was negligible.

Scaup *Aythya marila*

Scarce, a spring/autumn passage migrant and winter visitor; its breeding distribution is circumpolar, but those wintering in Britain originate mostly from Iceland

'Regular winter migrant. Hawker's bag amounted to a hundred and twelve and Coles has often seen the bird in the harbour' (K&C).

During 1814–1853 Hawker shot c.98 at Keyhaven, where 15 were accounted for during the winter of 1828/29 and 21 in 1829/30: others referred to by K&C were obtained elsewhere, eg in Poole Harbour, Dorset. His first reference to Keyhaven Scaup, in mid-January 1823, was possibly a first for Hampshire, but note that one in the Alton Museum (presumably shot) from King's Pond at that place, was undated (Curtis 1896). Taverner, writing of the county as a whole, described it as 'very scarce' and C&T considered it 'far from common' and suggested that the decline had begun 'at some stage between 1900 and 1940.' Curiously, in neighbouring Dorset, the reverse appeared to be the case, with Scaup being rare in the nineteenth century and only increasing from the mid-1940s (see Green 2004). There were just two reports, both singletons in the 1950s, ie at Sturt Pond on 30 November 1953 and at Keyhaven on 7 November 1958. The 1960s yielded only five records, of which two in 1963 reached double-figures, when 46 flew west at Hurst Spit in cold weather on 9 February (noted as east in C&T) and 12 that flew east, at the same locality, on 20 April. Scaup were frequently noted during the following decade. The most notable records involved 12 that flew east at Hurst Spit on 9 May 1974 and a total of 36 during 4 January–17 February 1979, including 15 that flew east at Hurst Spit in cold weather on 15 January. The 1980s saw a slight increase in records, perhaps as a result of greater observer coverage. About 15 reports included a male at Keyhaven on 7 October 1980, a female on 10 October 1981 (also at Keyhaven) three in 1982 (two at Lymington on 17 January and a male at Pennington Marshes on 12 April) and three (one male) that flew east at Hurst Spit on 18 December 1983. The majority, however, occurred during November 1985–early March 1986. Though numbers were generally small, the largest flock by far was 38, of which at least 12 were males, at Tanners Lane in cold weather on 9 February 1986; they were possibly displaced from Little Sea, Poole Harbour (Dorset). Also of note was a flock of ten that flew west at Pennington Marshes on 12 January 1987 and a female at Keyhaven during 17–21 August 1992, which was the first county record for that month.

Post-BoH, Scaup were recorded in all but three years during 1993–2015, but no count exceeded five and only four reports occurred outside the period of late October–late April. Exceptions were singletons on 9 May 1997, 8 May 2000 and a first-winter female at Keyhaven during 17–24 September 2008.

At Hurst Spit, five flew east on 2 January 1997, five flew west on 15 January 2005 and a male was present on 1st and 18 January 2009. Spring migrants there included one on 12 March 1993 and three on 9 April 2012. In autumn two occurred on 29 October 1994, one flew east on 15 October 2002, a male flew east on 1 November and a female flew east on 29 November 2008.

The five-year average of British WeBS maxima during 2007/08–2011/12 was 2,413; Hampshire and NW Solent contributions were negligible.

Eider *Somateria mollissima*

Common, has bred, a spring/autumn passage migrant and winter visitor

'Rare winter migrant. Hawker wrote in his "Instructions" that "the only three I ever heard of on the Hampshire coast appeared in the severe winter of 1838. I stopped them all, though got but one, as the other two beat me in a sea"' (K&C).

The above incident occurred on 11 January and probably involved the first record for Hampshire, as K&M cited no earlier county record.

Eiders were once scarce visitors to coastal southern England as a whole (Saunders 1899). K&M were unable to add to Hawker's account, merely noting them as rare visitors in Hampshire. No more were reported on the NW Solent until the winter of 1949/50 when an immature male was seen at 'Pennington' on 28 December and 11 January, a record which, together with two other Hampshire records in 1946 and 1947, was perhaps an early indication that a change in status was underway. In this connection, however, it should be noted that Taverner (1959) who documented the post-Second World War spread of the Eider in Britain, wrote that in Hampshire the 'first signs of change were in 1953/54.' This bird greatly extended its English wintering range from the mid-1950s, which was attributed to a large increase in the breeding population on the Friesian Islands (Taverner 1959, 1963). The scant ringing evidence lends some support to this notion; recoveries in Britain of Eiders ringed in the Netherlands, show a more southerly distribution than those from Germany and Denmark (Wernham 2002). The next at Hurst Spit/ Pennington Marshes occurred during the winter of 1955/56, with up to 12 in January (a singleton was still present on 16 April) and double-figures were again reached in 1957/58, when up to 14 were recorded. By the early/mid-1970s it occurred on the Hampshire coast in small–moderate numbers, which included occasional summer records of three at Pennington Marshes on 17 June 1972, up to ten there in June 1974 and an adult male at Hurst Spit on 31 May 1975. The Frisian population subsequently declined and those at present wintering in Great Britain are thought to originate from the Baltic Sea (Owen 1986, Lack 1986). A wintering flock at Hurst Spit that peaked at 71 on 2 February 1963 was a county-maximum and was followed during the second winter period by a group of 55 in November 1963. In 1975, 61 in two flocks flew west at Hurst Spit on 22 October and a single flock of 130 flew west there on 10 November. Eiders, present throughout the year for the first time in 1976, included up to 34 in February, 41 in March, 42 in April, 11 in July and 13 in August. Fewer occurred during the following five years, but 97 that included six adult males (the largest group reported in Hampshire since 1975) were off Hurst Spit on 4 December 1982. Interestingly, a flock of 35 Greylag Geese (qv) arrived at Keyhaven on the same day.

A flock of up to 32 in August 1989 was at that time, the largest to summer in Hampshire.

Post-BoH, a pair that attempted breeding in 2003 appeared to be the first such record for southern England. During 2006–2014, at least four pairs, of up to a further 16 possible breeding attempts, were known to hatch a combined total of at least 15 young. Offshore in summer, small groups included five on 19 June 1996 and three on 1 June 2003. In autumn up to 32 occurred, in October 2011 and winter-counts included up to 100 on the sea on 15 January 2012. Off-passage Eiders elsewhere on the NW Solent probably included those recorded at Hurst Spit, though day-maxima during the 1990s barely attained 20. However, peaks in excess of 50 were regularly reported during 2002–2012; the all-time maximum of 191 in Oxey Lake on 14 March 2003 was given as a 'winter' peak in HBR. Autumn migration followed earlier patterns and no count during 1993–2003 exceeded that of 64 in late October 2003. Winter populations remained low, typically fewer than 20, until 35 in early December 2002, 64 in late February 2003 and 66 in December 2011.

The five-year average of British WeBS maxima during 2007/08–2011/12 was 19,369; Hampshire and NW Solent contributions were negligible.

Long-tailed Duck *Clangula hyemalis*

Scarce, a winter visitor and spring/autumn passage migrant; breeds in Fenno-Scandia and Russia

With only five records to 1938, this attractive diving duck was a rare visitor to Hampshire until found to occur in Langstone Harbour in the early 1950s. Subsequently it was recorded more widely along the coast and Hurst/ Lymington also became a favoured wintering site. During 1952–1992, c.100 individuals included two in the Lymington River on 27 December 1952, possibly NW Solent's earliest report and one in Hurst Narrows in December 1955. Of about 40 that occurred in the Hurst Spit/Keyhaven area, ten were on spring passage during 9 April (in 1958)–13 May (in 1961). Fifteen on 22 February 1992 was a NW Solent day-maximum, of which 12 were present on 10 April and one on 18 April, though another flew east at Hurst Spit on 4 May and eight were reported at Keyhaven/Oxey Lake on 31 December 1991. One that flew east on 23 September 1961 was the earliest Hampshire autumn record to 1992.

Post-BoH, at least 94 individuals during 1 November (in 1999)–13 June (in 2010) included 55 in the vicinity of Hurst Spit, in November (12), December (7), January (8), February (3), March (2), April (19) and May (4): of these, 16 flew east during 22 March (in 2005)–26 May (in 2002). The NW Solent day-maximum was six in Oxey Lake on 22 November 1993, while a female during 25 April–13 June 2010, remained for much of its stay on Keyhaven Marshes' lagoon.

The five-year average of British WeBS maxima during 2007/08–2011/12 was 1,865; Hampshire and NW Solent contributions were negligible.

Common Scoter *Melanitta nigra*
Common, a spring/autumn passage migrant; also occurred in summer and winter

'Regular winter migrant. On January 28th 1829, Hawker "saw two scoter ducks, birds I never met with before, except stuffed in museums ... and floored them both." These birds usually frequent the open sea, which probably accounts for Hawker seeing so little of them' (K&C).

Those possibly represented the first Hampshire reference to this bird, as K&M cited no earlier records. Cohen noted the presence of occasional offshore flocks in the west of the county in 1952, ie c.300 off the Needles on 17 April and 50 off Hurst Spit on 27 December, but the paucity of sightings was presumably due to lack of observation, as they were found to be of regular occurrence, particularly on spring migration, during 1966–1992. Not all, however, flew into The Solent and many were seen to return seawards, when they presumably continued their migration around the Needles and along the southern shore of the Isle of Wight. The heaviest movement recorded at Hurst Spit occurred on 5 April 1966 when 1,380 flew east into The Solent, followed by a further 500, four days later. Flock sizes exceeded three-figures in at least 19 seasons and gatherings on the sea included 400 on 4 April 1987, 390 on 1 April 1990 and 600 on 10 April 1991.

Passage sometimes occurred during July, eg in 1981, when 72 flew west on 11th and in 1985, when at least 54 flew west off Pennington Marshes during 21st–28th and in August such as 70 that flew west at Pennington Marshes on 3rd in 1989. Summering populations included c.1,000, the largest by far, on 7 June 1992, which decreased to 200 on 3 July and to 80 on 8 August. Scoters were less regular during September–December, but 60 flew west at Hurst Spit on 16 September 1984 and 133 flew east on 14 September 1986, while monthly-maxima during October–December were 89 (in 1978), 65 (in 1988) and 95 (in 1988) respectively.

Flocks occasionally wintered, eg during 1988/89, when 65 off Hurst Spit on 27 November, increased to 95 on 21 December, to 100 on 21 January, but decreased to about 30 on 11 February and to 24 on 8 March; 300 off Hurst Spit on 27 March were presumably migrants.

Post-BoH, at least 8,000 that flew east on spring passage at Hurst Spit during 4 March (in 2001)–31 May (in 2003) included an annual-maximum of c.1,270 of which 440 flew east on 1 April, during 18 March–30 May 2004, a day-maximum of 571 on 9 April 1993 and a flock of 400 on the sea on 22 May 2006. Offshore summer flocks included up to 216 on 1 June 2006 and 125 on 4 July 2012, while autumn monthly-maxima were: 40 on 2 August 2001, 43 that flew east on 25 September 2001 and 65 that also flew east, on 19 October 2003.

It is of interest that Scoters were particularly scarce in February, with a peak of just 15 in 2010. Otherwise, winter monthly-maxima were 80 on 9 November (in 2007), 50 on 5 December (in 1995) and c.100 on 30 January (in 1993).

Surf Scoter *Melanitta perspicillata*
Rare, a spring/early winter passage vagrant; breeds N America where it winters on both coasts

Three accepted records: a drake, among a small flock of Common Scoters, that flew east on 15 May 1976, another male, also with Common Scoters, that flew east on 23 April 1999 and a female/immature, with Eiders, off Hurst on 19 November 2011, were the first, second and fourth county records.

The Hampshire total to 2015 was five individuals (but see below).

For the sake of completeness, it is worth noting that a first-winter Surf Scoter was seen in flight (with a small group of Common Scoters) off Hurst Spit on 17 November 1996, by three experienced observers. For reasons now unclear, the record seems to have become lost in the submission process and has thus never been considered by the HOS Records Panel.

Velvet Scoter *Melanitta fusca*
Scarce, a spring/autumn passage migrant and winter visitor, also occurred in summer; breeds in N Eurasia and North America

'Rare winter migrant' (K&C).

Hawker wrote in his *Diary* for 17 February 1840: 'Went off about two, when it was quite calm and rowed off in Channel, where I made a capital shot at six black velvet ducks. I floored the whole lot of them at about 120 yards. The only dead one floated out past Hurst, where I dare not follow him' (K&C).

The above was possibly the first reference for Hampshire, as K&M cited no earlier county records. The next were three (a drake and two females) off Hurst on 7 January 1950 and a drake, found dead, at Keyhaven on 5 April 1951. During 1958–1992, the Velvet Scoter was recorded principally as a spring passage migrant. The earliest was one that flew east off Keyhaven on 11 March (in 1990) but at least 230 flew east at Hurst Spit during 30 March (in 1958)–17 May (in 1973). Day-maxima included 30 that flew east on 12 April 1974, 20 on 1 May 1984 and 27 offshore on 10 April 1991; also, 19 flew east at Pennington Marshes on 10 April 1981 and nine were off Keyhaven on 1 April 1990. Autumn passage was much less pronounced. Of 13 during 29 September (in 1991)–30 October (in 1983) the day-maximum was four on 30 October 1983. A further 85 individuals were reported during November–February, with a day-maximum of 18, around the sewage outfall off Pennington Marshes, on 22 November 1975.

Post-BoH, about 352, recorded mostly off Hurst Spit during 3 March (in 2000)–11 June (in 2010) occurred in March (20), April (275), May (55) and June (2). The monthly day-maxima were nine on 31 March (in 2002), 28 on 13 April (in 2003), 14 on 4 May (in 2008) and a singleton on 10/11 June (in 2010). Of 19 individuals reported in October, the day-maximum was 11 on 28th in 2012. A further 124 individuals were recorded during 2 November (in 2003)–13 February (in 1999) in November (58), December (32), January (28) and February (6); monthly day-maxima were eight that flew west on 24 November (in 2007), nine that flew west on 11 December (in 2009), seven that flew west on 31 January (in 2011) and three on 13 February (in 1999).

Goldeneye *Bucephala clangula*
Common, a spring/autumn passage migrant and winter visitor; also occurred in summer

'Regular winter migrant' (K&C).

According to Hawker the Goldeneye was known at Keyhaven by the local names 'gingler' and 'ginging curre', seemingly references to the sound made by its wings. Curiously, despite this apparent familiarity, Hawker's bag was just 19 that included eight during the very severe winter of 1837/38. Together with Wise's opinion that it was among the rarer visitors and stragglers to the New Forest coast, this suggests that though the Goldeneye was a well enough known winter visitor to the NW Solent to be given local names, it was not a particularly numerous one. Taverner considered that they were no more than 'occasional' on the NW Solent, a description that may have reflected the paucity of active observers during the post-Second World War era, rather than the lack of a regular presence of a few Goldeneyes. Whether or not this was indeed the case, there is no doubt that numbers of this duck increased during the 1970s when, during the ebb tide, they were attracted to the vicinity of a broken sewage pipe off Pennington Marshes. However, the largest count of 28 during that decade, included 25 in Mount Lake on 7 January 1979, though this was soon eclipsed by one of 40 off Pennington Marshes, still the record count for the area, on 3 February 1980 and another of 36 in January 1987. A few, eg two that flew east on 21 April 1971, were recorded on passage at Hurst Spit and out-of-season occurrences included a female off Pennington Marshes on 29 May and 12th and 26 June 1974. Few were reported east of Lymington River, but three were at Pylewell on 18 December 1981.

Post-BoH, double-figure counts occurred in 17 winters, with day-maxima of 20 on 13 January 1998 and on 22 January 2011. Goldeneyes often frequented Mount Lake with 11 on 7 January 2006, but were less often observed at sea off Hurst Spit, where one flew east on 23 March 2002, one was on the sea and then flew northwest, on 16 October 2003, and one flew east on 20 July 2012.

Goldeneyes continued to occur less frequently east of the Lymington River where, other than three on 31 January and two on 19 November, in 2010, singletons were reported on 25 October 2003, 16 October 2005 and 20 February 2011.

The five-year average of British WeBS maxima during 2007/08–2011/12 was 12,152; Hampshire and NW Solent contributions were negligible.

Smew *Mergellus albellus*
Scarce, a winter visitor, usually during hard weather, also an occasional spring passage migrant; breeds from Fenno-Scandia to central Siberia

'Regular winter migrant' (K&C).

However, K&C specifically cited only a female, shot by Hawker at Keyhaven on 15 January 1830, who added 'the first I ever saw, or heard of, on our coast.' This now probably constitutes the first Hampshire record, as an earlier report of one, shot at Heron Court on 20 January 1823, was conceded to Dorset following local government boundary changes in 1974. It is of interest to note that K&M, only eight years prior to K&C, described the Smew as 'an irregular winter visitor to the coast.' The next NW Solent record appears to be of two redheads at Keyhaven on 5 February 1947 and off Hurst Spit on 30 December at the commencement of the 1962/63 cold–spell. At least 37 individuals were reported during 1963–1992. Other than three on 2 December 1969 and one that flew east, with Common Scoters, off Hurst Spit on 8 April 1979, all occurred in January/February, of which one remained in the Keyhaven area during 28 January–30 April 1972 and five during 6–17 February 1985. Day-maxima were eight that flew east at Hurst Spit on 6 January 1963 and six, of which one was a male, on 17 January 1987.

Post-BoH (1993–2015) just 18 individuals were reported during 19 November (in 1999)–8 January (in 1994) in November (1), December (11) and January (6, one of which remained to 20 February). The day-maximum was seven that included two first-winter males, on Normandy Farm lagoon on 1 December 1998.

Red-breasted Merganser *Mergus serrator*
Common, a spring/autumn passage migrant and winter visitor; sometimes during summer

'Regular winter migrant' (K&C).

Garrow did not mention this species and Hawker records only five individuals, ie one on 10 January 1833, three on 12 January 1841 and one during the winter of 1841/42. According to K&C, the fishermen knew it as the saw-bill or spear-wigeon (spear or spear-grass is a local name for *Spartina*) which suggested it was more commonly met with during the early twentieth century, when *Spartina* became established between Keyhaven and Lymington.

At a time when there was no Hampshire record of this bird for June, July or September and only one for August, Taverner stated that it was 'regular in small numbers between Hurst and Lymington River' and quoted 30 as a post-Second World War NW Solent maximum. It apparently became more numerous during 1963–1992, when October–March monthly day-maxima were: 32 (in 1976),50 (in 1972 & 1975), 49 (in 1976), 40 (in 1991), 44 (in 1990) and 45 (in 1989) respectively. Increases in Hampshire post-1980 reflected the national trend and were attributed to an expansion of the British breeding population (Owen 1986), though birds from Fenno-Scandia were also involved.

The first June sighting was in 1971 and one at Keyhaven on 5th and 30 July 1966 was the second post-Second World War Hampshire occurrence for that month. Additional June–August records occurred in a further seven years to 1992. Summering was recorded in 1975 (up to two on 18 June) and in 1980 (a female in Oxey Lake during 22 July–25 August 1984) and three flew east at Hurst Spit on 3 July 1992. Singletons also occurred in September 1975, 1983 and 1984.

The commencement of regular seawatches at Hurst Spit during the 1960s revealed it to be a regular spring passage migrant. Between 1968 and 1992, at least 617 flew east during 12 March (in 1983)–17 May (in 1978). Annual spring-totals exceeded three-figures in 1971 (105) and 1974 (139) with day-maxima of 71 on 13 April 1971 and 45 on 4 April 1987.

Diurnal autumn passage was predominately westwards and included 22 at Hurst Spit on 11 November 1962, 27 off Pennington Marshes on 3 November 1979, 37 off Keyhaven on 26 October 1980 and nine at Hurst Spit on 19 October 1987.

Post-BoH, further increases occurred in the NW Solent autumn–early spring populations when October–March day-maxima were: 32 (on 6 October 2010, an early date for such a number), 92 (in 2002), 85 (in 1999), 74 (in 2004), 72 (in 2003) and 71 (in 2006) respectively.

Easterly spring passage at Hurst Spit occurred during 1 March (in 2000)–31 May (also in 2000) when a total of 205 included a season-maximum of 69 in 2000, but a day-peak of just 19, on 27 April. Autumn passage peaked at 27 at Hurst Spit on 2 November 1998 and 35 that flew west on 11 November 2002.

Five-year averages of British, Hampshire (where it is a declining winter visitor) and NW Solent WeBS maxima during 2007/08–2011/12 were 3,366, 337 and 78 respectively.

Goosander *Mergus merganser*
Scarce, a winter visitor, often in hard weather, also occurred in summer/autumn
'Rare winter migrant, apparently unknown to Hawker' (K&C).

The Goosander was described as a scarce and erratic winter visitor to Hampshire (BoH), though by 1992 it was on the increase in the county. Between 1950 and 1992, some 69 were reported on the NW Solent during 7 November (in 1989)–30 April (in 1978). The day-maxima were nine, of which three were males, off Hurst Spit during very cold weather on 13 January 1963 and seven in flight over Salterns on 14 January 1985. Spring occurrences included singletons on 1 April 1967, during 28 January–30 April 1978, a very late date for a wintering Hampshire Goosander, on 13 March 1981 and on 25 April 1988.

Post-BoH (1993–2015) at least 51 reported during 22 July (in 2002)–28 April (in 2008) included day-maxima of five (two males) on 1 November 1993 and up to five during 2–27 December 2010.

Five-year averages of British and Hampshire WeBS maxima during 2007/08–2011/12 were 3,458 and 194 respectively; the NW Solent contribution was negligible.

Ruddy Duck *Oxyura jamaicensis*
Rare, has bred; it is a native of North America
A pair apparently nested successfully in 1997 when four young were seen near Pennington Marshes.

The first records for the area occurred in 1989 when a male was on the sea off Hurst Spit on 22 July and one was in The Solent off Pennington Marshes on 2 December.

Post-BoH, a further 15 individuals included up to three on Keyhaven Marshes' lagoon during 27 December–14 January in 2000/01 and two juveniles on Normandy Farm lagoon on 13 September 2005. Ruddy Ducks were reported on the NW Solent in all months except March and October.

The British feral population stemmed from about 70 unpinioned juveniles from the Wildfowl and Wetlands Trust at Slimbridge, which were allowed to fly away between 1956 and 1963 (Kear 1990). Their descendants have now almost been exterminated by a DEFRA eradication programme.

Quail *Coturnix coturnix*
Rare, a late spring/summer/early autumn vagrant
'Regular summer migrant' (K&C).

Though probably overlooked, it was an irregular passage migrant with six records (seven individuals) ie two at Lymington on 11 April 1950 and singletons at Milford-on-Sea (dead) on 4 June 1974, flushed from a field-edge at Keyhaven on 25 July 1981, at Keyhaven (a male) on 23 June 2003, at Normandy Farm on 9 August 2005 and Keyhaven Marshes' lagoon on 25 May 2015.

Red-legged Partridge *Alectoris rufa*
Common, a resident
'A common resident but of foreign origin. Though the original importation from France took place in Suffolk about the year 1770, it does not appear that the bird was introduced into this part of Hampshire until nearly a hundred years later, when they were turned out onto the estates at Beaulieu (about 1864) and Heron Court (1867). At the present day the species is particularly common along this part of the coast' (K&C).

It still occurs commonly throughout the recording area, on farmland, where a group of about 30 was reported from Vidle Van Farm in early March 2005, as well as on the grazing marshes. The odd stray is sometimes found in unlikely spots, such as on Hurst Spit shingle crest in September 2009.

Grey Partridge *Perdix perdix*
Scarce, a resident
'Common resident' (K&C).

This bird remained a common resident on NW Solent farmland and on the grazing marshes until the latter decades of the twentieth century, since when it has become scarce. Numbers in the Keyhaven area were boosted by releases by a local shoot syndicate. During 1966–1992, coveys usually consisted of fewer than ten individuals, with a maximum of 18 at Keyhaven on 2 December 1993. The last record on the grazing marshes was of two on Oxey Barn fields (Lower Woodside) on 5 October 1999, but they continued to occur in small numbers elsewhere within the recording area, on Vidle Van Farm and Manor Farm/Efford, as well as on Pylewell and Sowley estates. Two were at New Lane, Milford-on-Sea, on 1st and 27 February, 10 March and 8 May, in 2015.

Pheasant *Phasianus colchicus*
Common, a resident
'A common resident' (K&C).

Occurs commonly on the grazing marshes as well as on farmland throughout the recording area. Game-shoot syndicates released large numbers, particularly onto the estates east of Lymington. Unusually, one appeared in the vicinity of Hurst Castle, in early March 2005.

Red-throated Diver *Gavia stellata*
Common, a spring and autumn passage migrant and winter visitor, also occurred in summer
'A regular winter migrant, occasionally seen in summer plumage. Hawker mentions the divers in his bag of "various", without specifying the numbers shot. In his "Instructions" he gives directions for shooting these birds' (K&C).

This is the most numerous member of the diver family to be seen on the NW Solent. During 1950–1992, most were recorded in winter, with day-maxima of nine on 1 February 1958, seven on 14 November 1992 and six on 1 December 1973.

An easterly spring movement was detected as long ago as 1954, when three migrated past Hurst Spit on 1 May. An additional 151 individuals were subsequently recorded to 1992 during 5 March (in 1989)–31 May (in 1972 and 1978). Singletons on 26 June 1989 and 21 July 1985 were the second and first Hampshire records for those months respectively. One at Keyhaven/Pennington Marshes during 16 July–18 September 1988 was the earliest autumn record for the county at that time. One on 22 August 1992 was only the second for NW Solent in that month and others occurred in September (5) and October (7).

Red-throated Diver

Post-BoH (1993–2015) the easterly spring passage involved about 480 individuals, mostly off Hurst Spit, during 3 March (in 1996 and 2012)–2 June (in 2013). Peak movements occurred during 19 April–2 May, with a day-maximum of ten that flew south beyond The Needles on 21 April 2013. One flew east on 17 June, but none were reported in July/August. The earliest autumn migrant occurred on 13 September 2011, with three on 19 September 2007, one on 30 September 2009 and about 19 during October. An increase in winter numbers, particularly post-2006, included an all-time day-maximum of 218 transients off Hurst Spit on 7 February 2011, which followed a 96-hour spell of gale-force south-westerly winds.

Black-throated Diver *Gavia arctica*
Scarce, a spring and autumn passage migrant and winter visitor

'A rare winter visitor' (K&C).

This was the least common of the diver species to frequent the NW Solent between 1950 and 1992. Spring passage during 13 April (in 1990)–30 May (in 1972) involved just seven individuals, while in autumn one was at Hurst on 30 October 1972. In winter, at least 33, of which six flew east at Hurst Spit on 6 January 1979, included one on Salterns Eight Acre Pond during 23 February–8 March 1988.

Post-BoH (1993–2015) an increasing frequency of sightings probably reflected a real trend. Spring passage during 6 March (in 2011)–6 June (in 2007, the latest for the county) involved at least 103 individuals, with a peak during 19–25 April. The few reported in autumn included singletons on 25 September 2003, 28 September and 17th and 21 October, in 2005.

At least 92 individuals occurred in winter, with a day-maximum of six at Hurst on 7 December 2008. Some remained for considerable periods, eg one during 16 November–20 December 1999, up to five during 21–30 November 2004 and one during 1 January–28 February 2010.

Great Northern Diver *Gavia immer*
Scarce, a spring and autumn passage migrant and winter visitor; at least one remained into early summer

'An occasional visitor in the winter months. Mr. Hart has fine specimens obtained locally, both in summer and winter plumage' (K&C).

Between 1950 and 1992, at least 18 records during 20 March (in 1973)–1 June (in 1957) included 13 individuals that flew east at Hurst Spit during 20 April (in 1985)–9 May (in 1959). The earliest in autumn (one on 24 October 1991) remained until the end of December. Of at least 31 individuals recorded in winter, all were singletons except for doubletons during 15–21 November and 24–28 December, in 1991.

Post-BoH (1993–2015) easterly spring passage involved at least 68 individuals between 17 March (in 2013) and 9 June (in 2012) most of which occurred during 19–25 April. One, with a damaged foot, off Hurst Spit on 17 May and 9 June in 2012, was possibly the same individual, in summer plumage, off Milford-on-Sea on 14th and 28 May and until 22 June (the latest county record) in 2013.

Autumn passage involved just ten singletons during 16 September (in 2003, the earliest for the county)–31 October (in 2003 and 2008). At least 79 individuals in winter included day-maxima of three during January/February 2002, in late January 2004 and in December 2010 and 2011.

White-billed Diver *Gavia adamsii*
Rare, a winter vagrant; breeds in high Arctic on coasts and tundra, mainly from Yamal peninsula to NW Canada

An adult in winter plumage, in Oxey Lake on 14 February 1991, was only about the sixth for southern England at that time (Garr 1994). Once considered extremely unusual in Britain (Burn & Mather 1974) this bird is now known to be a scarce passage migrant in north-west Scotland (Scott & Shaw 2008) though a rarity elsewhere.

Fulmar *Fulmarus glacialis*
Common, a spring and autumn passage migrant; also occurred in summer and winter

Singletons at Hurst on 15 January and 27 August, in 1956, were the second and third records for Hampshire; the first was a corpse, found on the coast in the east of the county, on 28 December 1954. Between 1957 and 1970, about 18 recorded during 13 April (in 1970) and 24 June (in 1966) included one off Lymington on 14 May 1958 and one that flew into The Solent at Hurst Spit on 17 June 1969.

The establishment of breeding colonies on the Isle of Wight and in Dorset was probably the principal factor in the increase in numbers and frequency of sightings off Hurst Spit post-1970. At least 330 individuals occurred during 1971–1992, of which 120 flew east at Hurst Spit during 16 March (in 1980)–17 June (in 1991). Almost a quarter of the spring-total was reported between 26 April and 2 May, though the day-maximum of 12 occurred on 7 April 1985 and 24 April 1992; also, a corpse was found at Pennington Marshes on 2 June 1979.

Autumn records involved some 39 individuals during 8 August (in 1982)–21 October (in 1989) with a day-maximum of six on 1 September 1988, but just one in October. In winter, two occurred during gales on 16 January 1984 and on 22 February 1991 and singletons on 27 January and 19 February, in 1989.

Post-BoH, about 700 at Hurst Spit (many flew east) were recorded during 11 March (in 2001)–15 June (in 1996 and

2009) and of which more than half occurred between 19 April and 2 May. Though duplication may have occurred, the day-maximum was c.50 on 20 April 1999. A further 231 were reported during 16 June (in 1994)–18 September (in 1999) with a day-maximum of 21 on 26 August 2000. Relatively few occurred in winter; about 43 during 11 November (in 2000 & 2005)–27 February (in 2000) included a day-maximum of 15 on 26 February 2001.

Cory's Shearwater *Calonectris borealis*

Rare, a spring, autumn and early winter vagrant; breeds North Atlantic islands (particularly Azores) and at one site in W Mediterranean

Three records: singletons on 12 May 1982, 18/19 August 2001 and 22 November 2012, were the first, second and sixth county records.

The Hampshire total to 2015 was six individuals.

This shearwater was for many years considered as being conspecific with Scopoli's Shearwater *C. diomedea* that breeds on Mediterranean islands and at one site on the French Atlantic coast.

Sooty Shearwater *Puffinus griseus*

Rare, a spring, autumn and early winter visitor; it breeds on Antarctic islands and winters at sea in the North Atlantic and Pacific Oceans

One off Pennington Marshes on 2 October 1994 was the second county record, but first of a live bird. A further 23/24, all singletons other than five on 10 September 2010 and three on 11 September 2011, occurred off Hurst Spit/Milford-on-Sea during 28 April (in 2002)–3 November (in 1996) in April (1), August (3), September (13/14), October (5) and November (1). Individuals in 1996 (1), in 2000 (3), in 2002 (1) and in 2004 (1) constituted the third–seventh and ninth county records.

The Hampshire total to 2015 was 32 individuals.

Manx Shearwater *Puffinus puffinus*

Common, a spring and summer visitor, also occurred in autumn and winter

'Regular winter visitor to the coast' (K&C).

Specimens obtained near Yarmouth (Isle of Wight) in 1836 and near the Needles on 14 June 1867 (K&M) probably occurred within the recording area's waters. Cohen was unable to cite a single NW Solent record between 1909 and 1960, but six off Hurst on 31 May 1961 were the forerunners of at least 109 individuals recorded to the end of 1992, in April (13), May (64), June (11), August (10) and September (11) of which day-maxima were a flock of 22 on 4 May 1974 and ten (groups of three and seven) on 17 May 1986.

Post-BoH, a significant increase occurred from the late 1990s, most of which occurred during mid-April–early July. Many were at long range, often beyond the Needles, but some were seen to enter or leave The Solent through Hurst Narrows. At least 3,614 recorded during 9 April (in 2009)–31 October (also in 2009) included about 640 during 31 May–6 June, of which the day-maximum was 418 on 2 June 2001. Other day-counts in excess of 100 were 255 on 28 June 2002, 339 on 13 May 2003, 134 on 8 June 2003 and 133 on 18 June 2011. Numbers tailed-off in late August and only 48 were reported during 23–29 August and the latest was a singleton on 31 October 2000. Winter occurrences were unusual in Hampshire and the sole NW Solent record involved two that flew west at Hurst Spit on 23 January 2002.

Large numbers breed off the coast of Wales (on the islands of Skokholm and Skomer) and smaller numbers on the Isles of Scilly, the Channel Islands and north-west France.

Balearic Shearwater *Puffinus mauretanicus*

Scarce, a spring, summer and autumn visitor; it breeds in W Mediterranean and disperses into North Atlantic

One that flew west off Oxey/Pennington Marshes in calm, sunny conditions on 21 July 1971 became the first Hampshire record, as the individual shot in Christchurch Bay in August 1859 was conceded to Dorset in 1974, following local government reorganisation. Others off Hurst Spit on 2 August 1981, 11 May 1982 and 4 July 1993 were the second–fourth county records.

Post-BoH (1993–2015) Balearics became more frequent in NW Solent waters. Singletons on 11 August 1996, 6/7 August 1998, 18 September 1998 and 23 July 1999 were the fifth and eighth–tenth county records; others occurred on 11 August and 3 October, in 1999. A further 178 individuals during 3 March (in 2009)–23 October (in 2013) occurred in March (3), April (8), May (5), June (5), July (42), August (81), September (24) and October (10) and included day-maxima of at least 22 on 2 August 2001 and 11 on 15 August 2012. Most were recorded off Hurst Spit, though at least 20 were in, or were seen to enter The Solent. The March record is particularly interesting, as not only was it the first for Hampshire for that month, but one of only two others recorded in Britain in March 2009 and which followed other South Coast sightings in January/February (HBR 2009).

Storm Petrel *Hydrobates pelagicus*
Scarce, but increasing spring, summer and autumn visitor; also occurred in winter
'An occasional visitor to the coast' (K&C).

The first for the NW Solent and for Hampshire was one attracted to Hurst lighthouse during the night of 15/16 December 1835; it was taken alive and acquired by Hawker (Payne-Gallwey 1893). It thus pre-dates one found near Stockbridge in about 1884 (K&M) and previously thought to be the first for the county (BoH). The second NW Solent occurrence was a singleton that flew west at Hurst Castle on 14 August 1954. There was just one record in the 1960s (two at Hurst Spit on 28 October 1967) and none in the 1970s, but the 1980s saw two October singletons, at Pennington Marshes on 4th in 1985 and Hurst Spit on 18th in 1987.

Post-BoH, the 1990s produced four records at Hurst Spit: two on 24 June 1994 (the first for Hampshire in that month), singletons on 12 July and 21 October and two on 28 October, all in 1998. Beginning with a 'wreck' in October 2000, which resulted in counts of 55 on 30 October and 16 the next day, the turn of the millennium and the early years of the twenty-first century saw an increase, both in records and numbers, at Hurst Spit/Milford-on-Sea. In 2002, singletons were seen on three dates in May and two were noted on 22 October. A remarkable series of records occurred in May 2006 when birds were recorded on 11 dates during 13th–28th. Counts reached double-figures on five of those dates, peaking at 19 on 22nd, but the only other report for that year came on 7 December. During 2007–2015, some 24 individuals were reported, eight of which occurred during 5–11 July, day-maxima were three on 27 May 2007 and three on 25 August 2014 and one was found, long dead, at Hurst Castle on 23 September 2013. The sharp increase in seawatching effort during the 1990s and the use of modern, tripod-mounted prismatic telescopes, were factors that presumably contributed to the increase of sightings of these and other tubenoses.

Petrels not specifically identified as either Leach's or Storm, together with a few records for which details were not forthcoming, have been excluded from this and the following account.

Leach's Petrel

Leach's Petrel *Oceanodroma leucorhoa*
Scarce, an autumn and winter visitor, usually associated with south-westerly gales
Doubtless due to a paucity of observers in the early decades of the twentieth century, let alone any with an active interest in seawatching, it was not until 1960 that the first Leach's Petrel for the area was recorded, at Hurst Spit on 4 December. A huge national 'wreck' of this species during October/November 1952 yielded not a single record,

though included in the 23 seen elsewhere in the county, was one found 'dying' at nearby Barton-on-Sea (Boyd 1954). Since then, however, Hurst Spit and the area of The Solent eastwards to Pennington Marshes provided the lion's share of Hampshire's records. There were reports of singletons in 1962 (28 October and 3 November), in 1967 (28 October), in 1983 (4 September), in 1986 (28 September) and in 1988 (9 October). In 1987, associated with the aftermath of the 'Great Storm' that led to unprecedented numbers of Sabine's Gulls (qv) four were seen on 17 October. In 1989, doubletons were seen on 21st and 22 October and a 'wreck' in late December brought 12 into Hurst Narrows on Christmas Eve and at least 15 to Hurst Spit/Milford-on-Sea the next day. One, found by a wildfowler on Keyhaven saltings on 3 January 1990, flew strongly towards The Solent when released into Oxey Lake, later that day.

Post-BoH, there were five records, all singletons at Hurst Spit/Milford-on-Sea, during the 1990s, in 1996 (one that flew east on 2 November), 1998 (singletons on 8 January and 24th and 27 October) and 1999 (one on 9 December). The Hurst Spit/Milford-on-Sea monopoly continued during 2000–2015, with reports in 12 of the 16 years (2003, 2011, 2012 and 2015 were blanks) in January (2), September (2), October (10), November (53) and December (9, which included a dead specimen). All records involved one–four birds, except for ten on 5 December 2006 and eight the next day, and the NW Solent's (and Hampshire's) day-maximum of 44 on 29 November 2009.

Gannet *Morus bassanus*
Common, a spring and autumn passage migrant and summer visitor; also occurs in winter
'A rare winter migrant, chiefly seen in the open channel' (K&C).
Between 1950 and 1992, day-maxima were 200 during the last week of August 1953 and 150–200 on 10 July 1969. Double-figure counts included 18 that flew east in April 1980, 20 in May 1973, 13 in June 1961 and 1991, 26 in July 1987, 32 in August 1988 and 20 in September 1987: none were recorded in March or November/December. Dead Gannets, of which singletons in January 1990 and 1991 were visibly oiled, were reported in January (6) and February (4 that included 2 in 1982).

Post-BoH, there were records of Gannets in all months, ie small numbers during January–March, substantial spring movements in April/May, large numbers, often fishing offshore, during June–October, but many fewer during November/December. At least 23 day-counts in excess of 300, included two of 1,000 or more, in May (1), June (2), July (12), August (6), September (1) and October (1). Most observations were of birds at sea off Hurst Spit/Milford-on-Sea. They were often observed fishing in large numbers, over the Shingles and Dolphin Banks or off the Needles, though many were seen to enter and leave The Solent through Hurst Narrows. Early year day-maxima were 39 (mostly adults) on 16 January 1995 and 50 off the Needles on 6 February 2011, while eastwards spring passage included monthly-maxima of 41 on 22 March 2012, 250 on 20 April 1999 and 407 on 27 May 2007. Day-maxima during June–October were 385 that flew east on 17 June 2011, 568 that flew east on 24 July 2005, 1,454 offshore on 14 August 2007, 2,000 (the area's all-time day-maximum) that flew west in 30 minutes on 16 September 2001 and 434 that flew south on 23 October 2011.

Many of those that fished in Christchurch Bay were presumably from breeding colonies closest to the Hampshire coast (the Channel Islands, Brittany and Wales) but one found dead at Milford-on-Sea in October 1949 was ringed as a chick in that year on the Bass Rock in Scotland. Detailed observations over many years (particularly by one observer — see Ornithological History) of this and other seabirds in Christchurch Bay highlighted the ornithological importance of the Bay.

Cormorant *Phalacrocorax carbo*
Common, a visitor at all seasons
'A common resident, nesting in the Freshwater Cliffs and constantly visiting Sturt Pond and the Harbour at all seasons of the year' (K&C).
In Hawker's day, this bird was known in Hampshire as the 'Isle of Wight Parson'. Though few 1950–1992 data were available, annual maxima usually occurred between August and January, the day-maximum during that period being 58 in October 1990. A favoured roost site was on Keyhaven saltings (Stony Point) where up to 19 roosted on 3 September 1976.

Post-BoH, the day-maxima of 82 occurred on 17 October 2009. Peaks usually occurred in September/October, but also in August (once), November (three occasions) and January (once). A flock of 27 that flew west, high over Keyhaven on 17 September 2005, possibly involved passage migrants.

Shag *Phalacrocorax aristotelis*
Scarce, a visitor at all seasons
'Resident and nesting in the Isle of Wight, but not nearly so common as the last species' (K&C).

This bird was presumably a frequent and regular visitor to the area, though few pre-1992 data were available. It was observed fishing in Christchurch Bay and was not uncommon in The Solent between Keyhaven and Colgrims; most were presumably from nesting groups on the West Wight cliffs, or from Durlston Head (Dorset). During 1950–1992, at least 104 individuals were reported. Though observed throughout the year, the majority occurred during mid-April–late May, with a day-maximum of just four in April/May 1974; few were recorded during late May/late June.

Post-BoH, this bird, though possibly overlooked, was recorded in every month in only seven years. However, the timing of spring occurrences was remarkably similar to those during the previous period. In at least 13 of the 20 seasons, most occurred up to late May with very few in June; only in 2010 did up to five or six consistently fish off the Spit in that month. However, late-year day-maxima were higher than pre-1992, with up to 43 off Hurst Spit on 20 September 1999 and 25 on 17 October 2006 and 7 October 2009.

The status of those observed in spring off Hurst Spit is intriguing. If they are from the West Wight or Dorset breeding colonies, the paucity of June sightings suggests that young are then fully fledged and families have moved from the area, there are food shortages at that time or, for other reasons, they are obliged to fish elsewhere. They are able to fish in deeper waters than Cormorants (Sharrock 1976).

Bittern *Botaurus stellaris*
Scarce, a winter visitor particularly during cold weather, but also occurs in spring and autumn
'A rare winter migrant' (K&C).

Three obtained within a few miles of Lymington during a three-week period during late December 1848–early January 1849 (Wright 1849) were possibly within the recording area. One, roughly 200 metres upstream of Efford Bridge on 25 December 1938, was outside the recording area, as was perhaps another that was shot at Milford-on-Sea in 1946. Sightings on Vidle Van Farm on 17 January and 19 February, in 1947, perhaps involved one individual. Only four singletons were reported during 1950–1990; at Walhampton on 21 December 1964, Pylewell during 22 October 1969–22 March 1970, Keyhaven on 1 January 1982 and on Oxey Marshes on 24 November and 18 December, in 1987.

Post-BoH (1993–2015) at least 13 individuals reported in January (5), February (1), March (2), April (2), November (1) and December (2) included long-stayers at Keyhaven/Pennington Marshes during 3 March–1 April 1996 and at Keyhaven during 18 January–12 March 2011, and one that flew south-east at Hurst Spit on 30 April 2007.

American Bittern *Botaurus lentiginosus*
Rare, a winter vagrant; breeds N America and winters south to Mexico
A singleton, shot at Woodside (Lymington) by Mr Bran in January 1876, was the first for Hampshire. It was in the collection of Edward Hart, who probably remounted it following its original preparation by Francis Edwards. Hart was a taxidermist living at Christchurch and 'possessed the most complete and most admirably arranged collection of birds in the county' (K&M). The specimen remains in a remnant of Hart's collection, which is owned by Hampshire County Council. Another, killed at Cadnam in February of the same year as the Woodside specimen, was the only other county record.

Night-heron *Nycticorax nycticorax*
Rare, a summer vagrant; nominate race breeds Europe, Asia and Africa (other races in the Americas)
One record: an adult, seen intermittently on Smith's Pond at Lower Pennington in 2012 during 2–4 June, 12–21 June, on 19 July and 3–19 August, was the ninth county record. A first-winter individual on the Danes Stream in Milford-on-Sea during 30 October–16 November 1988, was just outside the recording area.
The Hampshire total to 2015 was 18 individuals.

Cattle Egret *Bubulcus ibis*
Rare, an autumn vagrant; breeds on all continents, though in Europe, mainly in Iberia
One at Normandy Farm during 17–19 August 2001 (but at Sowley Pond during 11–13 August) was the fifth county record. The second NW Solent record involved two individuals in 2009, the first of which was at Keyhaven on 1 October–16 December. Finally, two were on Keyhaven/Pennington Marshes during 27–29 September 2015.

The Hampshire total to 2015 was at least 49 individuals.

The Spanish and Portuguese populations expanded rapidly northwards during 1970–1990 and this bird became more frequent in Britain during the 1990s. A major influx in 2007 was the forerunner to the first reported successful breeding in Somerset in 2008, during which two or three pairs reared at least two young (Balmer *et al* 2013).

Little Egret *Egretta garzetta*
Common, a resident and spring and autumn passage migrant
The first NW Solent records were singletons in 1968, at Pennington Marshes during 29 May–6 June and 24 August–12 September; they constituted the sixth and eighth county records. Another on 30 May 1970 was the ninth for Hampshire and a further eight individuals were recorded during 1972–1988, of which one at Keyhaven on 14 November 1987 was the first Hampshire record for that month. An unprecedented influx into southern England in mid-July 1989 was believed to have originated in north-west France (Combridge & Parr 1992). Initially detected on the NW Solent on 30 July, up to four occurred to 25 August and what was a county record at the time, a day-peak of 17 on 28 August. Numbers declined to an estimated 10–12 during 1–5 September, up to six during 6–24 September, two during 19 November–12 December and one during 14–31 December; by 1992, other than April, the Little Egret had been recorded on the NW Solent in all months.

Post-BoH (1993–2015) continued colonisation of Hampshire was characterised by pronounced late summer/ autumn influxes, which led to proved breeding in the county in 1998 (Carr 2003). Seventy-five on 7 October 2006 (given as 49 in HBR) constituted one fifth of the county-total at that time and the day-maximum of 78 occurred in September 2014. A nocturnal roost within the recording area dated from about 2003 and numbers peaked there at 77 individuals on 4 September 2010 and 5 September 2011.

Great White Egret *Egretta alba*
Rare, a summer, autumn and winter vagrant; range almost cosmopolitan, nominate race breeds Europe to temperate Asia (other races Asia/Australasia, Africa and Americas)
Seven records involved eight individuals as follows: Singletons on the Lymington River on 19 August 1997 and at Hurst Castle on 10 December 2003 were the sixth and tenth county records. Others occurred at Pennington Marshes on 27 July and on Oxey Marshes on 9 September, in 2010, at Keyhaven on 12th and two on 30 September 2011, one that flew north-east over Normandy Farm on 21 September 2012, one at Keyhaven and Oxey Marshes on 3rd and 26 September 2014 respectively and one Lymington/Hurst on 7th and 29 September 2015.

The Hampshire total to 2015 was about 63 individuals.

Numbers wintering and summering in Britain have increased dramatically since 2007; a pair may have nested in Somerset in 2010 and 2011 and two pairs bred successfully there in 2012 (Anderson 2013).

Grey Heron *Ardea cinerea*
Common, has bred, a spring and autumn passage migrant and winter visitor
'A common resident, the nearest nesting places being the heronries at Sowley' (K&C).

The above statement remained true until Grey Herons were discovered nesting on Manor Farm. Though the exact year is unknown, two or three, possibly four pairs, nested from at least the early 1990s, before disturbance by continued landfill and reinstatement activity, followed by the loss of nest trees, forced them to abandon the site. A heronry was subsequently established immediately north of the A337 at Efford (but outside the recording area) where up to at least eight pairs nested during 2001–2009.

Observations indicative of spring and autumn migration between 1969 and 1992 included seven individuals that flew in off the sea at Hurst Spit during 1 April (in 1984)–2 May (in 1969).

Post-BoH (1993–2015) nine similarly did so during 25 March (in 2001)–8 May (in 2003) and a flock of nine flew high to the west over Keyhaven on 9 May 2006. In autumn at least 98 were reported moving in all directions during 29 June (in 2002)–16 October (in 2002) and included groups of 13 that flew south-west out to sea at Hurst Spit on 12 September 2002 and 11 that flew east high over Normandy Farm on 13 October 2006. Monthly day-maxima, January–December were 20 (in 2000), seven (in 1999), five (in 1997), 11 (in 2015), five (in 1994), eight (in 2010), nine (in 2000), 17 (in 2003 – see below), 20 (in 2007), 13 (in 1995), ten (in 1999) and ten (in 1994) respectively. Unusually, a group of 17 preyed on a profusion of eels, in very shallow water in Keyhaven Marshes' lagoon on 30 August 2003.

Purple Heron *Ardea purpurea*
Rare, a spring and autumn vagrant; nominate race breeds Africa and Iberia/Maghreb to central Asia
(other races Cape Verde, Madagascar and south and east Asia)
Four records: a first-summer at Keyhaven on 19 May 1968 was the fourth county record (stated as the eighth in HBR 1968) but some of those were from the Isle of Wight (see C&T). An adult flew from Keyhaven towards the Isle of Wight on 10 May 1984, a juvenile was on Smith's Pond (Lower Pennington) on 21 August 1986 and another adult flew west over Normandy Farm on 9 May 2006.
The Hampshire total to 2015 was 38 individuals.

White Stork *Ciconia ciconia*
Rare, a spring and summer vagrant; nominate race breeds Europe, North Africa and the Middle East
(larger *asiatica* breeds central Asia; black-billed *boyciana* of E Asia now usually treated as separate species)
Two records: one soared inland over Keyhaven saltings (last seen at long range to the north-west) on 18 July 1976 and one was over Lower Pennington Lane and at Keyhaven on 18 May 2004.
The Hampshire total to 2015 was 57 individuals.

Glossy Ibis *Plegadis falcinellus*
Scarce, a spring, autumn and winter visitor; it breeds discontinuously from south-east Europe to Australia and southern Africa, also south-east USA and Caribbean
The first NW Solent record concerned a singleton at Pennington Marshes during 17–19 May 2008; it was the sixth county record and sixth individual. Since then a further 34 birds occurred during 14 August (in 2010)–4 May (in 2012, remained until 20 June) in August (1), September (26), October (2), November (2), April (2) and May (1). Those reports included a group of six that flew east over Pennington Marshes' Butts Lagoon on 19 September 2009 and no fewer than 21 in 2010 (one on 14/15 August, a flock of 19 that flew east on 13 September and one that also flew east on 26 September). Those in 2009 and 2010 were the seventh–tenth county records.
The Hampshire total to 2015 was 49 individuals.
As recently as 1970, the Glossy Ibis nested no nearer than the Balkans. Four decades later, during which the first major influx of 18 individuals occurred in 1986, it became such a frequent visitor to Britain that from January 2013 it was omitted from the list of species considered by British Birds Rarities Committee.

Spoonbill *Platalea leucorodia*
Scarce, but increasing spring and autumn passage migrant; also occurs in summer and winter
The first for the NW Solent occurred in January 1920 (Troubridge 1921) and was followed by a further 18 individuals during 1967–1992, in April (3), May (5), July (2), August (2), September (3), October (2) and November (1). The records, all singletons except for doubletons on 23 April 1987 and 15 August 1992, fell between 23 April (in 1987) and 4 November (in 1991).
Post-BoH, some 132 individuals were recorded during 23 February (in 2008)–16 November (in 2007) in February (7), March (20), April (23), May (16), June (4), July (11), August (9), September (21), October (7) and November (14). Those included at least 49 that over-flew the marshes, with day-maxima of 12 that flew west on 1 November 2001, six that flew south towards the Isle of Wight on 16 September 2011 and six that flew west at Hurst Spit on 31 March 2012. Off-passage gatherings included a maximum of six at Keyhaven Marshes on 19/20 July 2010.

Little Grebe *Tachybaptus ruficollis*
Common, a resident, spring and autumn passage migrant and winter visitor
'A common resident, frequently to be seen on Sturt Pond and above the hatches at Keyhaven. When frozen out during the winter months it may often be seen off the coast' (K&C).
Few NW Solent data appear in the record until the 1950s, when up to 12 were on the Lymington River on 22 January 1952; they continued to frequent Sturt Pond and the Avon Water at Keyhaven in the 1960s.
During the CBC, though present at Normandy Farm in three seasons (1996, 1999 and 2000) and at Salterns in 1995, nesting did not occur on either plot, presumably because of lack of emergent vegetation and high salinities, which were close to, or that of, seawater. During the Atlas Survey, breeding was confirmed at Keyhaven, Lower Pennington and Lisle Court, but not at Sturt Pond, where it was probably overlooked.
Favoured wintering areas during 1967–1992 were in the vicinity of Keyhaven and Salterns Eight Acre Pond. Here,

maxima were 21 on 8 December 1974 and 15 on 21 January 1986, latest spring and first autumn occurrences were on 11 April (in 1979) and 14 April (in 1975) and 14 September (in 1973) and 10 August (in 1987) respectively. Day-maxima at Sturt Pond, where an isolated high count of 44 on 28 October 1967 was exceptional, were usually fewer than five. Little Grebes were seldom recorded on the open estuary (one on The Solent, off Pennington Marshes' Butts on 5 November 1983, was an exception) but were frequently reported within the intertidal in Hawkers Lake and Keyhaven Harbour and River.

Post-BoH, breeding became more widespread due to newly created freshwater habitats on Manor Farm gravel-extraction site, as well as declining salinities in the grazing marshes' lagoons. Breeding probably occurred annually at most of the following locations, but specifically, at Vidle Van Avon Water (single pairs in 2002 and 2010) Keyhaven Marshes' Fishtail lagoon (single pairs in 2002, 2003, 2007 and 2010) Manor Farm Balancing Pond (pair in 2005) Manor Farm Water Treatment Works (nest with one egg in 1999) Iley Lane Lake (eight pairs reared at least 37 young in 1993 and three pairs nested in 1994) Newbridge Copse (pair in 2002) Pennington Marshes' lagoons (single pairs in 1995, 1999, 2000 and 2012 and four pairs in 2004 and 2005) Smith's Pond at Lower Pennington Lane (pair in 1993 and 1998) and Bulls Saltern at Lisle Court (pair in 1995 and 2009 and two pairs in 1997). Breeding also probably occurred in Sowley Marshes.

The wintering population also increased and the Normandy Farm lagoon (newly flooded in November 1990) together with Salterns Eight Acre Pond, attracted a significant proportion of those on the NW Solent, where combined monthly day-maxima during November–February were: 52 (in 2007), 34 (in 2007), 35 (in 2007) and 30 (in 2008).

One, first seen at long range to the west of Hurst Spit, flew east on 3 April 2000 and two drifted eastwards on the sea past Milford-on-Sea on 22 April 2001.

Perhaps unsurprisingly, at least some in the vicinity of Keyhaven Harbour and River and Hawker's Lake, apparently roost at night in the lee of moored craft.

Great Crested Grebe *Podiceps cristatus*
Common, has bred, a spring and autumn passage migrant and winter visitor

'A regular winter migrant to our coast, of which Mr Hart has specimens in both summer and winter plumage obtained locally. Wise writes that it "appears every winter in Christchurch Harbour and may be seen just cresting the waves, as they break under the Barton cliffs"' (K&C).

During the Atlas Survey, breeding was confirmed in Pitts Deep tetrad (Pylewell Park in 1989). Those reported at sea off Hurst Spit in April and May and on the estuary between June and August, probably included failed and non-breeders.

Of the large number of records available for 1970–1992, at least 20 individuals included up to three on single March and May dates off Hurst Spit during 23 March (in 1984)–17 May (in 1971, 1975 and 1986). Autumn passage usually began in late August (up to seven on 31 August 1981) and double-figure counts included ten on 18 September 1988 and 13 on 6 October 1980. Winter-maxima, eg 23 on 27 November 1969, possibly involved transients. Great Crested Grebes were rarely reported on the marshes' lagoons, but singletons were on Salterns Eight Acre Pond on 5 January and 5 February in 1979 and on 7 June 1981.

Post-BoH, a pair and two young were observed on the Avon Water flood at Keyhaven in June 2003.

Wintering populations increased at several Hampshire coastal localities during the 1980s and double-figure counts subsequently became more frequent on the NW Solent, where monthly day-maxima were 25 (in November 1994), 22 (in December 1999), 19 (in January 2003) and 12 (in February 2008). Other maxima, March–October were: 12 (in 2008), 11 (in 1995), 15 (in 2008), ten (in 2001), nine (in 2008), eight (in 1993), 14 (in 1995) and 22 (in 1995). All maxima, other than those in March, May and September that occurred east of Lymington River, were reported west of Lymington River.

Red-necked Grebe *Podiceps grisegena*
Scarce, a spring and autumn passage migrant and winter visitor

'Rare visitor during the winter months, of which Mr Hart has specimens both in summer and winter plumage. Mr G C Sitzler has a specimen killed near Milford in the winter of 1912–13' (K&C).

It is unclear where those in Hart's collection were obtained, though K&C were presumably of the opinion that some were from within Milford-on-Sea parish. Whatever the situation concerning Hart's records, Mr Sitzler's specimen appears to be from Hampshire; it thus pre-dates the one that visited the Hampshire section of Frensham Great Pond in 1949 and considered to be the first Hampshire record since 1894 (BoH). As the exact location of the Milford individual is unknown, two 1953 records that involved a singleton at Hurst Spit on 1 February and two in the Lymington River on 20 December, were possibly the first for the NW Solent. Between 1954 and 1992, when extreme dates were 19 September (in 1982) and 16 April (in 1988) at least 28 individuals included single dead specimens during severe weather in early 1963 and badly oiled on 6 February 1982, and a day-maximum of three off Hurst Spit on 20 January 1985. An influx into Britain during the early 1979 cold spell (Chandler 1981) was probably the result of a north-west European breeding-range expansion (Spencer 1993).

Post-BoH (1993–2015) at least 45 individuals were recorded during 18 September (in 1993)–22 April (in 2006) in September (1), October (7), November (11), December (3), January (12), February (3), March (3) and April (5). At least six individuals were present for considerable periods, eg singletons during 23 October 1994–30 January 1995, 28 October–19 November 1995, 15 October–11 December 2005 and 16 November–16 December 2006 and two during 20 November 1996–19 January 1997. Those in September 1993 and in April 1994, 1995 and 2006 were in summer plumage. With the exception of 2004, 2012 and 2015, Red-necked Grebes were reported annually on the NW Solent from 1993. No fewer than six were recorded in 1996 (a record year for the county, with 30 noted) since when they have become much scarcer in Hampshire.

Slavonian Grebe *Podiceps auritus*
Common, a spring and autumn passage migrant and winter visitor.
'A regular winter migrant to the coast. Hawker shot a "dusky Grebe" on 14 January 1814, which was probably a bird of this species. In his game-list he calls it "a kind of black and white sea-dabchick"' (K&C).

The above record was also cited by K&M, but it is clear from Hawker's *Diary* that this bird was shot at Poole in Dorset, not at Keyhaven. Neither K&M nor Cohen mention other pre-1945 NW Solent records, but singletons were recorded on 25 February 1947, on 24 December 1948 and on 12 January 1949 and doubletons on 7 March 1947 and on 15 December 1949. During 1950–1992, at least 158 individuals were reported between 6 October (in 1972) and 11 May (in 1978) in October (2), November (11), December (54), January (40), February (30), March (10), April (10) and May (1) and day-maxima were seven on 24 November 1957, on several dates during November/December 1972 and on 14 February 1982 and six at Pitts Deep on 18 February 1979.

Post-BoH (1993–2015) it remained a frequent visitor and an estimated 287 individuals were recorded during 18 September (in 2009)–3 May (in 1993) in September (1), October (13), November (7), December (104), January (78), February (52), March (27) and April (5, one of which remained into May 1993). Day-maxima peaked at 16 on 20 January 1998; nine on 1 February 2009 occurred during cold weather. Singletons flew east at Hurst Spit on 13 April 2013 and 17 October 2010.

Those occurring in Hampshire probably originate from around the Baltic.

Slavonian Grebe

Black-necked Grebe *Podiceps nigricollis*
Scarce, a spring and autumn passage migrant and winter visitor

'An occasional visitor during the winter months, of which specimens may be seen in Hart's museum' (K&C). During 1949, two were in Oxey Lake on 12 January, five in the Lymington River on 15 December and one in Oxey Lake on 28 December. Regular wintering occurred during 1950–1979 and included day-maxima of seven on 7 January 1957 and nine on 24 December 1960 and 10 January 1962. Only eight individuals were reported during 1980–1992, the earliest of which was one in the Lymington Estuary on 23 November 1992 and the latest were a singleton off Pennington Marshes on 18 April 1970 and two, in summer plumage, off Hurst Spit on 16 April 1989.

Post-BoH (1993–2015) some 82 individuals were reported between 17 June (in 2000)–23 April (in 2001) in June (1), July (1), August (4), September (5), October (8), November (9), December (14), January (23), February (5), March (6) and April (6) and the day-maximum was three on 8 March 1997. Some were apparently long-stayers, eg singletons during 1 January–15 February 2000, 17 June–27 August 2000, 25 September 2006–4 February 2007 (with two on 25 January) and 27 December 2008–13 February 2009.

Unlike the previous species, which breeds predominately in Iceland, Scotland and Fenno-Scandia, the Black-necked Grebe is a denizen of more southerly latitudes in central and southern Europe; a small number of pairs breed in Britain.

Honey-buzzard *Pernis apivorus*
Scarce, a spring and autumn passage migrant

'The Honey-buzzard is a scarce summer visitor to the New Forest, where it nested regularly until driven away by egg-collectors. We have no record of its occurrence in this parish' (K&C).

There were eight records that involved nine birds, the first at Hurst Spit in October 1973. Others occurred at Keyhaven/Pennington Marshes as follows: singletons on 21 October 1973 (soared inland, having earlier been seen at Alum Bay on the Isle of Wight), 7 September 1975 (flew south), two in 1976 (flew south-west on 3 October 1976 and west on 30 October), 15 September 1979 (flew east), 12 May 1980, 23 May 1991 and two drifted north on 5 September 1988. Those in 1976 were associated with a large arrival of Honey-buzzards in eastern England, a dark juvenile on 30 October being the latest Hampshire record.

Post-BoH (1993–2015) at least 12 were recorded during 4 May (in 2001)–8 June (in 2005) and 36 during 20 August (in 2003)–13 October (in 2012) in May (11), June (1), August (4), September (29) and October (3). Perhaps unsurprisingly, peak autumn-totals occurred during 'invasion years' in 2000 (when nine were reported on the NW Solent during 23–30 September with a day-maximum of seven on the last day) and 2008 (when seven were reported during 7–20 September).

Black Kite *Milvus migrans*
Rare, a spring and autumn vagrant; it breeds Palearctic, Afro-Malagasy, Indomalayan and Australasian regions and European breeders (nominate migrans) winter mainly sub-Saharan Africa

Three records: one that arrived from the south at Hurst Spit on 4 May 1987 and flew west towards Hengistbury Head was the third county record, one flew east over Keyhaven on 21 September 2009 and one was at Lower Pennington on 19 May 2013.

The Hampshire total to 2015 was 38 individuals.

Red Kite *Milvus milvus*
Scarce, a spring, autumn and winter visitor

One that flew south at Hurst Spit on 5 January 1979 appeared to be the first modern-day NW Solent record.

Post-BoH (1993–2015) at least 27 individuals (25 of which were during 2001–2012) included nine that flew north in spring. All occurred during 5 August (in 2006)–10 June (in 2012) in August (1), September (2), October–February (1 in each month), March (11), April (2), May (4) and June (2). Three singletons (close to, but outside the recording area) were at Milford-on-Sea on 10 April 2001 and over the Isle of Wight on 14 November 1988 and 7 May 2004.

White-tailed Eagle *Haliaeetus albicilla*
Rare, a winter vagrant; breeds SW Greenland/Iceland and Continental Europe (reintroduced Scotland) east to Kamchatka and Japan

'A very rare visitor in the winter months' (K&C).

K&C also included details of Hawker's encounters with this bird. Fossil remains of this species, discovered during archaeological excavations, were indicative of a widespread distribution in lowland England during Anglo-Saxon and Roman periods. Arnewood (in Old English earn, wudu, meaning Eagle wood) indicates that this was probably a White-tailed Eagle site in by-gone days (Yalden 2007). Hawker's record of one at Keyhaven on 10 February 1827 appears to be the first specifically dated Hampshire reference; he reported others on 28 December 1829, 9th and 15 January 1837 and 22/23 January 1841. Nesting in England, eg on the River Plym in Devon and at Culver Cliff on the Isle of Wight, seems to have ceased in the 1700s (Warner 1795, Love 1983) though despite fierce persecution, White-tailed Eagles persisted in Scotland throughout the nineteenth century and into the next; the last known breeding attempt was on Skye in 1916. It is thus possible that Hawker's birds were from the then-declining Scottish population.

Post-BoH, a juvenile (initially in Sussex and on the east Hampshire coast in December 2010) wintered at Hordle (only a kilometre or two from Arnewood) during 1 January–12 February 2011; it visited Keyhaven/Normandy Farm on 9/10 January and on 12 February.

The Hampshire total to 2015 was 13 individuals.

Marsh Harrier *Circus aeruginosus*
Scarce, has bred, spring and autumn passage migrant and winter visitor and occurred in summer

K&M listed four nineteenth-century records for Hampshire, but other than a 'probable', recorded by a competent ornithologist near Sturt Pond on 1 December 1947, there appear to be no other county records during the first half of the twentieth century. Marsh Harriers were increasingly reported from Poole Harbour (Dorset) from 1943, where breeding took place in 1950 and possibly even earlier. At least five pairs were present in 1954 but numbers then decreased, the last pair nesting just eight years later in 1962 (Green 2004). The Poole Harbour population was considered to be the catalyst for its Hampshire appearances in the 1950s (BoH). Between 1952 and 1992 at least 41 individuals, of which ten were males, were reported on the NW Solent during 12 August (in 1967)–3 June (in 1989) in August (6), September (9), October (2), November (2), January (1), February (2), April (7), May (11) and June (1).

Post-BoH, the Marsh Harrier became a more frequent visitor to Hampshire, particularly in mid-winter from 2009. Between 1993 and 2014 an estimated 168 individuals, of which at least 28 were males, were reported on the

NW Solent during 29 July (in 2002)–12 June (in 2002) in July (1), August (21), September (20), October (21), November (5), December (10), January (16), February (6), March (12), April (26), May (29) and June (1). Nesting material was taken into potential breeding habitat at one NW Solent site in early May 1996, but it was not until 2015 that a pair bred and reared two young, on private land within the recording area. This was the first confirmed breeding in Hampshire since 1957 when a pair unsuccessfully nested at Needs Oar.

Hen Harrier *Circus cyaneus*
Scarce, a spring and autumn passage migrant and winter visitor; has occurred in summer
Unlike the previous species, Hen Harriers were known to occur in Hampshire during the first half of the twentieth century, though Cohen considered that there was 'practically no evidence to substantiate' claims of nesting during, or before, that period.

A female was reported over Pylewell saltings on 13 November 1955. During 1967–1992, at least a further 49 individuals, of which 15 were noted as (presumably grey) males, were reported during 11 September (in 1985)– 10 June (in 1986) in September (2), October (7), November (7), December (9), January (13), February (7), March (2), April (1) and June (1). A few individuals, eg a grey male during 1 January–15 March 1979 (a winter in which a major influx occurred in southern England) and one during 18 January–12 March 1986, hunted over the marshes and adjacent farmland on many occasions, though it is uncertain whether they roosted locally or commuted to the New Forest.

Post-BoH (1993–2015) in spite of an increasing observer force, only about 51 individuals were reported during 31 August (in 2013)–2 June (in 2002) in August (1), September (2), October (9), November (10), December (6), January (7), February (8), March (2), April (2), May (3) and June (1). A female or juvenile regularly hunted the marshes during 1 January–2 April 2010, while singletons flew north on 2 June 2001, 11 April 2004 and 3 May 2012.

Montagu's Harrier *Circus pygargus*
Scarce, a spring and autumn passage migrant, has occurred in summer
'A rare summer migrant, nesting in the county most years. A slender hawk with very long wings and tail, the male bird being of such a pale ash grey as almost to resemble a gull' (K&C).

Hen Harrier. Salterns Marshes

No further records were forthcoming from the NW Solent, until a female was seen to leave northwards from Keyhaven Marshes on 23 June 1962. A further 11 individuals during 1966–1992 included juveniles on 19 August 1966, 18 August 1968, 31 July 1982 and 10 September 1989, and a male on 30 September 1980. All records fell between 1 May (in 1997) and 31 May (in 2003) and 31 July (in 1982) and 30 September (in 1980) in May (2), July (1), August (4) and September (4). Ringtails, probably of this species flew south on 26 September 1976 and 8 September 1985.

Post-BoH (1993–2015) 14 individuals, that included two juveniles in August 2014, occurred during 1 May (in 1997) –31 August (in 2014) in May (11) and August (3). Other than a male and female, which flew high to the north at Milford-on-Sea on 2 May 2005, all were singletons.

The last known Hampshire breeding attempt occurred in 1998.

Goshawk *Accipiter gentilis*
Rare, a summer, autumn and winter visitor
At least nine, all singletons, occurred in January (1), March (1), July (1), September (2), October (2), November (1) and December (1). The first was reported at Lymington on 11 July 1972 and the next in 2002, in which year breeding was proved for the first time in the New Forest.

Sparrowhawk *Accipiter nisus*
Common, resident and probable spring and autumn passage migrant
'Resident and nesting in our big woods. Not so common as formerly owing to the strict preservation of our game preserves, where we must admit that it is destructive. But those who complain of the increase of Thrushes and Blackbirds must remember that this hawk, if allowed to live unmolested, would be a severe check upon them' (K&C). Locally, Sparrowhawks were probably less numerous than Kestrels. During the CBC, territories adjacent to Normandy Farm were occupied and breeding was confirmed in 1983, so it was no surprise that they were recorded on the Farm in at least seven seasons and also at Salterns in seven seasons. During the Atlas Survey, breeding was confirmed at Waterford and was considered likely at Lower Pennington, Lisle Court and Pitts Deep.

According to Wernham (2002), British Sparrowhawks are 'remarkably sedentary' with ringing indicating that just 23 per cent of juveniles disperse more than 20 km, though birds from Fenno-Scandia and the Low Countries occur in Britain in autumn and again in spring. Thus, while some reports, such as two that flew north at considerable height at Hurst Spit on 27 April 2000 and singletons that flew in off the sea there on 27 April and 2 May, in 2013, may refer to migrants, it is impossible to differentiate them with any confidence from local birds that regularly commute to and from the Isle of Wight and also those that hunt over the intertidal. Sparrowhawks sometimes hunted up to 5 km from their nesting or roosting sites (Newton 1986).

Post-BoH, a NW Solent total of at least 235 records were submitted during 1993–2015, of which 36 were for October and 31 for December. All were of singletons, other than two on at least seven dates. However, it must be noted that as with other common species, it was probably under-reported. At least three territories within the recording area, west of Lymington, were occupied in 2003.

Buzzard *Buteo buteo*
Common, a resident, greatly increased as a breeding species in Hampshire in relatively recent times
'As this bird was formerly common in the Forest and still visits the big woods occasionally, it is likely to be seen in the district during periods of migration' (K&C).

The Buzzard was not recorded during the CBC, but two (possibly a territorial pair) over Efford on 12 April 1987 were apparently overlooked during the Atlas Survey. There appeared to be no documented NW Solent record during the first half of the twentieth century, but one flew from Alum Bay (Isle of Wight) towards the Hampshire mainland on 9 September 1954. A further 67 records, which included the 1987 Efford pair, involved at least 69 individuals, of which most occurred in August (10, of which one was long dead on Hurst Spit shoreline on 9 August 1966), September (27) and October (9); most were probably dispersing juveniles. Others were reported in November (2), December/February (1 in each month), March (2), April (8), May (6) and June (2).

Post-BoH, more than 560 records were submitted, though as with other common species, it is known that not all sightings were reported. Though few were specifically indicative of local breeding, the annual nesting population within the recording area was probably up to three or four pairs. The status of those moving to and from the direction of the Isle of Wight is impossible to assess, but many were probably local residents. Beginning in the 1990s as the population increased, Buzzards soaring out over The Solent towards the Isle of Wight were common sights: if watched long enough, many of those birds returned to the mainland and so were clearly neither migrants nor dispersing juveniles. Such movements were reported in all months other than January and June.

Reported day-maxima of 35 (16 flew south) on 22 August 2001, 26 (20 flew south) on 5 October 1999, 20 (five flew south) on 12 April 2001 and 11 (eight flew north) on 29 March 2001 were, however, considered by the observers, to be passage migrants. Some groups of soaring individuals, however, though not necessarily all from within the recording area, almost certainly involved residents. Gatherings of ten or more were reported in February (once), March and April (four occasions each), May (once), August (eight occasions), September (ten occasions) and October (four occasions).

Rough-legged Buzzard *Buteo lagopus*
Rare, an autumn vagrant; breeds in N Eurasia and North America and winters south to S Europe, central Asia and southern US

One record: an adult female flew north at Hurst Castle on 17 October 2004. At least one (in early April 1969) that appeared in the Hampshire Bird Report was insufficiently documented, so was excluded from BoH.

Osprey *Pandion haliaetus*
Scarce, a spring and autumn passage migrant and occurred occasionally in winter

'A rare visitor, chiefly in autumn. Coles saw one over Sturt Pond, early in the nineties, which afterwards settled on a post in Keyhaven Harbour and Kelsall saw one at Barton on September 10th 1897' (K&C).

One (originally observed at Yarmouth, Isle of Wight on 4/5 December 1953 and which was seen at Keyhaven on 7 December (Cohen 1955) and also at Needs Ore on that day (Cohen & BoH) was the first December record for Britain. During 1954–1992, at least 37 individuals were recorded during 7 April (in 1973)–27 October (in 1981) in April (7), May (6), June (4), July (1), August (3), September (10) and October (6); up to an annual maximum of three was recorded during 1975–77 inclusive, in 1982 and 1984. One at Pennington Marshes on 27 August 1987 was the sole Hampshire autumn record in that year.

Post-BoH (1993–2015) NW Solent annual maximum increased to at least 11 individuals, of which eight were in spring, during 2015. Submitted records referred to about 130 individuals during 19 March (2005)–28 November (in 2014) in March (5), April (26), May (19), June (2), July (3), August (25), September (40), October (8) and November (2). All were singletons, other than doubletons on 1 April 2000, 27 August 1997, five dates during September 1997 and on 8 October 2006.

One of its last known English breeding sites was on The Solent in 1570 (Martin 1992).

Water Rail *Rallus aquaticus*
Common, a resident, spring and autumn passage migrant and winter visitor

'A resident but commonly overlooked on account of its skulking habits' (K&C).

Water Rails were recorded at Keyhaven in 1947, but were clearly under-reported during 1950–1992. During the CBC, it was apparently absent from Normandy Farm and Salterns, but probably nested near Keyhaven during the Atlas Survey. An estimate of about 12 at Keyhaven on 3 April 1969 may have included potential breeders; otherwise, it was reported principally as a winter resident, but with a day-maximum of just seven on 11 February 1988. The first autumn returns were usually in late August, though reported day-maxima did not exceed two.

In winter they also frequented the saltmarshes and were sometimes observed as they flew landwards during rising high spring-tides. This bird also foraged on the foreshore, eg one at Iley Point on 12 November 1969.

Post-BoH, the Water Rail was frequently reported, particularly from the grazing marshes' lagoons during the breeding season. Here, as some lagoons became progressively less saline (see A Site History) there were noticeable increases, from a single pair in 1996, to about ten pairs in 2000 and 35 pairs in 2008, of which at least nine pairs produced young. The size of the wintering population was unknown but was presumably greater than reported day-maxima of 25 on 10 January 2009 and 22 on 9 November 1996.

Spotted Crake *Porzana porzana*
Rare (perhaps overlooked) an autumn passage migrant and winter visitor; breeds from W Europe (locally in Britain) east to SW Siberia and NW China, winters mainly Africa and India region

'A scarce resident, though not proved to nest in the parish' (K&C).

The next reports for the NW Solent were in 1967, ie a singleton at Normandy Farm on 12th and 16 November and again on 3 December. Between 1968 and 2015 at least 15 individuals were reported during 2 August (in 2009)–11 December (in 1983) in August (6), September (1), October (6), November (1) and December (1). All were singletons, other than two (an adult & juvenile) at Lisle Court on 27 August 1989 and two at Pennington Marshes (Butts lagoon) on 14 October 2009.

Baillon's Crake *Porzana pusilla*
Rare, a spring vagrant; race *intermedia* breeds locally NW Africa and Europe, other races east to Japan, in the Afro-Malagasy region, Asia and Australasia
One record: one, caught by Arthur, Normandy Farm's household cat on 17 March 1990 (AW in HBR) and released, apparently unharmed, on the Farm later that day, remains the sole Hampshire occurrence to 2015.

Corncrake *Crex crex*
Rare, now an autumn vagrant
'Regular summer migrant, seldom nesting in this neighbourhood, but always to be met with in clover and rough grass in September. Hawker's bag amounted to fifty-six, doubtless all killed at Longparish' (K&C).
K&M described the Corncrake as a common visitor to all parts of Hampshire, though they commented that 'Kelsall has not heard the corn-crake for the past seven years at Milton, but has seen one in spring and he believes that it occurs regularly there in autumn.' They also stated that Corncrakes were unusually scarce 'throughout the county' in 1904, which in retrospect, was perhaps one of the first local signs of the catastrophic decline in both range and numbers that affected Britain as a whole during the twentieth century (see Holloway 1996).
Due probably to a lack of active ornithologists, the disappearance of the Corncrake was not documented for NW Solent, though by the middle of the twentieth century it was clearly no more than a rare passage migrant. During 1950–2015, just three records, all singletons, came to light, ie at Lymington on 17 September 1956, Keyhaven on 28 August 1964 and Pennington Marshes on 5 September 1983.

Moorhen *Gallinula chloropus*
Common, a resident, spring and autumn passage migrant and winter visitor
'A very common resident' (K&C).
During the CBC, though present in a further five breeding seasons, this bird was proved to breed on Normandy Farm only in 1995 and 1999, but nested almost annually at Salterns (up to three occupied territories in 1980 and 1995). During the Atlas Survey, breeding was confirmed at Sturt Pond, Keyhaven, Lower Pennington, Pennington Marshes, Woodside, Lisle Court and Pitts Deep.
Only four double-figure day-counts were traced for the period 1953–1992, ie 76 at Sowley Marshes on 19 January 1985, up to 37 at Keyhaven (Avon Water) in November and December 1953, 13 at Keyhaven on 5 December 1956 and 11 at Sturt Pond on 9 November 1983.
Post-BoH, a post-breeding maximum of 70 at Iley Lane Lake on 26 September 1993 was probably a reflection of a significant, concentrated, but short-lived nesting population in the early 1990s that peaked at ten pairs in 1993. An apparent increase in the grazing marshes' breeding populations (at least 19 territories in 2003 and up to 20 territories in 2004) was presumably indicative of the decrease in lagoons' salinity levels (see Water Rail); five pairs in 2005 and four pairs in 2006 on Normandy Farm were also in freshwater habitats (Ward pers.comm.).
There was also a corresponding increase in autumn-maxima and winter-maxima; at least 14 counts in excess of 20 included up to 40 in February and March 2004 and 32 in October 2003 and August 2007.

Coot *Fulica atra*
Common, a resident, spring and autumn passage migrant and winter visitor
'Resident and nesting. In winter this bird may be seen in large flocks on the open sea' (K&C).
Hawker recorded large flocks of Coots on salt water in the vicinity of Lymington (Payne-Gallwey). Coots nested in small numbers during 1966–1992, on the Avon Water at Keyhaven (single pairs in 1967/68, 1970 and 1987) Pennington Marshes (single pairs in 1985 and 1988) at Lower Pennington (up to three pairs on Smith's Pond during 1979–1985) and on Bulls Saltern at Lisle Court (six pairs in 1973, single pairs in 1980/81 and 1986).
Coots were often recorded calling in flight after dark over Salterns during 6 February–29 March in 1978 and also on 23 October 1977. One on the sea off Hurst Spit on 21 April 1973 was presumably a spring passage migrant.

Day-maxima were usually fewer than ten, the most being 11 on Sturt Pond on 28 January 1979.

It was unclear when Coots ceased wintering in numbers on saltwater on the NW Solent, but this habit continued in a Hampshire eastern harbour into the early 1960s. The few reported on saltwater on the NW Solent post-1950 included two in the Oxey Marshes/Salterns area on 5/6 January 1979, one off Pennington Marshes on 15 July 1979 and four in Keyhaven Harbour on 22 January and 1 February, in 1985, though note there were considerable freshwater flows into the harbour during ebb tides.

Post-BoH, increases occurred in the breeding and wintering populations, as well as those on spring and autumn migrations. In the early 1990s, the principal NW Solent breeding locality was Iley Lane Lake (up to 11 pairs nested in 1993). Other breeding sites were Salterns (up to three pairs in 1994), Keyhaven/Pennington Marshes (up to ten pairs in 2012), Keyhaven (up to two pairs on the Avon Water in 2003), Normandy Farm (a pair in 2008 and 2011), Bulls Saltern (one or two pairs in 2003) and Sowley Marshes (at least two pairs in 2010).

Iley Lane Lake was an important NW Solent site where monthly-maxima January–December (all in 1993 other than those in January, February, June and July in 1994) were: 95, 101, 65, 40, no count, 122, 173, 154, 176, 158, 161 and 225 respectively. Following modifications to the lake in the mid-1990s, most then occurred on the Keyhaven/Pennington Marshes' lagoons where monthly-maxima, January–December were: 150 (in 2009), 105 (in 2011), 100 (in 2011), 71 (in 2009), 37 (in 2010), 48 (in 2009), 68 (in 2008 and 2009), 110 (in 2010), 158 (in 2008), 246 (in 2007), 183 (in 2008) and 156 (in 2008) respectively. Other than those reported on Normandy Farm lagoon, saltwater records were confined to singletons in Hurst Narrows on 9 March 1994, in Mount Lake on 5 January 2003 and one that drifted east on the sea at Hurst Castle on 29 March 2005.

One ringed at Abberton Reservoir in Essex in November 1962 was recovered at Milford-on-Sea in January 1963.

Five-year averages of British, Hampshire and NW Solent WeBS maxima during 2007/08–2011/12 were 112,617, 3,585 and 141 respectively.

Crane *Grus grus*
Rare, a spring and autumn visitor; breeds N Europe (reintroduced Britain) east to Siberia, winters SW Europe, N Africa, Middle East and Asia

Four records involved some 63 birds. A flock of about 50 at Milford-on-Sea on 31 October 1963 was part of a massive influx into southern England that involved around 500 individuals. No more were reported on the NW Solent until 17 October 1994, when a flock of 11, calling loudly, circled low over Vidle Van Farm at Keyhaven then flew high towards the Isle of Wight; they were probably the group that was seen later in the day at Hengistbury Head and The Fleet (Dorset). An immature, seen earlier at three sites east of Southampton Water, was at Keyhaven and Pylewell on 16 September 2011 and an adult flew north-west over Hurst Spit on 24 April 2013.

The Hampshire total to 2015 was about 141 individuals.

Stone-curlew *Burhinus oedicnemus*
Rare, a spring and autumn vagrant

'An occasional visitor at seasons of migration, but not nesting in this part of Hampshire. A specimen was procured in the parish of Milton about eight years ago, which had apparently been injured by contact with a telegraph wire and Coles has seen one on Blackfield Common, near Fawley. Hawker's bag of five was no doubt obtained at Longparish' (K&C).

There were just five NW Solent records since 1950: one flew south at dusk at Pennington Marshes on 24 October 1951, one called after dark at Keyhaven on 18 August 1972, one was over Keyhaven saltmarshes on 14 October 1989, one at Keyhaven on 13 May 2010 was possibly present a few days before and one was in fields near Keyhaven on 10 April 2013.

Black-winged Stilt *Himantopus himantopus*
Rare, one breeding attempt, otherwise a spring vagrant; nominate race breeds Europe (winters tropical Africa) east to Mongolia, Africa, Madagascar and south Asia (other races Oriental Region, Australasia and Americas)

Five records that involved eight individuals were as follows: a pair at Pennington Marshes during 3–7 May 1987 (the fifth Hampshire record and ninth–tenth individuals) together with four others in Hampshire, formed part of an influx of about 30 individuals into southern England (Rogers 1988) one at Normandy Farm lagoon on 30 March 1998 moved to Oxey Barn fields the next day, where it remained until 5 April, two at Normandy Farm lagoon on 29 April

2000 and a male at Keyhaven Marshes (Fishtail lagoon) on 21 June 2005. Finally, a female arrived at Pennington Marshes on 27 May 2012 and was joined by a male on 2 June. Breeding was attempted, but marauding Crows and poor weather forced them to abandon the site on 9 June.

The Hampshire total in 2015 was 27 individuals.

Avocet *Recurvirostra avosetta*
Scarce; four breeding attempts to 2015, but mainly a spring and autumn passage migrant and winter visitor

The first report for the area was of two at Keyhaven on 30 July 1934, though no more were noted until 1945 when two were at Keyhaven on 9 May and five, the largest group recorded in the county during the first half of the twentieth century, on 22 May 1947. Subsequent occurrences were almost annual and a total of at least 141 individuals were recorded during 1950–1992, in January (2), February (3), March (4), April (45), May (24), June (21), July (1), August (2), September (1), October (16), November (13) and December (9). Day-maxima were 12 that flew east at Hurst Spit on 16 April 1968, 16 that arrived from the west in over the Spit on 21 June 1974 and 12 at Keyhaven on 12 October 1991. The latter left eastwards during the morning and later that day a flock of 11 reported at Titchfield Haven were probably of the same group.

Avocet

Post-BoH, single pairs attempted to breed in 2010, 2012, 2013 and 2015. The first was predated, the second was flooded-out, the third pair lost their clutch to egg thieves and the last also failed to raise young.

Some 456 individuals occurred in January (31), February (37), March (26), April (42), May (57), June (14), July (15), August (45), September (89), October (47), November (33) and December (20). Of a combined 104 that flew east and west during 4 March (in 2002)–18 November (in 1995) in March (7), April (17), May (11), August (24), September (23), October (15) and November (7) maxima were eight east on 25 August 2002 and 28 October 2001 and seven west in September, on 4th in 1999 and 29th in 2011. Annual totals peaked at 48 in 2002 and included a day-maximum of 24 at Keyhaven on 8 September 2006. One individual remained in Oxey Lake during 10 January–20 February 1993 and seven were on Normandy Farm lagoon during 2–9 May 1996.

Oystercatcher *Haematopus ostralegus*
Common, a declining resident, spring and autumn passage migrant and winter visitor

'A regular winter visitor, more common in autumn and spring than in the dead season' (K&C).

Garrow did not mention this species and Hawker, who used an old name of Olive, shot only eight in the Keyhaven/Lymington area. Wise, however, said it was 'by no means uncommon' along the New Forest shore.

Oystercatchers, though nesting (but rarely) on the Isle of Wight and (uncommonly) in Sussex and Dorset in the late nineteenth century, did not breed in Hampshire until 1934 (Cohen). During the following two decades, one or two pairs possibly regularly nested between Lymington and Hurst Spit (single pairs certainly did so in 1947 and 1952) though by the mid-1960s up to ten pairs were breeding on saltmarshes between the Lymington River and Keyhaven. Numbers increased further and no fewer than 48 pairs nested between Hurst Spit and Pitts Deep in 1977, 90 pairs in 1990 and 129 pairs, of which one pair were on the grazing marshes at Pennington, in 1992.

During 1945–1960, outside the breeding season, up to 100 were to be found at high-water roosts between Keyhaven and Lymington River. During 1955–1989, annual autumn-maxima averaged about 65, with a day-maximum of 250 in August 1969 and winter-maxima during 1955/56–1989/90 averaged about 90 with a day-maximum of 300 in December 1968. Oystercatchers were regularly recorded on passage at Hurst Spit, the day-maxima being 40 that flew east on 29 April 1976.

Post-BoH, breeding territories gradually declined to about 35 in 2012, due principally to habitat loss brought about by rising sea level and increasing wave attack on the saltmarsh seaward edge. Despite this, Oystercatchers continued to breed at suitable locations on the saltmarsh (often in Sea Purslane *Halimione portulacoides*) on shingle spreads, on Hurst Spit and on islands in Normandy Farm lagoon.

The average at spring roosts during 1992–2012 was about 100, with a day-maximum of 166 in April 2009. In autumn, those at roosts increased to an average of about 107 and peaked at 264 in September 2003. Similarly, the winter average rose to c.185, with a day-maximum of 284 in November 2002.

In spring, a total of 148 that flew east at Hurst Spit during 1993–2012 included a season-maximum of 63 during 20 April–19 May 1996 and a day-peak of 28 on 9 May 1998. A noteworthy autumn report was of 36 that flew east on 22 September 1999.

Oystercatchers were very catholic in their choice of high-water roost sites; those included the saltmarshes between Iley Point and Pennington Marshes Butts, fields on Manor Farm and at Lower Pennington (particularly around the caravan site) and the grazing marshes' lagoons between Keyhaven and Normandy Farm. Major low-tide feeding areas were the foreshores fronting Pennington/Oxey Marshes and in Oxey and Crooked Lakes around Normandy Farm. A juvenile, ringed at Keyhaven on 3 July 1970, was found dead at Felixstowe, Suffolk, on 19 August 1979. Five-year averages of British, Hampshire and NW Solent WeBS maxima during 2007/08–2011/12 were 228,856, 3,110 and 235 respectively.

American Golden Plover *Pluvialis dominica*
Rare, a spring, autumn and winter vagrant; breeds Arctic and subarctic tundra of N America, winters S America

The NW Solent accounted for the first four Hampshire individuals, ie at Lower Pennington Lane on 20 November 1994, Pennington Marshes during 20 May–2 June 1998, Keyhaven Marshes/Normandy Farm during 31 October –28 November 1999 and Pennington Marshes shore during 4–13 October 2006; the spring bird was an adult and the three autumn birds were juveniles.

The Hampshire total to 2015 was five individuals.

Golden Plover *Pluvialis apricaria*
Common, a spring and autumn passage migrant and winter visitor

'A regular autumn and winter visitor. Coles has shot this bird from Hurst Beach, but it is impossible to give Hawker's bag, as his editor includes it with the Grey and Green Plovers in a grand total of 351' (K&C).

Garrow described this species as an uncommon hard-weather visitor to the neighbourhood. Hawker shot at least seven at Keyhaven, but most of his fowling was carried out from gunning-punts in the intertidal zone, not with shoulder guns in the fields and grazing marshes. Pennington Marshes, where winter-maxima during 1960/61–1989/90 averaged about 163 and numbers peaked at 700 on 9 February 1985, was one of three regular 1970s Hampshire wintering sites. As a spring migrant it occurred mostly in March/April, with up to 85 on 14 March 1976 and 53 on 1 April 1991. Also, two were at Keyhaven on 15 June 1966, singletons at Pennington Marshes on 22 May and 4 June, in 1976 and at Hurst Spit on 11 May 1982; there were only two other June records for Hampshire (C&T). One on 26 June and two on 30 July, in 1988 were returning autumn passage-migrants, but they were most frequently recorded during August–October. At least 400 individuals that were reported during 12 August (in 1973)– 31 October (in 1976) included 70 on 28 August 1978, 36, of which 32 flew west, at Keyhaven on 30 August 1972 and 23 at Lymore on 26 October 1986.

Post-BoH, Golden Plovers were recorded in increasing numbers, but other than an isolated estimate of 1,100 in December 1995, it was not until January 2004 that the previous maximum of 700 was exceeded; the winter-maxima during 2004–2012 then averaged about 520 with a peak count of 2000 in January 2005. High numbers, particularly during 2004/05–2006/07, mirrored the national trend.

High counts in spring included 250 on 5 April 1995 and 1,000 on 6 March 2005. Easterly spring passage at Hurst Spit occurred during 3 March (in 1995 and 2006)–26 April (in 2000) with monthly-maxima of 200 on 3 March, in 1995 and 2006 and 150 on 15 April 1995.

Autumn migration occurred during 3 July (when one flew east at Hurst Spit in 2005)–17 October (in 1994 and 2009) and day-maxima were 69 on 30 September 2004 and 300 on 16 October 2008.

Many British wintering Golden Plover were not counted during WeBS surveys, but were routinely detected on the NW Solent, where the recording area included farmland and the grazing marshes.

Grey Plover *Pluvialis squatarola*

Common, a spring and autumn passage migrant and winter visitor and also occurs in summer;
it breeds in north Russia and north N America and winters in west and southern Europe, Asia, Africa, Australia
US and S America

'Spring and autumn visitor to the coast. Hawker apparently killed a few of these birds at Keyhaven in most seasons and notes in his account of a battle between an eagle and Ravens (Jan 22nd, 1841) that the former dropped a Grey Plover ...' (K&C).

Only about five entries in the *Diary* specifically referred to Grey Plovers, but the account of a White-tailed Eagle having (presumably) caught one is of interest as Grey Plover was not included in listed prey in BWP. Garrow called this species the Whistling Plover and wrote that it 'abounds in the winter season about our shores. The young of these birds appear about August and may be shot at this time about Hurst and Keyhaven.' Wise described it as 'not uncommon' during severe winters along the New Forest coast. C&T reported that Pennington [sic] was a principal Hampshire Grey Plover wintering area, but that any count over 200 would be abnormal. Research of the period up to 1971 (the cut-off data for C&T) revealed no documented count of more than 150, in February 1966, on plough-land at Keyhaven. Numbers increased substantially during 1972–1992 with average winter-maxima of c.320 and a day-peak of about 500 in November 1988.

Of some 1,900 reported on diurnal passage at Hurst Spit during 29 March (in 1981)–31 May (in 1978) at least 226, of which 140 flew east, occurred on 6 May 1976. Though March day-totals were sometimes greater, eg 379 in 1991 and 300 or more on several other occasions, grounded migrants included an exceptional spring gathering of 290 in April 1985.

Grey Plovers were apparently more numerous in autumn during 1972–1992 and maxima included at least eight counts in excess of 300. Other than single August (in 1980) and September (in 1986) counts of this magnitude, all occurred in October, with an average of about 235 and a day-maximum of 424 in 1982.

Post-BoH, the underlying British trend in Grey Plover numbers remained downwards (Austin 2008). Winter-maxima between Hurst Spit and the Lymington River declined to an average of roughly 240 with peak counts of 400 in December 1993 and 412 in December 1994. The average of autumn-maxima west of Lymington, also decreased, to about 156 with day-peaks of 300 or more only in October 1993 and in September 1994 and 2003.

At Hurst Spit, some 2,350 flew east during 10 February (in 2012)–31 May (in 2000); day-maxima usually occurred during the first fortnight in May and included the highest-ever count of 391 on 9 May 2001.

Since at least the 1950s, principal Grey Plover roosts were on the Keyhaven saltings (Hawker's Lake–Stony Point) and Oxey Lake–Lymington River, but sites east of Lymington River were poorly monitored in the 1950s/1960s. During periods of exceptionally high spring-tides, Grey Plovers often resorted to inland fields, traditionally on plough-land, but latterly on fields hosting autumn-sown cereals, such were the changes in agricultural practices. Small numbers fed at numerous locations along the entire Hurst/Colgrims coast, often in the narrower creeks and channels, but favoured zones were the extensive and open areas in the vicinity of Hurst Camber/Keyhaven River, Oxey Lake and at Tanners Lane.

Five-year averages of British, Hampshire and NW Solent WeBS maxima during 2007/08–2011/12, were 35,813, 1,824 and 433 respectively.

Those that occur in Britain breed on the western Siberian coast (Cramp & Simmons 1983).

Lapwing *Vanellus vanellus*
Common, a resident, spring and autumn passage migrant and winter visitor

'A common resident, nesting in the parish and largely increased numbers in winter. Hawker often shot these birds, but they are not separated from the other plovers in his total bag' (K&C).

Garrow, who records the Lapwing as breeding 'in the swampy districts of the New Forest', presumably included the Lymington area; it was certainly an abundant breeding bird across Hampshire during the late nineteenth century (see Holloway 1996). There were few historical records of Lapwing breeding on the grazing marshes, but one or two nests were found at the Lymington end of the marshes in 1926/27, though their discovery was perhaps incidental, as Redshanks were the principal targets on those occasions (Campbell 1979). Anecdotal evidence of Lapwing nesting on the marshes shortly after the Second World War came to light in the early 1960s. Local marshmen reported the Lapwing as a common breeder in the late 1940s/1950s, an indication that the marshes were heavily grazed and perhaps wetter at that time. The population crashed, possibly due in part to a perceived increase in ground predators, following domestic refuse tipping at Pennington Marshes in the late 1950s. Also, myxamotosis drastically reduced the Rabbit population, a fact that may also have contributed to increased predation of eggs and young of ground-nesting birds. Lapwings continued to nest in fluctuating numbers, mostly on Pennington Marshes and Manor Farm, where one or two pairs did so in most years during 1966–1973 and up to 25 pairs in the 1980s, though none were proved to nest in 1986. Other than the brackish lagoons and temporary freshwater pools, much of the grazing marsh remained very dry during summer, but habitat management since 1980, designed to maintain and increase areas of standing water and damp grassland at Keyhaven Marshes Fishtail, Pennington Marshes and Normandy Farm, was successful and maintained modest numbers of breeding waders.

The Lapwing was principally a winter visitor to the NW Solent where the average of annual maxima during 1971/72–1991/92 was some 1,450 and peaked at about 2,120 in February 1976 and 2,000 in December 1979 and in January 1973/74 and 1984. Numbers decreased considerably by mid-March, by which time counts rarely attained 500, but an exceptional 950 was reported on 14 March 1976. Numbers increased slowly during June–October and monthly-maxima during 1971–1992 were 150 (in 1971), 200 (in 1983), 400 (in 1979 and 1985), 400 (in 1979) and 700 (in 1980) respectively. Significant cold-weather influxes included 4,000 that flew south–south-west on 31 January 1976, 2,200 at Oxey/Keyhaven Marshes on 5 February 1977 and 5,000 that flew south–south-west over Keyhaven/Hurst Castle during heavy snowfall on 31 December 1978.

Post-BoH, some 29 pairs nested on the grazing marshes, west of Lymington River, in 1994 and other counts of nesting pairs were 14 in 1996/97, 15 pairs (six at Normandy Farm, eight at Keyhaven/Pennington Marshes and one on fields at Tanners Lane) in 2005 and an overall 21 pairs during 2010–2012.

Post-breeding gatherings included 315 in July 1993 and six other reported autumn-counts in excess of 300 included a day-maximum of 470 in October 2006. Wintering populations averaged about 1,860, which included day-maxima of 4,400 in February 2009, 3,000 in January 2008 and 2000 in December 1994 and February 2005, 2007 and 2009; 770 remained on 13 March 2005. There was little evidence of Lapwing migration at Hurst Spit; 76 that flew north on 29 November 2000 and 14 that flew east on 17 September 2002 were possibly local movements.

Lapwings occurred throughout the recording area, but principally in fields at Vidle Van and Manor Farms, grazing marshes between Keyhaven and Normandy Farm and saltings in the vicinity of Keyhaven. During late autumn and in winter, dawn and dusk flights took place to and from the saltmarshes.

Five-year averages of British, Hampshire and NW Solent WeBS maxima during 2007/08–2011/12 were 291,768, 5,516 and 1,296 respectively.

Little Ringed Plover *Charadrius dubius*
Common, a summer resident and spring and autumn passage migrant

One at Milford-on-Sea during 26–31 July 1951 was the first for the NW Solent and closely followed Hampshire's first, at Fleet Pond in June 1951: no more were reported on the NW Solent until one at Pennington Marshes on 19 August 1967. During 1968–1992, at least 100 individuals during 31 March (in 1982)–2 October (in 1976) included a day-maximum of five at Keyhaven Marshes on 17 July 1988. The first autumn return was one at Oxey Marshes on 29 June 1986; the origin of juveniles recorded on the marshes was unclear.

Post-BoH, breeding was reported for the first time in 1996, when two pairs were display-flighting and at least three broods were seen in late June; a further 21 breeding attempts during 1999–2012 produced c.20 young.

The presence of nesting pairs obscured spring and autumn migration patterns, but an estimated 413 individuals were recorded during 12 March (in 2011)–25 September (in 2012), in March (32), April (73), May (23), July (180), August (25) and September (28). Those included at least 22 singletons that arrived off the sea or over-flew Hurst Spit/Keyhaven during 18 March (in 2003)–15 May (in 2006) and a day-maximum of eight at Keyhaven Marshes on 2 April 2000. The autumn day-maximum of 21 individuals, of which 14 were juveniles, occurred on 14 July 2010; four other double-figure counts for July, also probably included passage migrants from elsewhere.

Ringed Plover *Charadrius hiaticula*
Common, a declining resident, spring and autumn passage migrant and winter visitor

'A common resident, nesting on the shingle near Sturt Pond. Hawker shot twenty-eight in fifty years' (K&C). Hawker called them Ring Dotterels, but Garrow noted that 'the Sea Lark or Bull Plover breeds in the disused saltpans at Keyhaven and adjoining spots. They appear in May and quit us early in October.' Most nineteenth-century Hurst Spit Ringed Plover nesting attempts were probably doomed to failure. Not only was there a resident garrison manning the Castle, but also a civilian population that included children, presumably always on the lookout for birds' eggs. Munn, writing in 1918/19, considered it had increased on the coast since 1905, by which time the Hurst civilian population had declined. Ringed Plovers were certainly breeding on Hurst Spit during the 1930s, at least one pair nested at the mouth of the Lymington River and probably at Pennington Marshes in 1947 and at least 11 pairs nested on Hurst Spit in 1961. Post-1966, when an increasing breeding population was probably the result of sustained protection measures, the Keyhaven/Lymington coast became one of Hampshire's principal breeding areas, with up to 18 pairs in a single season (C&T).

Ringed Plover

The majority of Ringed Plovers nested on the shingle and shell spreads fronting the saltmarshes and on Hurst Spit. A few pairs also bred landwards of the seawalls, ie a pair in 1981 and three pairs, of which two were on the abandoned Pennington Rubbish Tip, in 1982. National BTO censuses in 1973 and 1984 revealed NW Solent totals of 29 and 50 pairs respectively. During the Atlas Survey, breeding was considered likely at Sturt Pond and was confirmed specifically at Hurst Castle, Keyhaven, Stoney Point, Pennington Marshes, Cockleshell Island, Lisle Court, Pitts Deep and Colgrims; another survey in 1989 revealed a total of 34 pairs.

Ringed Plovers regularly flew east on spring passage at Hurst Spit during late April–mid-May, eg 42 during 22 April–17 May 1973, of which 31 occurred on 3 May and 34 on 7 May 1981.

Populations increased at autumn roost sites west of Lymington River post-early 1950s when during 1955–1990 they averaged about 140 with day-peaks of 350 in September 1976 and 344 in September 1989. Winter-maxima were similar and roost-counts during 1955/56–1989/90 also averaged c.140 with a day-peak of 310 in November 1981 (BoH).

Post-BoH, though islands in the newly created Normandy Farm attracted up to six nesting pairs during 1993–2012, breeding territories on the NW Solent declined. Some 33 pairs were present in 1993, but the 2007 HOS/BTO breeding survey found just 24 pairs, though there was a small increase to 27 in 2009. At Hurst Spit, c.700 flew east in spring, the season maxima was 123 during 13 April–20 May 2012 with a day-peak of 32 on 2 May. Autumn movements were also detected, eg 130 that flew east during 11–25 August 1999 and 32 that flew east on 23 September 2012.

The average of annual roost-count maxima increased to about 245 with a peak of 390 in October 2007. Winter populations also increased, to an average of roughly 170 and included a day-maximum of 230 in March 1995. Fewer Ringed Plover were found east of Lymington River but three-figure counts included 150 in October 2000 and 160 in September 2003.

Favoured autumn roost sites were on Normandy Farm lagoon and at Hurst Spit where, unfortunately, there was often much disturbance; alternative high-water sites were on fields around the base of the Spit. Feeding zones occurred all along the NW Solent coast, though Ringed Plovers tended to concentrate where the intertidal was coarser in nature, eg along the Pennington/Oxey foreshore or where spreads of sandy mud tended to accumulate. An adult, ringed at Pennington Marshes on 24 August 1971, was killed by a cat on at Kopasker, North Thingeyrar, Iceland, on 25 May 1983; it was the first recovery of this species between Hampshire and Iceland.

Five-year averages of British, Hampshire and NW Solent WeBS maxima during 2007/08–2011/12 were 18,398, 691 and 272 respectively.

Killdeer *Charadrius vociferus*

Rare, an autumn vagrant; nominate race breeds North America where it is migratory in northern part of its range, wintering south to S America (other races Caribbean and South America)

A first-winter on 28 September 1980, located by call before it landed on Iley Point, was last seen on 29th on an offshore shingle/shell spit at Pennington Marshes Butts.

This was the sole Hampshire record to 2015; the first British occurrence was also in Hampshire (at that time) at Knapp Mill (now Dorset) near Christchurch, in April 1859.

Kentish Plover *Charadrius alexandrinus*

Rare, spring and autumn migrant; nominate race breeds Eurasia, northern Africa and parts of Middle East and Asia (other races, some now treated as full species, in Asia and Americas)

NW Solent records all involved singletons, the first of which was at Hurst Spit on 24 April 1962 and others between 1972 and 2008 during 22 March (in 1974)– 9 September (in 1972) in March (1), April (4), May (3), July (1), August (3) and September (1).

Lesser Sand Plover *Charadrius mongolus*

Rare, a summer vagrant, *mongolus* group of 2 ssp (breeding NE Asia) and *atrifrons* group of 3 ssp (breeding S Central Asia) are possibly 2 spp (races *atrifrons* and *mongolus* on British List) winters Asia, Africa and Philippines to Australia

An adult on the intertidal mudflats close to Pennington Marshes' Butts during 22–26 July 2003 was the third occurrence in Britain and the first report of subspecies *mongolus* (though an earlier record of *mongolus* was accepted retrospectively).

It remains the sole Hampshire record to 2015.

Dotterel *Charadrius morinellus*

Rare, an autumn and winter vagrant; breeds arctic and alpine zones of Eurasia, wintering N Africa and Middle East (those recorded in Hampshire are of the British or Fenno-Scandian breeding populations)

Garrow informed us that 'the Dotterel *Charadrius morinellus* has been discovered in a few instances in the Oxeye and Keyhaven Marshes.' It is possible he confused this species with Ringed Dotterel, an early name for Ringed Plover, but though he used the correct scientific name, he provided no evidence to support his claims. Those reports have previously been overlooked, ignored or rejected by later Hampshire authors, but for completeness is included here. Otherwise, the first NW Solent records were of singletons at Keyhaven Marshes during 27–29 August 1969 and Pennington Marshes on 17/18 August 1975; they constituted the fourth and seventh county records (and twelfth and fifteenth individuals). The remaining records were likewise all singletons: at New Lane/Cut Bridge (Keyhaven) during 2 December 1994–29 January 1995, Keyhaven Harbour on 14 October 1995 and a juvenile, seen only in flight, that flew west at Hurst Spit on 15 September 2001.

The Hampshire total to 2015 was some 117 individuals.

Whimbrel *Numenius phaeopus*
Common, a spring and autumn passage migrant but also occurred in summer and winter

'Spring and autumn visitor to the coast, but more common at the former season. Hawker writes in his "Instructions" that they appear in small flocks about April and May; his total bag was twelve. On May 8th, 1838, he notes "plenty of Whimbrel about and quite tame." Mr Philip Munn saw a flock at Keyhaven as late as June 30th, 1894 and a small number of immature birds remain for the summer. Its local names are May-bird, from the season of its appearance and Titterel from its common call-note' (K&C).

A limited number of available records during the 1930s/1940s included 15–20 at Keyhaven on 13 May 1935 and 50 at Pennington Marshes on 4 May 1947. Two flew high out to sea over Hurst Spit on 21 July 1952 and an overall spring-total of at least 8,240 during 1956–1992, included some 6,255 that flew east, mostly at Hurst Spit, during 18 March (in 1970)–9 June (in 1984). Of those, the season-maxima was about 1,110 during 16 April–27 May 1978, a day-peak of 198 at Hurst Spit on 22 April 1976 and an off-passage gathering of 160 at Keyhaven on 1 May 1981. Also, all-season totals of 500 or more, occurred in 1971, 1976 and 1984. An additional 1,105 were reported, ie 27 in June that included one throughout the month in 1985 and a day-maximum of ten on 18th in 1989, 354 in July that included day-maxima of 45 on 17th in 1983 and 42 on 14th in 1984, 647 in August that included a day-maximum of 50, of which 40 flew south-west out to sea on 18th in 1966, 63 in September that included a day-maximum of 12 on 12th in 1992 and six in October that included one on 10th in 1981; others, recorded in November (4), December (1), January (1) and March (2) possibly over-wintered.

Post-BoH, at least 14,145 flew east at Hurst Spit during 27 March (in 2002)–5 June (in 2008); these included 1,647 during 13 April–5 June 2008 with a day-maximum of 440 on 20 April (a county record) and a June maximum of five on 18th in 2011. Grounded individuals, many of which were recorded on Pennington Marshes, peaked in 2012 when 24 on 21 April increased to 72 on 29 April then to no fewer than 200 on 2nd and 6 May and to 400 (a Hampshire day-record) on 4 May.

Of a autumn grand total of 741, 198 occurred in July, of which 25 flew east on 27th in 2001, 440 in August, of which 52 were reported on 16th in 2012, 97 in September, of which 17 were on 7th in 1997 and 2010 and 26 in October that included 12 on 3rd in 1993. At least 28 individuals that wintered included up to two during 2011/12.

Curlew *Numenius arquata*
Common, a spring, summer and autumn passage migrant and a winter visitor

'We consider that this bird may be classed as a resident, although not actually nesting within our borders and most numerous in autumn and winter. During high water large flocks rest on the shingles, between the mainland and the Isle of Wight, on the edge of the Needles Passage and return to their feeding grounds on the mudflats, the moment they are uncovered by the ebbing tide. Hawker includes no less than a hundred and eighteen in his total bag' (K&C). Garrow informed us that 'Curlew continue with us the winter through and retire to their breeding haunts in March. They feed on the mud where they procure small crabs and other marine food.'

This wader was recorded on eastwards spring migration at Hurst Spit in 1955, when 35 flew east over Hurst Castle on 30 April. Subsequently, migrating Curlew were reported there between mid-February and mid-May during 1969–1990. About 970 that flew east included 199 during 5 April–4 May 1974, 265 during 29 March–7 May 1981, of which 199 flew east on 12 April and 140 during 7 March–13 May 1982.

Annual autumn roost-count maxima, west of Lymington River, averaged about 320 during 1960–1990, with a peak of 600 in September 1975. Winter-counts during 1955/56–1989/90 averaged roughly 325 with a peak of 800 in February 1962. Fewer occurred east of Lymington River, but 130 were at roost on Pylewell saltings on 28 July 1990.

Post-BoH, noteworthy spring-totals at Hurst Spit included 262 during 18 February–8 May 2002 and 226 during 17 February–7 May 2003. Numbers peaked during the third week of April and three day-counts of 100 or more included a maximum of 148 on 13 April 2002.

During 1991–2012, autumn roost-count maxima averaged about 254 with a day-peak of some 415 in October 1992. Annual wintering populations during 1990/91–2011/12 averaged roughly 300, with a day-maximum of about 500 in February 1997.

Favoured high-water roost sites were the Keyhaven saltmarshes between Hawker's Lake and Stony Point and the west bank of the Lymington River. The fields and intertidal east of Lymington River hosted fewer Curlew and largest gatherings included up to 190 on 17 October 2004, but other than about 130 on 14 December 1997, mid-winter flocks seldom exceeded 100.

During the ebbing tide, most that roosted at Keyhaven flighted westwards to the muds and saltings west of Hawker's Lake, those on the Lymington roost flew into Oxey Lake and others at Pylewell flew both westwards and eastwards, into the upper reaches of the Lymington River intertidal and to Pylewell Lake respectively. Fewer fed elsewhere on the NW Solent, but Curlew regularly flew to wet pasture inland of the seawalls, eg on Vidle Van, Manor and Normandy Farms, at Lower Pennington and to fields on or close to the coast to the west of Milford-on-Sea.

Five-year averages of British, Hampshire and NW Solent WeBS maxima during 2007/08–2011/12, were 81,297, 2,933 and 376 respectively.

Black-tailed Godwit *Limosa limosa*

Common, a spring, summer and autumn passage migrant and occurred in winter

'Occasional visitor in spring and autumn. There is no evidence that Hawker distinguished this species from [Bar-tailed Godwit]' (K&C).

This bird was classed as a regular autumn migrant, but in small numbers, in Hampshire in the early twentieth century (Cohen). Black-tails increased in the county from about 1930, but apparently remained scarce on the NW Solent. Two, during 12 May–2 June and one on 15 September 1935, were considered worthy of publication in *British Birds*, though not until the early 1960s was the NW Solent population of sufficient significance to warrant mention in Hampshire Bird Reports. Thereafter the area figured prominently in the county literature and C&T were able cite wintering populations that often exceeded 100. Those on spring passage also increased and voraciously feeding Black-tailed Godwit flocks, which peaked at 490 on 16 April 1976, became anticipated NW Solent March/April ornithological events. In contrast, annual autumn and winter-maxima during 1960–1992, averaged only about 55 and 90 respectively.

Relatively few were recorded on diurnal spring passage at Hurst Spit, eg 40 flew north on 29 April 1961, 17 flew north-west on 6 May 1979, 12 flew east on 10 May 1981, 21 flew east during 6–12 May 1982 and 60 flew east at Milford-on-Sea on 30 April 1992.

Post-BoH, spring off-passage birds on the intertidal included day-maxima of 417 on 28 March 2009 and 525 on 16 April 2011; three-figure counts also occurred during May, eg 282 on 23 May 2004. Those on diurnal spring passage at Hurst Spit totalled at least 252 that flew east during 9 April (in 1993)–27 May (in 2007) with a season-peak of 96 during 2–4 May 2012 and a day-maximum of 60 on 13 May 1998.

Autumn/winter populations increased during 1990–2012. The autumn average rose to about 310, with a day-peak of 676 in October 2012 and winter populations averaged about 418, with day-maxima of 610 in January 2008 and 600 in December 2009. Forty-six that flew west at Hurst Spit on 26 December 2009 were probably local individuals. Prime low-water feeding areas were in the vicinity of Keyhaven harbour and river, in the upper reaches of Mount Lake and in the Walhampton intertidal as far north as Bridge Road. Major high-water concentrations were to be found on Manor Farm and on the grazing marshes and lagoons between Keyhaven and Normandy Farm.

As far as is known, this species never attempted to breed on the NW Solent but an immature found dead at Keyhaven on 22 October 1945 was of such small measurements that, in the informed opinion of BW Tucker, it could barely have crossed the Channel (Cohen).

Five-year averages of British, Hampshire and NW Solent WeBS maxima during 2007/08–2011/12 were 32,001, 2,210 and 560 respectively.

Bar-tailed Godwit *Limosa lapponica*

Common, a spring, summer and autumn passage migrant and winter visitor; it breeds in northern Fenno-Scandia and Siberia

'A regular spring and autumn migrant to the coast. Hawker writes on May 16th, 1842, that he "found the whole shore near Keyhaven lined with godwits, all working to the eastward" and on the following day he brought home twenty-one, some in summer and some in winter plumage. On the next day again he went about seven miles to the eastward and "fell in with the rearguard of their army", of which he killed eighteen. His total bag was eighty-seven' (K&C).

A record of 'a large flock' at Keyhaven on 12 May 1935 and 100 there on 3 May 1936, erroneously given as 3 November (Cohen) provided indication of continued NW Solent spring migration. Early-1960s seawatches revealed a significant up-Channel diurnal migration and during April 1962, 220 flew east on 27th and 1,100 on 28th, at Hurst Spit. Though possibly overlooked, no earlier large-scale movements were documented, even in Sussex, where seawatches were carried out from the late 1940s. Subsequent regular and intensive observation at Hurst Spit during 1963–1992, produced day-totals that exceeded 1,000 on 13 occasions with a grand total of at least 50,260 en route from their winter quarters in Mauritania and Morocco to their northerly breeding grounds. Fifty that flew east on 31 March 1973 were the vanguard of one of the heaviest spring migrations of this species to be recorded in Hampshire. During 8 April–16 May 1973, more than 10,000, which included 3,090 on 21 April, flew through The Solent. Yet this massive day-total was eclipsed on 29 April 1984, when of a spring-total of almost 10,000, at least 5,510 migrated across the area. Grounded migrant flocks rarely exceeded 100, but 130 were at Pitts Deep on 28 April 1974 and 105 at Keyhaven Marshes on 25 April 1975. Those observers fortunate to witness such major Bar-tailed Godwit migrations could not fail to be impressed; such spectacles were rarely encountered in Hampshire.

In contrast, other than an exceptional 300 that flew east at Hurst Spit on 19 January 1963, it was an autumn/winter visitor in only modest numbers, eg noteworthy reports included 42 that flew west at Pennington Marshes on 1 September and 38 during October 1988 and 74 that flew west at Hurst Spit on 7 September 1991.

Post-BoH, fewer were reported at Hurst Spit where, during 1993–2012, only 17,900 were logged during 1 April (in 2000) and 2 June (in 2007). Four-figure day-counts were attained on six occasions, of which the maximum was 1,850 that flew east on 28 April 2007, but which excluded an off-passage flock of c.400 in Mount Lake. Otherwise, except for 160 in April 2011 and 200 in May 2012, spring off-passage day-maxima were usually fewer than 50. Autumn and winter day-maxima were also unexceptional, monthly-maxima being just 30 in August 1994, 26 in September 2010, 38 in October 2001, 90 in November 1994, 23 in December 2002, 80 in January 1994 and 120 in February 1997; the three highest counts all occurred east of Lymington River.

Turnstone *Arenaria interpres*

Common, a spring and autumn passage migrant and winter visitor, some over-summer; it breeds in north Eurasia and northern N America and winters in Europe, Africa, south Asia, Australasia and the Americas

'A regular winter visitor to the coast. Hawker does not mention this bird, but Coles shot one in December 1890 and Mr G. C. Sitzler saw several in May 1911' (K&C).

Hawker did mention the Turnstone; K&C overlooked a *Diary* entry for 18 April 1842 when Hawker related the shooting of '18 godwits and 2 Turnstones.' Wise considered it 'not uncommon' in the New Forest area and C&T cited roosts of 100 at 'Pennington'. A diurnal easterly movement occurred at Hurst Spit during late March–early June, notably 119 during 19 April–3 May 1969, 127 during 10 April–12 May 1981 (maximum of 49 on 7 May) and a day-peak of 140 on 3 May 1980, the largest such Hampshire count during 1955–1989. A flock of about 20 at Pennington Marshes on 5 June 1974 were presumably also spring migrants. A northerly movement that often occurred in May, possibly involved individuals heading for Greenland, whereas the easterly passage were possibly those that were heading for northern Eurasia; the day-maxima of northerly-bound birds were 71 which departed over Salterns on 18 May 1976 and 35 from Oxey Lake on 19 May 1984.

Annual autumn high-tide roost-maxima between Hurst Spit and Lymington River averaged roughly 80 during 1960–1989, with a day-peak of some 280 in October 1986. Similarly, winter-counts averaged around 120, with a peak of about 260 in November 1984. High-tide gatherings east of the Lymington River were smaller and typically in the order of c.35 individuals.

Post-BoH, around 160 individuals were reported on easterly up-channel spring migration at Hurst Spit during 1990–

2012, with a season-maximum of 41 in 1995 and a day-peak of 26 on 2 May 1994; off-passage gatherings included a day-maximum of 162 in April 2009.

Though reported at other Hampshire coastal sites, northerly movements were undetected on the NW Solent. Annual autumn high-tide roosts averaged about 130, with a maximum of 215 in September 2012. Winter roost counts during 1989/90–2011/12 averaged some 118 and peaked at around 220 in February 1990. Favoured feeding areas, also used by Ringed Plovers, were in the upper reach of Mount Lake, the Pennington Marshes' Butts/Oxey Marshes' foreshores, Aden Bank (the foreshore around the southern perimeter of Normandy Farm) and Tanners Lane shore. Roost sites included craft moored in Keyhaven harbour and the top of the seawall fringing the harbour's north shore where they accepted morsels of food offered by fascinated onlookers, but it is known that Turnstones have a very catholic diet, eg see Bell (1961) and Mercer (1966).

Knot *Calidris canutus*
Common, a spring, summer and autumn passage migrant and winter visitor; it breeds in arctic N America, Greenland, northern Siberia and winters in Europe, southern Asia, southern Africa, Australia and South America

'Autumn and winter migrant to the coast' (K&C).

K&M regarded this species as 'not uncommon on the shores of the mainland during autumn and winter and often remains until May, after assuming the red plumage of summer.' NW Solent data for 1960–1992, confirmed the Knot as principally a spring and autumn passage migrant; a majority were present during 15 April–12 May.

At Hurst Spit about 580 that flew east during 5 April (in 1965)–6 June (in 1970) included a day-maximum of 102 on 7 May 1981, though fewer than half were detected east of Southampton Water on that day.

Autumn migration was less pronounced. In August 1978, a flock of 65 flew west out to sea on 20th and three flocks, totalling 91, did likewise on 28th; also, two flew east on 13 September 1986 and five (with four Ruffs) flew eastwards the following day. Elsewhere on the NW Solent, summer/autumn migration during 1960–1992 spanned the period 23 June (in 1971) –30 October (in 1983). Most occurred between mid-August and mid-September, though clear-cut peaks during 10–16 September and to a lesser extent during 22–28 October, were boosted by significant counts of 230 on 16th in 1962 and 50 on 27th in 1963 respectively. A protracted series of records during the late 1970s/mid-1980s may have reflected successful breeding seasons, though counts of 80 on 6 September 1985 and 64 on 5 September 1987 occurred at times when autumn concentration in excess of 20, at other county sites, were unusual.

It was a less frequent winter visitor and occurred mostly during December/January. A marked peak in the latter month was largely accounted for by a count of 180 in severely cold weather in 1963 and other noteworthy winter day-counts included 35 in December 1967, 45 in December 1991 and 80 in January 1992.

Post-BoH, about 730 that flew east at Hurst Spit included a season-maximum of 248 during 29 April–11 May and a day-peak of 87 on 9 May, in 1993.

Knots apparently became more frequent, particularly in winter east of the Lymington River, during the early twenty-first century. However, notable counts of 250 on 29 January 2005, 300 on 6 December 2009, 350 on 13 January 2010 and 400 on 23 January 2011 were presumably birds that were wintering in the Beaulieu Estuary. Meanwhile, at Keyhaven in 2010, no fewer than 166 occurred on 28 February, 178 on 8 March, 70 on 5 April, seven on 5 May, one on 7 June (though a later bird was reported on 9 June 2006) and 163 in December.

In autumn, 152 that included day-maxima at Hurst Spit included 31 that flew west on 29 August 2004 and 71 that flew east on 23 September 2012; also, additional off-passage groups were recorded in adjacent Mount Lake.

The peak week for Knots on the NW Solent was during 5–11 September, though the day-maximum of 124 occurred on 13th, in 1998.

Five-year averages of British, Hampshire and NW Solent WeBS maxima during 2007/08–2011/12 were 255,521, 1,045 and 226 respectively.

Ruff *Philomachus pugnax*
Common, formerly a predominately winter visitor, now a spring, summer and autumn passage migrant

'An autumn and winter visitor to the coast. Coles has a Reeve, the female of this species, which lost its right wing by contact with the telegraph wires running down the shore road towards Hurst Beach and was retrieved by his spaniel from the marshy meadow adjoining, in August 1890. The accident must have happened some time previously, as the wound was quite healed and the bird in good condition' (K&C).

Half a century later the Ruff had been recorded in all months in Hampshire, with county-wide winter increases post-late 1950s. By the late 1980s, regular wintering was confined to one Hampshire locality, by which time NW Solent spring-counts and autumn-counts in excess of five were of county significance. At Keyhaven/Pennington Marshes, up to nine occurred during 21 February–16 April 1956, 33 in early April 1957, eight on 12 February 1959, ten on 8 February 1960 and 16 on 20 April 1987. A few were recorded on-passage at Hurst Spit, eg three flew east on 4 May 1989.

Autumn-counts attained double-figures in at least 14 seasons during 1958–1981, with peaks of 47 on 21 September 1980 (see also Redshank account) and 17 in September 1981; no other autumn-count exceeded eight.

Ruff apparently began wintering at Keyhaven in 1956, when nine were recorded during February's cold weather. Between 1958 and 1961, up to 22 were noted on a few dates during January/March and up to 17 were continuously present during December/March, in 1962. Numbers soared spectacularly during subsequent winters and attained an all-time maximum of 171 in February 1970. During winter 1975/76, an influx of 350 into Hampshire included about 125 at Keyhaven on 21 February and 140/150 at Needs Ore on 15 February, though 100 at Sowley Marshes on 22 February 1976 were presumably part of the Needs Ore population, where 140 were reported on 31 January. However, 60 at Pitts Deep in December 1978 and 68 at Sowley on 5 December 1982 apparently occurred when no similar-sized counts were reported at Needs Ore. During the early 1980s, Keyhaven day-maxima were 43 in January and December, in 1980 and 33 at Tanners Lane on 24 November 1985.

Post-BoH, the Ruff occurred only in modest numbers throughout the spring/autumn/winter periods. Double-figure counts were seldom attained and maxima were 36 on 19 September 1999, 12 on 12 March 2005 and 12 on 27 March 2011. Other than those recorded from Hurst Spit, where a group of 18 that consisted of 16 males and two females, flew east on 24 March 2002, the only other notable counts were 13 on 26 July 1999 and 21 on 19 September 1993.

Broad-billed Sandpiper *Limicola falcinellus*
Rare, a spring vagrant; breeds mainly Fenno-Scandia to eastern Siberia, wintering E Africa to Australia
Two records: singletons at Pennington Marshes during 2–7 May 1994 and at Hurst Spit/Pennington Marshes on the evening of 2 May 2006, were the fourth and fifth county records. The Hampshire total to 2015 was five individuals.

Curlew Sandpiper *Calidris ferruginea*
Common; a spring, summer and autumn passage migrant, occurred less often in winter; it breeds in northern Siberia and north Alaska and winters in western Europe, south Asia and south to southern Africa and Australia
'Spring and autumn visitor to the coast. Several specimens, both in summer and winter plumage, may be seen in Mr Hart's Museum at Christchurch, obtained in the harbour there. This remark applies to many of the shore birds which visit our coastland no doubt include Milford in their line of flight' (K&C).

A singleton on mudflats at Sowley on 18 January 1936 was reported in the Field. Curlew Sandpipers were subsequently recorded at Keyhaven/Pennington Marshes in 35 out of the 41 years during 1952–1992 (BoH). At least 31 occurred during 12 April (in 1984)–1 June (in 1963) in April (7), May (23) and June (1); those included a day-maximum of ten on 6 May 1971 and singletons in off the sea at Hurst Spit on 22 April 1983 and 12 May 1975. Some 455 individuals were reported during 21 July (in 1990)–31 October (in 1988) in July (15), August (136), September (250) and October (54); the day-maximum was 50 on 1 September 1972. At least four November individuals were recorded during 1st (in 1991)–18th (in 1972).

Post-BoH, about 42 were reported during 20 April (in 1997 and 2006)—15 June (in 2008) in April (5), May (36) and June (1) of which the day-maximum was four (perhaps five) during 2–5 May 1994 and singletons flew east at Tanners Lane on 29 April 1995 and at Hurst Spit on 15 May 1998. An unprecedented 46 adults in partial summer plumage on 1 August 2009 were among a total of around 591 reported during 5 July (in 2012)–26 October (in 1996 and 2002) in July (54), August (212), September (259) and October (66). Also singletons were recorded in November on 24th, in 1993 and 6th–11th, in 2006.

Stilt Sandpiper *Micropalama himantopus*
Rare, a summer vagrant; breeds on tundra of N America and winters in S America

One record: an adult, moulting out of summer plumage, on Pennington Marshes Butts Lagoon during 21 July–3 August 2002. It remained Hampshire's sole occurrence to 2015.

Temminck's Stint *Calidris temminckii*
Scarce, a spring and autumn passage migrant

Four on 12th (not five as in BoH) and one on 25 May 1935, at Keyhaven, were the first Hampshire records; earlier dated reports in K&M were from Christchurch. Between 1951 and 1992, a further 13 individuals were reported at Keyhaven/Pennington Marshes during 4 May (in 1972)–11 September (in 1968) in May (7), July (2), August (2) and September (2); all were singletons except for two on 31 May 1963 and 11 September 1968.

Post-BoH, 14 individuals occurred at Keyhaven Marshes/Normandy Farm during 6 May (in 2006 and 2008)–16 September (in 1999) in May (8), June (1 on 3rd in 1996), July (3), August (1) and September (1): all were singletons, except for doubletons at Normandy Farm on 26/27 May 1998 and during 17–19 July 2001.

Sanderling *Calidris alba*
Common, a spring and autumn passage migrant and winter visitor; it breeds in arctic N America, Greenland and northern Siberia and winters in Europe, south Asia, southern Africa, Australia and S America

'A winter migrant to the coast. Two birds of this species are included in Hawker's bag' (K&C).

K&M wrote that it was 'a common winter visitor to all our coasts, very rare inland' and cited two spring specimens in Hart's collection. Writing of Hampshire as a whole, Cohen stated that it had been 'recorded in every month, could no longer be called a common winter visitor, were uncommon in spring, rare in summer, not infrequent in August and September and small parties moved east along The Solent in April/May.' C&T reported easterly movements of 148 on 9 May 1968 and 120 on 22 May 1961 at Hurst Spit and emphasised the lack of wintering birds away from Hayling Island.

Analysis of personal records and those published in Hampshire Bird Reports, during 1971–1992, revealed that roughly 2,740 flew east at Hurst Spit during 2 April (in 1971)–3 June (in 1979) and that an additional 360 off-passage individuals occurred during 10 March (in 1989)–10 June (in 1979). Those involved annual-totals of 220 that flew east during 12 April–12 May 1980 (47 on 11 May) and 257 that flew east during 10 April–11 May 1981 (182 on 7 May). Other day-maxima included 104 on 10 May 1975 and protracted migration into the first half of June was illustrated by, eg four at Hurst Spit on 9th in 1973 and ten off-passage individuals at Pennington Marshes on 10th in 1979. The Sanderling was a scarce and irregular autumn migrant and appeared during late July–October; reports from Hurst Spit of 20 on 24 August 1984 and 13 on 1 September 1988 were the largest autumn-counts in Hampshire at that time. One was at Keyhaven on 11 November 1985 and two December records (probably the same individual) occurred on 1st and 12th in 1974 and one was at Keyhaven on 1 January 1982.

Post-BoH, about 2,960 that flew east at Hurst Spit during 17 March (in 2002)–17 June (in 2006) included a day-maximum of 109 on 8 May 1998, an off-passage group of 26 on 22 May 2008 and one that flew high to the north-east from Pennington Marshes on 19 May 2004.

Autumn migration at Hurst Spit involved some 165 individuals during 12 July (in 2002)–25 October (in 2012) with a day-maximum of 22 that flew east on 15 August 2004. Autumn passage elsewhere on the NW Solent involved at least 270 individuals during 11 July (in 2007)–25 October (in 2012); the day-maximum was 17 on 23 August 2009. Otherwise, they were infrequently recorded and 14 winter individuals included four that flew west on 6 November 2002 and two on 14 January 1998.

A flock of 250, reported at Pennington on 1 November 1950, were probably misidentified; they were observed in 'frosty weather' and were probably Dunlin, a species, which often appears much whiter when in flight in such conditions.

Dunlin *Calidris alpina*
Common, a spring, summer and autumn passage migrant and winter visitor

'Usually reckoned as a winter visitor, when vast flocks may be seen along Hurst Beach, but often occurring in the summer months and in breeding plumage. Hawker shot a hundred-and-forty-six in three shots in March 1827 and his total bag amounted to 1329' (K&C).

The Dunlin was a numerous winter visitor to the NW Solent from at least the early 1800s, though estimates for bygone days were lacking. Garrow referred to 'prodigious flocks during the winter months all over our shores and saltpans.' C&T cited estimates of 1,000–2,000 and one of 7,000 at high-tide roosts, which in Hawker's day included the Shingles (west of Hurst Spit) where they presumably sought respite from high disturbance levels or shooting pressures, but note that no saltmarsh sites existed at that time.

Tubbs (1992) concluded that Dunlin increased in The Solent from about the early 1950s, probably in response to lower shooting mortality resulting from the Bird Protection Act 1954. Documented data, however, revealed a NW Solent decline from the mid-1970s (also detected at two other Hampshire coastal sites) though Langstone Harbour's population apparently increased.

A marked spring migration into and through The Solent was observed at Hurst Spit during 1969–1990. About 10,000 flew east between 1 April (in 1984) and 23 May (in 1976) with a day-maximum of 561 on 3 May 1973. Annual-totals exceeded 1,000 in 1973 (1,820 during 15 April–17 May) and in 1974 (1,244 during 1 April–16 May) and off-passage gatherings peaked at 1,200 in Oxey Lake on 29 April 1970 and at least 1,000 at Keyhaven/Pennington Marshes on 1 May 1973 and 4 May 1985. Systematic watching on the east Solent and at Selsey Bill in West Sussex indicated that fewer migrated past those watch points. This implied that some deviated from their course, or dropped-out to feed, before continuing their journeys, conclusions that were supported by detection of northerly movements, principally at Langstone Harbour. On NW Solent, the few documented records included 23 that flew north from Oxey Lake on 13 May 1979, 12 from Keyhaven Marshes on 7 May 1982, 15 from Oxey Lake on 8 May 1983 and 12, also from Oxey Lake, on 4 May 1985; all occurred during late pm/early evening.

Returning passage migrants usually arrived at Keyhaven during mid–late-June; those in the first week of the month, eg 50 in 1973 and 1974, were almost certainly late spring migrants. Autumn passage (August–October) during 1970–1992, involved monthly-maxima of 826 in 1988, 1,550 in 1973 and 1,095 in 1990 respectively.

Five-year averages of annual winter-maxima during 1970–1990 were 7,200, 4,950, 3,800 and 3,050 respectively and included monthly day-maxima of 8,000 in November 1974, 7,000 in February and December, in 1973, 10,000 in January 1975 and 4,000 in March 1976.

Dunlin. Fishtail Lagoon

Post-BoH, those moving eastwards in spring at Hurst Spit during 1991–2012 totalled at least 11,800. The season-maxima were 1,010 during 21 April–14 May 1994, 1,652 during 19 March–26 May 2001 and 2,348 during 9 March–5 June 2004; the day-maximum was 683 on 27 April 2004. Off-passage gatherings, however, did not attain pre-1991 levels and maxima were only 630 in April 1991 and 600 in May 1994. Northerly movements included eight (with a Ringed Plover) that left Oxey Lake on the evening of 6 May 1996 and 27 that left Keyhaven Marshes during the morning of 12 May 2002.

Autumn/winter roost-maxima also declined during 1993–2012. August–October estimates peaked at 450 in 2010,

750 in 2009 and a little over 900 in 2004 and 2012 respectively and monthly winter-maxima averaged about 2,765 with a peak of 4,700 in January 1995. Wintering populations east of Lymington River were irregularly monitored pre-1990, but up to 2,000 occurred during 1992/93 and 2,200 during 1993/94.

The NW Solent Dunlin population suffered substantial losses during spells of severely cold weather. Fifty-one corpses were found along the Hurst Spit strand line in early February 1987 and 371 during the second week of February 1991: 42 Redshanks, seven Black-tailed Godwits, four Grey Plovers, three Oystercatchers, three Turnstones and two Lapwings were also found at that time. The latter Dunlin total represented almost 10 per cent of the wintering population present prior to the onset of the 1991 cold spell. Ten carried metal rings, of which three were ringed in Britain (Christchurch and Poole Harbour) two each in Sweden and Norway and singletons in Germany, Finland and Poland. The conclusion was that high mortality was due to inability to access food resources, particularly limited at that time, not only by the west Solent's peculiar tidal regime, but also by severely frozen conditions in the intertidal zone (Tubbs & Wiseman 1992). All were measured and a large percentage was found to have rather long bills. However, the JNCC Coastal Review Unit was of the opinion that all were within the bill-length range, particularly for females, of the UK wintering race *alpina*. Was it a possibility that a majority of smaller males, unable to withstand the rigorous conditions, departed at the onset of the cold spell?

Principal feeding areas were Keyhaven River, Hurst Camber, Oxey Lake and the vicinity of Tanners Lane: favoured high-tide roost sites were on Keyhaven saltings, at Pitts Deep and, more recently, on Normandy Farm lagoon.

Five-year averages of British, Hampshire and NW Solent WeBS maxima during 2007/08–2011/12 were 323,686, 24,140 and 2,765 respectively.

Purple Sandpiper *Calidris maritima*

Scarce, a spring and autumn passage migrant and winter visitor; it breeds in arctic and subarctic Eurasia and N America and winters south to southern Europe and southern US

'A winter migrant to the coast. Coles has a specimen which he shot on Hurst Beach in December, 1890' (K&C). The above appears to be the first record for Hampshire. Though listed by Cohen, it was overlooked during preparation of BoH, in which one at Southsea during 17–29 December 1939 was considered the first for the county. The NW Solent emerged as a significant Hampshire site during 1960–1992. At least 41 individuals (43 in BoH) were reported in all months other than June, during 7 July (in 1969)–31 May (in 1961, the latest ever Hampshire spring record) July (1), August (3), September (4), October (8), November (5), December (7), January (4), February (4), March (2), April (2) and May (1); day-maxima were four on 16 December 1989 and three on 4 January 1991.

Post-BoH, at least 87 individuals were recorded during 11 July (in 2001)–3 May (in 2001) in July (1), August (2), September (4), October (7), November (29), December (9), January (16), February (6), March (4), April (8) and May (1). The majority occurred in 2000 (14) and 2001 (16) with a day-maximum of nine at Hurst Castle on 5 November 2000. None were reported during 1993/95 inclusive or in 1997 and only two in 1996, 1999, 2004 and 2011. Most were recorded at Milford-on-Sea, Hurst Spit and along Pennington/Oxey Marshes' seawall.

Baird's Sandpiper *Calidris bairdii*

Rare, an autumn vagrant; it breeds in high arctic of NE Siberia and N America and winters S America

Four records: juveniles were at Keyhaven/Pennington Marshes during 7–18 September 1988, during 29 September–16 October 2005, during 14–17 September 2011 and on 14 September 2012; they were the second, fourth, seventh and eighth county records.

The Hampshire total to 2015 was eight individuals.

Little Stint *Calidris minuta*

Common, principally an autumn passage migrant, but also occurred in spring, summer and winter; it breeds in northern Eurasia and winters in Africa and India

'Autumn visitor to the coast, but not in large numbers' (K&C).

The occurrences of Little Stints at Keyhaven/Pennington Marshes during 1954–1992 were summarised in BoH. This revealed 36 years with records, 20 years when counts exceeded five and a day-peak of 56 on 4 October 1960, exceeded only by the county record of 60 (but see post-BoH) at Dibden Bay on 28 and 30 September 1973. Spring reports involved one in April (on 15th in 1984) eight in May, of which four occurred on 7 May 1961 and three that arrived off the sea at Hurst Spit and three in June (latest on 9th in 1973).

Analysis of NW Solent autumn data for 1966–1992, revealed seven July individuals (the earliest on 16th in 1988) and protracted autumn migrations in 1972 (2 August–29 October, with a day-maximum of nine on 9 September) in 1973 (2 August–21 October, with a day-maximum of five on 7 October) in 1975 (24 August–9 November, with day-maxima of six in September and October and four that departed seawards over Hurst Spit on 9 November) and in 1976 (one in July, then during 22 August–20 November that involved a day-maximum of nine on 9 October). Winter occurrences totalled six individuals, in December (4) and January (2).

Post-BoH, Little Stints became more frequent in spring and at least 30 individuals were recorded during 11 April (in 2003)–12 June (in 2008) with a day-maximum of four on 1 May 2011 and inclusive of singletons at Hurst Spit that flew east in May 1994. Autumn migration took place during 10 July (in 2009)–31 October (in 1993). The most prolific year was 1996 when passage occurred during 29 July–26 October, with day-maxima of 50 or more during 21–24 September, 90 (a county maximum) on 25 September and ten on 1/2 October. Conversely, only seven individuals were reported during 26 August–16 October, in 2000. Also, one flew west at Hurst Spit in October 1994. Winter records involved at least 13 individuals, of which one remained until 23 March 2000. An extended series of records during 10 November 2001–28 April 2002 probably involved one individual.

White-rumped Sandpiper *Calidris fuscicollis*
Rare, an autumn vagrant; it breeds in arctic N America and winter in S America
Three records: singletons occurred at Pennington Marshes on 10 August 1974 (the second county record) at Keyhaven Marshes on 4 August 2004 and at Hurst Spit (a juvenile) that flew east with six Dunlin on 24 September 2011. The Hampshire total to 2015 was 19 individuals.

Buff-breasted Sandpiper *Tryngites subruficollis*
Rare, an autumn vagrant; it breeds in N America and winters in S America
Six records: singletons were at Keyhaven/Pennington Marshes on 31 August 1975, 4 September 1977, during 12–22 September 1980, during 25–29 September 1982, on 6/7 October 1991 (killed by a Sparrowhawk) and on 20 August 2013. Those in 1975, 1977, 1980, 1982 and 1991 were the first, fifth–seventh and ninth county records. The Hampshire total to 2015 was 12 individuals.

Pectoral Sandpiper *Calidris melanotos*
Scarce, mainly a summer/autumn passage migrant, but has occurred in spring; it breeds on Siberian and N American tundra and winters mainly S America
The first reported on the NW Solent involved two individuals at Pennington Marshes in 1962, ie one on 25/26 August, two on 1/2 September and one on 8 September; they were the seventh and eighth county records. During 1963–2015, a further 37 were recorded, five of which occurred during 7 May (in 2011)–29 May (in 1983) of which one at Pennington Marshes on 19th in 1981 was the first Hampshire spring record. Autumn reports occurred during 14 July (in 2001)–30 October (in 1976) in July (5), August (7), September (18) and October (2). Of five during September 1970, four were present on 15th and singletons included a long-stayer at Keyhaven/Pennington Marshes during 19 September–30 October 1976. Those in 1997, 1999, 2001, 2004 and 2012–2014 inclusive, were adults. The Hampshire total to 2015 was 90 individuals.

Semipalmated Sandpiper *Calidris pusilla*
Rare, a summer/autumn vagrant; it breeds on N American tundra and winters in W Indies, C America and (mainly) S America
Four records: an adult 17/18 July 1994, juveniles during 4–19 September 2006, during 24 September–2 October 2011 and 6/7 September 2013, all at Keyhaven/Pennington Marshes, were the first and third–fifth county records. The Hampshire total to 2015 was five individuals.

Wilson's Phalarope *Phalaropus tricolor*
Rare, an autumn vagrant; it breeds in N America and winters in S America
One record: a juvenile moulting into first-winter plumage at Pennington Marshes during 9–11 September 1998, was the fifth county record.
The Hampshire total to 2015 was six individuals.

Semipalmated Sandpiper & Little Stint. Butts Lagoon

Red-necked Phalarope *Phalaropus lobatus*

Rare, a visitor in all seasons, but mainly in autumn; it breeds in the Holarctic and winters in tropical seas

A juvenile on 7 September 1969 (the first for the NW Solent) and an adult during 27–31 May 1972 (the first spring record for Hampshire) were the eighth and tenth county records. A total of 18 individuals, inclusive of the above, occurred during 10 July (in 1975)–29 May (remained until 1 June, in 1977) in July (1), August (6), September (5), October (2), November (1), January (1) and May (2). Other than singletons at Hurst Spit/Milford-on-Sea on 27 September 1981, 9 August 1995, 11 November 2005 and 21 January 2008, all were reported from Keyhaven/Pennington Marshes. The 2008 record, accepted by HOS, was the sole winter record for Britain. The Hampshire total to 2015 was 51 individuals.

Grey Phalarope *Phalaropus fulicarius*

Scarce, an autumn and winter visitor, usually after westerly gales; it breeds in Greenland, Iceland, northern Siberia and N America and winters in southern oceans south to Antarctica

'An occasional visitor, usually in autumn and sometimes in very large numbers. Hawker wrote on September 26th, 1839, "I saw a rare bird in the marsh, a Phalarope and got him with the cripple stopper." Coles had the good fortune to see something of the large invasion of these birds, which visited our shores from October 12th to the 24th, 1891. He saw six on Sturt Pond on the 12th and thirty-nine on the same pool on the 18th, besides numbers on the neighbouring mudflats and ten on a small pond in the meadow south of Saltgrass, where they were so tame that continual worrying by boys, who had succeeded in killing one bird with a stone, failed to drive them away. Many birds remained up to the 25th, when all had left, the Southerly gales, which prevailed for five days having ceased and the wind changed to east. Notable immigrations occurred in the years 1866, 1869 and 1886, the favoured counties being those to the South-East, South and South-West, but the visitation was more widely spread, writers to the "Field" recording birds in many counties, though the largest numbers seem to have been observed in Kent, Devon and Hants, particularly in the Isle of Wight, where, on October 14th, Mr. H.R.Leach saw near Blackgang, about a hundred passing towards the Needles in parties of fifteen to twenty. The birds — chiefly young — which visit us are usually in the grey plumage. Keyhaven Harbour and Sturt Pond provide a safe refuge for many migrants from the far North during October gales and are well worth a visit at that season on the chance of seeing uncommon species' (K&C).

The next on the NW Solent were at Keyhaven Marshes in 1935, ie one on 21 September, two (one dead) on 22 September, two or three on 4 October and one 5 October; another was on Keyhaven Marshes during 22–27 October 1946. Of 203 individuals recorded in Hampshire between 1951 and 1992, 94 were reported at Hurst Spit–Lymington, of which ten were recorded during 22–28 September and 23 during 6–12 October, with a day-maximum of 18 on 9 October 1960; also six occurred on 27 September 1981 and 19 October 1987. Other than singletons during 8–15 December 1979 and on 10 December 1961, extreme dates were 1 September (in 1988, the earliest for Hampshire at that time)–26 November (in 1960).

Post-BoH (1993–2015) c.43 individuals were recorded during 4 August (the earliest county occurrence, in 2013)–21 January (in 2007) in August (3), September (12), October (18), November (7), December (1) and January (2); the day-maxima were three on 9 October 2001 and two (with a Red-necked Phalarope) at Hurst Spit on 21 January 2008.

Terek Sandpiper *Xenus cinereus*
Rare, a spring/summer vagrant; it breeds from Finland to eastern Siberia and winters in tropical African east to Australia
Two records: a singleton on a small freshwater pool on Oxey Marshes on 25th and 31 May 1963 and one in the intertidal close to Oxey Island on 10 June 1986, were the first and fourth county records.
The Hampshire total to 2015 was five individuals.

Common Sandpiper *Actitis hypoleucos*
Common, a spring, summer and autumn migrant, also occurred in winter
'A summer visitor, but not nesting in this parish. Hawker calls this bird the Summer Snipe and Stone Runner, but his specimens were no doubt killed on the Test, which furnishes localities suitable to its habits. His bag numbered thirteen' (K&C).
Noteworthy records post-1950 included a spring-passage peak of 14 at Keyhaven on 26 April 1977, eight at Hurst Spit on 5 May 1989, 45 that moved along Milford-on-Sea beach on 13 July 1982 and the area's highest ever day-count of at least 50 on 15 August 1969, matched elsewhere in the county at Dibden Bay on 6 August 1973. Wintering individuals included one at Sowley Marshes in December 1968, three at Pennington Marshes on 13 January 1973 and one in the Lymington Estuary on 27 December 1988. A noticeable decline of passage-migrants at Keyhaven/Pennington Marshes during the 1980s paralleled the county trend.
Post-BoH, easterly spring passage at Hurst Spit involved about 90 birds during 9 April (in 2006)–26 May (in 1997); the day-maximum of 11 included a group of nine on 29 April 1994. Also nine, of which three flew east on 5 July 2012, were recorded during 5 July (in 2012)–14 October (in 2003).
Elsewhere on the NW Solent, spring passage took place during 5 April (in 2003)–3 June (in 1997) with a day-maximum of six on 23 April 2005. Return migration occurred during 22 June (in 2003 and 2006)–25 October (in 2012) with a day-maximum of just 13 on 5 August 2004. Late year/wintering records were singletons on 12 November 1994, 14 February 1999 and 27 February 2000.

Green Sandpiper *Tringa ochropus*
Common, a spring, summer and autumn passage migrant, also occurred in winter; it breeds in northern Eurasia and winters in southern Europe, south Asia, Africa and Australia
'An occasional visitor at various seasons of the year, especially on the spring migration. Hawker includes eight "Green Sandpipers or Ox-eyes" in his total bag, but they were probably killed on the Test' (K&C).
Wise wrote that this species was 'rather common between Lymington and Calshot Castle', though he was incorrect when he added 'In June 1862, I saw several pair near Leap, so that it probably breeds on the coast.' NW Solent occurrences featured meagrely in Hampshire's twentieth-century literature; the only record cited by C&T was of six that flew south-west over Hurst Spit on 14 August 1968.
During 1960–1992, spring migration was often characterised by the appearance of one-day singletons in March/April, but May records included seven (with ten Whimbrel) that flew east at Keyhaven on 13th in 1971, as well as singletons at Pennington Marshes on 16th, in 1971 and on 5th, in 1984; also one occurred on 5 June 1971.
Green Sandpipers were predominately autumn migrants from mid-June, eg two on 22 June 1972 and passage continued throughout July–September, when day-maxima were 15 on 29 August 1969 and ten on 21 August 1975;

also, one flew south towards the Isle of Wight as late as 25 October 1981. November records were difficult to pigeonhole; some were probably late-autumn transients. Winter occurrences were relatively unusual, but totalled some 16 individuals, in December/January (7) and February (9).

Post-BoH, with the exception of two on 10 April 1999, records of spring migrants involved singletons during 2 March (in 2002)–15 May (in 1998) and included those that arrived from the west at Hurst Spit and landed in the saltings on 29 April 1993 and on 6 April 2002. Elsewhere on the NW Solent, others flew east on 8th and 28 April 2007 and north on 29 April 2011.

A majority occurred during 29 June (one flew north at Hurst Spit in 2002)–15 November (in 2003). Another flew east at Hurst Spit on 21 August 1999 and two flew east on 10 September 2003, four flew west on 20 August 2001 and two west on 30 July 2004; the marshes' day-maximum was 14 on 21 August 1994. One on 12 December 2000 was the sole record for that month, but seven occurred in January and three in February.

Spotted Redshank *Tringa erythropus*
Common, a spring, summer and autumn passage migrant and winter visitor; it breeds in northern Eurasia and winters in the Mediterranean to south Asia and central Africa

'An occasional visitor to the coast, chiefly in autumn. Hawker shot a specimen at Longparish on Sept. 7th, 1815 and says that he had "often killed it on the coast", but this was before he had a house at Keyhaven' (K&C).

Spotted Redshank. Salterns Marshes

Two experienced observers, who saw one at Keyhaven on 22 April 1935, said they knew of only four other Hampshire records 'in the last 25 years' (*Proc.*). One, the first for the Island, flew towards Pennington from the Isle of Wight on 17 September 1951 (Cohen); others were reported at Keyhaven/Pennington Marshes on 12 September 1954 and 8 May and 13 October, in 1957. Observations by ever-increasing numbers of birdwatchers during 1966–1992 revealed this species to be a regular spring and autumn passage migrant, as well as a winter visitor, to the marshes west of Lymington (but see east of Lymington River below) where March–February monthly day-maxima were: 22 (in 1980), 12 (in 1978 and 1985), eight (in 1985), 14 (in 1976), five (in 1970), 23 (in 1983), 35 in 1976), 14 (in 1980), 11 (in 1980), 22 (in 1972), 33 (in 1981) and 16 (in 1966) respectively. Significant counts east of the Lymington River, eg 27 on 1 October 1969, 25 on 4 August 1973 and 34 on 7 July 1976, were presumably from the Beaulieu Estuary.

Post-BoH, singles were reported at Hurst Spit on 1 May 2004 and 2006, one flew east on 13 May and one west on 30 June. Spring, autumn and winter-maxima all declined, though day-maxima of 12 in April 2012, 15 in October 2012 and 15 in November 2010 and 2011, were indicative of improving fortunes. Fewer were reported east of Lymington River, where the day-maximum was seven on 9 February 1997.

Favoured feeding areas were the mouth of Moses Dock and on lagoons on Pennington/Oxey Marshes and Normandy Farm.

Greenshank *Tringa nebularia*
Common, a spring, summer and autumn passage migrant and winter visitor

'A spring and autumn migrant to the coast. Coles picked up a specimen on the shore at Keyhaven some years ago in the autumn' (K&C).

Cohen reported that it had been seen in all months in Hampshire, was more frequent on autumn passage and 'odd birds apparently remained through the winter now and then.'

Spring day-maxima were 20 on 17 May 1975 and on 5 May 1986, but autumn concentrations included at least 22 (nine of which left high to the south-west until out of sight, over Hurst Castle) on 23 September 1956, 65 on

25 September 1976, of which 29 flew west at Hurst Spit (14 also left westwards the following day) and 38 at Keyhaven on 11 September 1983. Small, but regular, wintering groups peaked at nine on at least three occasions.

Post-BoH, the status of this most elegant of waders underwent little change. At Hurst Spit, 57 (of which 28 occurred in April) flew east during 22 March (in 2012)–21 May (in 2001 and 2008) with day-maxima of eight on 5 May 2000 and 27 April 2007. Spring day-maxima elsewhere involved two flocks in flight across Salterns, ie 27 on 19 April 1999 and 22 that flew west on 7 May 2000.

In autumn, 14 flew south at Hurst on 20 September 2000, but the day-peak was 56 that included a compact flock of 52 (the largest single group ever recorded on the NW Solent) at Keyhaven on 6 August 1996. East of Lymington River, the only double-figure count was 11 on 10 September 1995. Greenshanks wintered annually during 1990–2012, the day-maximum being 15 in November 1997.

Lesser Yellowlegs *Tringa flavipes*
Rare, a spring and (mainly) an autumn vagrant; it breeds in boreal N America and winters S America

Six records: singletons at Keyhaven/Pennington Marshes during 28 September–2 October 1953, on 29 August 1954, on 18 September 1973, on 9 October 1976, during 5–7 May 1999 and on Normandy Farm lagoon during 5–9 September 2014. Those in 1953/54 were the first and second county records, the 1976 and 2014 individuals were aged as juveniles and the 1999 record was the first Hampshire spring occurrence.

The Hampshire total to 2015 was 15 individuals.

Marsh Sandpiper *Tringa stagnatilis*
Rare, a summer vagrant; it breeds across middle latitude of Palearctic from E Europe to central Siberia and winters in tropical Africa to Australia

One record: one at Pennington Marshes during 28 July–4 August 1983 was the third for the county.

The Hampshire total to 2015 was four individuals.

Wood Sandpiper *Tringa glareola*
Common, a spring, summer and autumn passage migrant; it breeds in northern Eurasia and Alaska and winters in southern Europe, Asia, Africa and Australia

Of 105 reported on spring passage in Hampshire during 1951–1992, 13 occurred at Keyhaven/Pennington Marshes during 16 April (in 1979)–7 June (in 1975). Of those, one was observed performing a song-flight over the Lymington end of the marshes on 6 May 1956 and another flew east at Pennington Marshes on 4 May 1989. Autumn records included day-totals of three or more in 16 seasons during 16 June (in 1968)–26 October (in 1975); a peak of 12 on Pennington Marshes on 24 August 1966 was a county-maximum at that time. October occurrences were unusual, but included a day-maximum of four at Sowley Marshes on 8th in 1972, one at Pennington Marshes on 22nd in 1973 and one at Keyhaven Marshes on 12th in 1989. None were reported in winter, the sole county record being one in the Avon Valley during 23 February–6 April 1984 (BoH).

Post-BoH, spring migrants totalled at least 19 individuals in 12 seasons during 27 April (in 2006)–3 June (in 2007) of which one flew east at Hurst Spit on 3 May 2006; other than two on 13 May 2001, all were singletons.

Return passage usually commenced in mid-July, but occurred as early as 11 June (in 2010). The previous day-maximum of 12 was equalled on 19 August 2012 and the latest was a singleton on 9 October, in 2004.

Redshank *Tringa totanus*
Common, a decreasing resident, a spring and autumn passage migrant and winter visitor

'Common resident, several pairs nesting in the Keyhaven Marshes, where those desirous of studying the bird's beautiful flight and interesting habits during the breeding season have plenty of opportunities of doing so in May and early June. Hawker's bag includes only four of this species' (K&C).

Wise records the Redshank as breeding in the New Forest but not on the coast, but when K&M wrote of Hampshire's birds of the early-twentieth century, the Redshank was a resident and increasing species in the county. Bruce Campbell recounts how as a 14-year-old schoolboy, together with his father and a family friend, they found four Redshanks nests with eggs, one nest of which contained six eggs 'plainly the product of two hens', near Lymington on 26 April 1927. In the following year they found 12 Redshank's nests during two more forays (Campbell 1979). Following Campbell's visits, Redshanks presumably continued to breed on the grazing marshes, but there appear to be no other documented records until the 1960s. Though detail of the exact year is lost, two nests with eggs were found within 10 m of each other, in long vegetation at the base of the inside of Keyhaven Marshes seawall during the late 1960s, an event now unheard of on NW Solent. In the wake of the severe winter of 1962/63, during which 30 were found dead at Hurst, only four breeding pairs were reported on the NW Solent, though a decade later about 20 pairs nested at 'Pennington' (C&T). Local marshmen were of the opinion that reductions in Redshank (and Lapwing) breeding populations during the early 1960s were caused by increasing predation by rats and foxes, attracted to the vicinity of the newly created Pennington Marshes Rubbish Tip. It must be recognised, however, that the grazing marshes were often very dry for much of each breeding season, doubtless exacerbated by constant removal of surface and groundwater from the adjacent Manor Farm gravel extraction and landfill site. During the second half of the twentieth century, most of NW Solent's breeding Redshanks favoured the saltmarshes outside the seawalls. Nesting densities were uneven and available evidence suggested that few Redshanks nested within the major Black-headed Gull colonies. Conversely, loose Redshank groups, eg those on the saltings west of Keyhaven River, where 23 pairs with young were recorded in June 1996, were established where breeding Black-headed Gulls were thin on the ground. During the CBC, a single pair nested on Normandy Farm in six of 15 seasons between 1976 and 1989, but following creation of the lagoon in November 1994, up to seven pairs nested in 1995 and 1996. At Salterns, a single pair nested in seven of 16 seasons between 1976 and 1999. During the Atlas Survey, breeding was confirmed at Hurst Castle, Keyhaven, Keyhaven saltings, Cockleshell Island and Pitts Deep and was considered likely at Waterford and Lisle Court.

This bird was rarely recorded on migration at Hurst Spit, eg one that flew east there on 27 April 1981 was one of few such reports. Redshanks began to flock during the second half of June, followed by a steady build-up at roosts during July/October. Autumn/winter-maxima at roosts between Keyhaven and Lymington River during 1955–1990 averaged about 415, with a peak of 975 in October 1976 and about 410, with a peak of about 1,000 in January and November 1974 respectively.

Post-BoH, a survey in 1992 revealed an overall breeding population of at least 51 pairs, most of which were on the saltmarshes between Hurst Spit and Pitts Deep. Grazing marshes' habitat improvements, instigated in the early 1990s, led to the return of nesting pairs, particularly on Normandy Farm (nine pairs in 1996) and Keyhaven Marshes Fishtail (six pairs in 2002).

During 2000–2007, 32 flew east at Hurst Spit between 9 March (in 2004) and 31 May (in 2000); season-maxima were seven during 2 April–10 May, in 2000 and during 10–21 May, in 2001. Fewer were recorded at the Spit in autumn when, of a total of ten that flew east during 28 July (in 2001)–20 October (in 1999) five occurred on 12 September 2005.

Autumn/winter roost-maxima between Keyhaven and Lymington River declined during 1991–2012 with averages of 258 and a peak of 390 in October 2001 and 222 and a peak of 390 in February 2007 respectively. Fewer were found east of the Lymington River, where during 1990–2007, the autumn/winter-maxima were 100 in October 2007 and 155 in November 1993 respectively.

Those on autumn passage, as well as the wintering populations, west of Lymington River, habitually roosted on Keyhaven saltings between Hawkers Lake and Stony Point, but when displaced by high spring-tides or otherwise disturbed, they often moved onto Keyhaven/Pennington Marshes' lagoons or onto the Avon Water flood. During the winter, when standing water accumulated on the grazing marshes and on inland fields, Pennington Marshes and meadows on the Lower Pennington caravan park were alternative sites. Important NW Solent low-tide feeding zones were in the Keyhaven River/Hurst Camber creeks and spreaders, Oxey Lake, Aden Bank and Norrey and Crooked Lakes in the Lymington Estuary. Some Redshank observations were among the more atmospheric and never-to-be forgotten NW Solent ornithological sights. Those included a vociferous group of 22 that flew seawards at Hurst Spit on 15 August 1967, a flock of 120 that 'appeared to drop out of the sky' at Keyhaven on 21 September 1980 and a tumultuous flock of c.1,000 observed at close range in fields around the Normandy Farm out-buildings, when very high spring-tides drowned the entire saltmarsh between Hurst Spit and Pitts Deep on a wild November day in 1974. British breeding Redshanks are of the nominate race *totanus*, but wing measurements of a Redshank found at Hurst Spit on 7 April 1956, fell well within the range of the race *robusta* that breeds in Iceland and the Faeroes. Further evidence of 'Icelandic' Redshanks reaching the NW Solent occurred in 1972 when one, ringed as a chick in Iceland on 28 June, travelled 2107 km to Pylewell, where it was killed two months later, on 2 September.

Five-year averages of British, Hampshire and NW Solent WeBS maxima during 2007/08–2011/12 were 84,175, 2,455 and 317 respectively.

Jack Snipe *Lymnocryptes minimus*

Common, a spring and autumn passage migrant and winter visitor; it breeds in northern Europe and northern Asia and winters in western and northern Europe, central and southern Asia and western and central Africa

'Regular winter migrant. This species has the distinction of being the first mentioned in Hawker's Diary, in the year 1802' (K&C).

The individual cited above was shot at Longparish, but Hawker also shot many Jack Snipe at Keyhaven; a *Diary* entry for 21 September 1836 records that he never saw so many Jack Snipe in so small space as in 'Mr Guy's mudlands' where 'about a dozen kept getting up under my feet one after the other.'

Though under-recorded, on account of its retiring nature and reluctance to fly, it remained a regular spring and autumn passage migrant and winter visitor to the marshes during 1950–1992; the earliest arrival was on 25 September, in 1975 and the latest occurred on 20 April, in 1969. The largest winter-count was just seven at Sturt Pond on 24 January 1982.

Post-BoH, it remained a regular visitor, with reports during 27 September (in 1990)–16 April (in 2003). Most occurred during January/February, with a peak of just eight on 2/3 February 1991.

Jack Snipes occurred in a variety of habitats, eg the grazing marshes, saltmarshes and reed stubble; the margins of Sturt Pond were a favoured locality.

Long-billed Dowitcher *Limnodromus scolopaceus*

Rare, a spring, summer and autumn vagrant and sometimes remained during winter; it breeds N America and NE Siberia and winters southern USA south to Guatemala

Six records: singletons occurred at Keyhaven/Pennington Marshes during 20–29 September 1975, during 5–24 April 1978, during 3 October 1981–11 May 1982, during 5–12 September 1989, a sporadically seen, but long-staying adult in 2013/14 on 31 July, during 2–23 August, on 9th and 28 September, during 6 October–19 November, on 20/21 January, 1 February and intermittently on at least a further 20 dates until 14 April 2014 and during 23 September–31 October and on 4th and 8 December 2015. Those in 1975, 1978, 1981/82 and 1989 were the first, second, fourth and eighth county records.

The Hampshire total to 2015 was 12 individuals.

There was one earlier report of a dowitcher on the NW Solent, ie at Pennington Marshes on 13/14 September 1970. Most likely a Long-billed, it was accepted by the BBRC as either that species or the closely related Short-billed Dowitcher *L. griseus*.

Woodcock *Scolopax rusticola*

Common, a resident inland of the grazing marshes, a spring and autumn passage migrant and winter visitor, usually during cold weather

'Resident, nesting in small numbers in many of the woods of the district, but better known in winter, when a large immigration takes place, the first flight usually occurring at the end of October or the beginning of November. Hawker mentions Arnewood, in his "Instructions to Young Sportsmen", as a place where he saw a nest with four eggs, apparently in 1843. It is remarkable that Hawker's total bag only amounted to sixty-eight, whereas at the present time the bird is fairly plentiful and it is no uncommon occurrence to flush ten or a dozen in a day's shooting in this neighbourhood. It should be remembered, however, that Hawker's birds were mostly, if not all, killed at Longparish. In the year 1910 the County Council made an order extending the close season for this bird, so that it now dates from February 1st, instead of March 1st, a very wise alteration, considering the early period at which this species breeds' (K&C).

Garrow alluded to the October autumn migration and commented that it was a numerous species around Lymington. Woodcock also frequented the Lymington Marshes in the severe winter of 1940/41, when they regularly flighted to the coast at dusk (Vesey-Fitzgerald 1946).

As a resident, its breeding haunts were confined to the private land within the recording area, although territories sometimes extended over the grazing marshes, where roding flights were occasionally observed. It was under-recorded during the Atlas Survey when breeding was considered likely at Sturt Pond, Waterford and Lisle Court. Most, if not all, of those observed on the marshes in winter were displaced by cold weather and were probably more frequent than records suggest; a mere 11 singletons were reported during 1967–1992 in November (1), December (3), January (4) and February (3).

Post-BoH, at least a further 11 were reported on or close to the grazing marshes, in November (1), December (2), January (7) and March (1, in territorial flight over Normandy Farm lagoon on 9 March 2006); all were singletons other than two over Manor Farm on 8 January 1996.

Common Snipe *Gallinago gallinago*
Common, has probably bred but mainly a spring and autumn passage migrant and winter visitor

'Resident, its numbers largely reinforced in winter. Hawker's total bag amounted to 2,116, most of which were no doubt killed at Longparish' (K&C).

According to Wise 'the greatest numbers occur in December.' Cohen reported that 97 in eight wisps flew out to sea from Keyhaven Marshes on 3 March 1959, the site at which 153 on 26 October 1980 (and at least this number the previous day) were noteworthy in a county context at that time.

Observations during 1966–1992 suggested a wintering population of 100–200 between Keyhaven and Normandy Farm and at least 21 counts of that magnitude were recorded in November (5), December (3), January (6) and February (7). High November counts were probably indicative of passage and occurred in 1978, 1989 and 1992, the day-maximum being 250 in November 1981, though 500 on 30 December 1981 occurred during cold weather.

The wintering population had usually departed by mid-March, counts to mid-May were typically fewer than 30, but 60 on 23 March 1966, 100 on 17 March 1973 and 50 on 2 April 1969 were exceptional. At Hurst Spit, singles flew east on 4 May 1969 and 3 May 1981.

Few were recorded during May/June, eg one in display-flight during the summer 1970 and pairs were present in 1981, 1983 and 1987.

The first post-breeding arrivals usually occurred in July, eg one at Keyhaven on 18th in 1982, two on 3rd in 1985 and 30 on 31st in 1971. Though probably under-recorded, reported autumn day-maxima seldom attained double-figures; the maximum was 70 in October 1969.

Post-BoH, the maximum counts occurred in February, ie 186 in 2009 and 150 in 2010/11. Few were recorded after March and noteworthy spring observations involved one in display-flight on 31 May 2003 and a group of 11 that left high to the north-east at dusk from Pennington Marshes, on 11 April 2004.

First autumn returns were again in July, but August–December maxima of 31 (in 2006), 85 (in 1993), 211 (in 1993), 65 (in 2008) and 95 (in 1995) respectively, were higher than pre-BoH. At Hurst Spit, five flew high to the north-west on 23 October 2003.

It was very difficult to obtain accurate counts or estimates of Snipe at Keyhaven, as normally they did not congregate into large, compact groups when disturbed. Substantial counts were often obtained as birds were washed off the saltmarshes by very high spring-tides, or when particularly visible on the ground. Daily dusk/dawn flights, from and to the intertidal saltmarshes, regularly occurred throughout the winter months, when on numerous occasions the marshes were alive with Snipe during the hours of darkness.

Collared Pratincole *Glareola pratincola*
Rare, a spring vagrant; breeds S Europe/N Africa east to central Asia and Pakistan
(other taxa formerly considered conspecific now generally treated as separate species)

One shot on Hurst Spit in May 1857 by Lieut. H Henn was the first county record and was subsequently preserved by the taxidermist Edward Hart of Christchurch. The specimen still exists and is held by Hampshire County Council's Museum Service.

The Hampshire total to 2015 was two individuals.

A pratincole, thought (in my view correctly) by the observer to be a Black-winged Pratincole *Glareola nordmanni*, was observed at the sewage outfall off Pennington Marshes, on 6 August 1983; it was, however, accepted by the BBRC as either a Collared or Black-winged.

Pomarine Skua *Stercorarius pomarinus*
Scarce, a spring, summer and autumn passage migrant, also occurred in winter; it breeds in arctic Russia to western Greenland and winters mainly in tropical seas

The first records for the NW Solent involved singletons in 1963 at Hurst Spit, ie one that flew east on 10 May, one that flew west on 21 September and one on 10th and 17 November (presumed the same individual). Of 428 recorded in Hampshire during 1963–1992, 339 (55 in April and 284 in May) were recorded at Hurst Spit during

21 April (in 1964)–27 May (in 1972); about 75 per cent flew east into The Solent while others returned south-west towards the Needles. A season-maximum of 93 in 1980 was largely accounted for by 57 on 11 May, of which no fewer than 55 (a single flock resting on the sea in poor visibility) of which 37 later departed eastward into The Solent. Mid-summer occurrences were unusual in Hampshire, the sole records, both on the NW Solent, being three that flew east at Keyhaven on 18 June 1969 and one at Hurst Spit on 9 July 1988.

It was scarce in autumn, when of 35 Hampshire records during 1958–1992, no fewer than 13 occurred in the Hurst Spit/Lymington area during 6 September (in 1992)–17 November (in 1963); those included two that flew west at Pennington on 10 October 1971 and one that also flew west, at Hurst Spit on 7 December 1964 (only the second Hampshire record for that month). Most reports involved pale morphs, but unusually, six out of a group of seven at Hurst Spit on 29 April 1986, were dark morphs.

Post-BoH, the Pomarine Skua remained a regular but increasing up-channel spring migrant and 614 were documented during 1993–2012. Other than a first-winter during 9 March–10 May 1995, the earliest was on 7 April 2002 and the latest on 8 June, in 1997 and 2012. Only in 1995, 1998 and 1999, did spring-totals fail to attain double-figures, the maximum being 109 during 2 May-8 June 1997, of which 103 occurred on 2 May, the highest ever Hampshire day-count.

Relatively few occurred during June–December. Eight were reported during 24 June (in 2002)–21 July (in 2006) and 30 during 10 August (in 1994)–19 November (in 1996); others occurred in January (2) and December (2). Of those, all were singletons except for doubletons on three July dates and in October and January (one date each). The largest autumn day-total involved ten that flew west on 7 September 2008.

As at other South Coast seawatch stations, this skua was seldom recorded feeding on spring migration. As a long-distance migrant it was apparently hell-bent on reaching its far northern breeding grounds as quickly as possible. An isolated report of Pomarine Skuas in 'great abundance' off the Devon coast on 16 May 1918 (Moore 1969) was perhaps indicative that they were under-recorded during the first half of the twentieth century. Only since 1959, when 27, that included a flock of 16, flew east at Dungeness (Kent) did the Pomarine Skua apparently become a regular spring migrant on England's Channel coast. A combined total of 525 at Portland Bill (Dorset) Beachy Head (East Sussex) and Dungeness, which included 128 off the former locality, occurred during 1967–1974.

Arctic Skua *Stercorarius parasiticus*
Common, a spring and autumn passage-migrant and also occurred in summer and winter.

'An occasional visitor in autumn and winter. Kelsall has seen this bird between Lymington and Yarmouth and Mr Alexander Paris has observed one off Barton Cliff in the winter of 1904/05' (K&C); they also referred to its alternative name of Richardson's Skua.

During the first half of the twentieth century, an adult at Hurst Spit on 28 June 1944 was of sufficient interest to warrant a mention in *British Birds*. Following a few occurrences, such as singletons on 8 October 1953 and 1 May 1954, a regular easterly spring passage was detected at Hurst Spit. Between 1960 and 1992, at least 680 were recorded during 7 April (in 1972)–18 June (in 1966) most of which occurred in late April and early May.

A season-maximum of 64 during 3–14 May 1974 included a day-peak of 27 on 3 May, one of four occasions when day-totals exceeded 20. Dark morphs predominated during the spring migration; of 421 for which plumage details were noted, 274 (65 per cent) were dark and 147 (35 per cent) were pale (BoH). Summer occurrences were unusual, with just nine during 1959–1986. Sightings became more frequent during the latter half of July and passage continued throughout August–October and on occasions into late November.

Autumn day-maxima at Hurst were 39 that flew west at Hurst on 24 September 1974 and 95 that also flew west, on 2 September 1976; also, 25 were off Pennington Butts on 21 September 1980. The latest were singletons at Hurst Spit on 23 November 1975 and at Keyhaven on 23 November 1985. Others were at Pennington Marshes on 16 December 1973 and on 18 January 1986 and at Hurst Castle on 30 December 1990.

Post-BoH, the Arctic Skua apparently became more numerous on the NW Solent where 1,736, of which 1,364 were reported during 16 March (in 2009)–30 June (in 2012) were recorded between 1993 and 2012. One observed off Oxey Marshes' seawall on 16 March 2009 was the earliest of four March occurrences and the second earliest spring county record. Those in April (694) May (612) and June (54) included a season-maximum of 120 during 30 April–30 June in 2012 and a day-peak of 31 that flew east on 30 April. Spring-maxima exceeded 100 in four consecutive seasons 2003–2006, with a clear-cut majority (496) during 1–15 May.

A few individuals, ie up to two, in 2007 and 2012, summered in the area during June and July. Otherwise a total of at least 367 were accounted for in July (61), August (116), September (125), October (49) and November (16) with monthly-maxima of four on 9 July 2002, ten on 26/27 August 2012, 11 on 19 September 2007, seven on 4 October 2008 and two on 2 November 1998 and 8 November 1999. Five December individuals occurred during 1st (in 1996)–10th (in 1994).

Arctic Skua

Timing of the peak (late April–early May) of the Hurst Spit spring passage, suggests birds accessing the English Channel probably breed in northern Europe. The Scottish population, which greatly decreased between 1986 and 2011, more so than any other British sea-bird (JNCC 2012) presumably return to their breeding stations by alternative routes, as they were often on their nesting grounds by late March or early April.

Arctic Skuas are infrequent in British waters in January and almost non-existent in February, so unsurprisingly there was only one NW Solent record in the former month and none in the latter.

Long-tailed Skua *Stercorarius longicaudus*
Scarce, an increasing spring and autumn passage migrant and sometimes occurred in winter; with a circumpolar distribution, its nearest breeding grounds are in southern Norway and it winters at sea in the southern hemisphere

An adult on 5 October 1963 and an immature (not aged) on 17 January 1982, at Hurst Spit, were the third and fifth Hampshire reports.

The 1990s amassed no fewer than seven NW Solent records in 1991 (1), 1993 (2), 1994 (2) and 1996 (2). Apart from adults over Normandy Farm on 30 June 1993 and at Hurst Spit on 10 May 1994, all were juveniles during 19 August (in 1991 at Pennington Marshes)–31 October (in 1996 at Hurst Spit). The trend of increasing reports continued into the twenty-first century, with 19 records that involved perhaps as many as 13 individuals during 2000–2015. Except for an adult at Hurst Spit on 10 May 2010 all occurred during 16 August (in 2003)–8 November (in 2014) of which three (an adult and two juveniles) were at Hurst Spit on 5 October 2008. While the increase in active observers, armed with tripod-mounted modern prismatic telescopes may have contributed, it is suspected that the increase in reports is at least partly real.

Great Skua *Stercorarius skua*
Scarce, a spring and autumn passage migrant and has occurred in summer and winter
Prior to the 1960s there were just three documented NW Solent records, ie singletons during 12–21 September 1953 and 8 August 1955 and two that flew east on 5 May 1956. Seawatching during the 1960s revealed this skua to be a regular spring passage migrant through The Solent. This was probably attributable to a continued increase (and a concurrent decrease in Iceland) in the British breeding population. Initially detected at the beginning of the twentieth century, the population more than trebled from about 3,170 pairs during the Operation Seafarer Survey of 1969/70, to some 9,634 pairs in 1998–2000.

Between 1960 and 1992, 47 were recorded between Hurst Spit and Lymington River in spring. With the exception of one that flew west at Pennington Marshes on 24 March 1989, all occurred during 11 April (in 1979)–19 May (in 1967) with a distinct peak during the second week of May and a day-maximum of four on 7 May 1972. One, in the wake of a south-west gale on 27 June 1966 and another on 8 July 1990, were the first and second Hampshire records for those months respectively.

An autumn county total of c.142 during 1953–1992 included 97 between Hurst Spit and Lymington River during 16 August (in 1973)–28 October (in 1984). Boosted by a day-total of 19 that flew west at Pennington Marshes on 14 September 1975, numbers peaked during the first half of September and again in the second and third weeks of October; those included 15 that flew east at Hurst Spit on 18 October 1987, following the 'Great Storm'. Most sightings involved one–three individuals, but six were at Pennington Marshes on 5 September 1976. Other than two off Milford-on-Sea on 25 December 1989, all other winter occurrences involved singletons during 2 November (in 1991)–late February (an oiled individual in 1983) in November (4), December (3), January (3) and February (3).

Post-BoH, 403 were reported during 4 March (in 2012)–8 June (in 2003/04 and 2012) in March (9), April (319), May (68) and June (7), of which no fewer than 229 occurred during the last ten days of April. The Great Skua spring passage of 2012 was the heaviest ever recorded in Hampshire (also recorded in other South Coast counties); the NW Solent season and day-maxima were 138 and at least 81 on 25 April respectively (Wynn 2012). An additional 195 were reported during 12 June (in 2011)–26 February (in 2002) in June (13), July (28), August (31), September (28), October (46), November (19), December (12), January (15) and February (3). Day-maxima were nine that flew west on 30 October 2000 and six that also flew west, on 20 November 2000.

Puffin *Fratercula arctica*
Scarce, a visitor at all seasons
'A summer visitor to the cliffs of the Island, where a fair number breed. Specimens are occasionally washed up along our beach' (K&C).

Those to which K&C referred had mostly disappeared by the early 1950s (BoH) and only 22 were recorded in Hampshire during 1949–1992. Nine, between Hurst Spit and Pennington Marshes, included a corpse at Milford-on-Sea in 1947 and an oiled individual at Keyhaven on 14 December 1978, as well as singletons at Hurst Castle on 26 October 1974 and 14 April 1979 and an adult that flew east off Pennington Marshes on 24 August 1985.

Post-BoH (1993–2015) a further 17 individuals were recorded between 1996 and 2012 (none 1993–1995) during 19 April (in 2011)–20 December (in 2000) in April (7), May (5), August (1), November (1) and December (3) with a day-maximum of three off Hurst Spit on 19 April 2011. Poor weather in the English Channel during winter of 2013/2014 resulted in great Puffin mortality and eight corpses were found at Hurst Spit between 9th and 27 February 2014, of which four were on the latter date.

Razorbill *Alca torda*
Common, a spring and autumn passage migrant and summer and winter visitor
'Resident, nesting in numbers in the cliffs of the Isle of Wight, but not on the Hampshire mainland. The season when this bird is most commonly met with at Keyhaven is during the autumnal gales, when many are washed up on the shore, but on July 4th 1892, a spaniel belonging to Coles brought him a living young bird, still in down, on the beach near Sturt Pond, which must have drifted nearly ten miles from the nearest nesting station in the Freshwater cliffs' (K&C).

As with Guillemot, the Isle of Wight's breeding population, estimated at about 60 pairs in the mid-1950s, exhibited significant declines from the 1940s. However, auks were difficult to count on the cliffs and estimates were based on birds observed on the water. The Razorbill, though less so than Guillemot, became more frequent in winter in Hampshire during the 1980s. A total of 180 on the NW Solent during 1957–1992, included 78 in summer/autumn, 60 in winter and 42 in spring; monthly day-maxima were seven on 14 July 1969, 17 that flew west on 4 October 1981, seven on 19 January 1986 and five on the sea on 12 May 1976. A single observer reported at least 20, of which 17 were victims of oil-contamination, during February 1957.

Post-BoH, 752, of which 356 occurred during winter months, included a day-maximum of 25 on 7 February 2011, 265 in spring, of which the day-maximum was 50 on 14 May 2010. Of 131 in summer/autumn, day-maxima were six on 25 September, 13 October 2004 and 5 October 2011. Four victims of oil-pollution were found on the shore, the last of which was reported in 2002.

Little Auk *Alle alle*
Scarce, an autumn and winter visitor; it breeds in western Greenland and Arctic Ocean islands from Spitzbergen to central Siberia and winters in the North Atlantic
'An occasional winter visitor, the only local records being those of dead birds found on our beach. These islands are occasionally visited by great irruptions of this species, the last occasion being in January and February 1912' (K&C). Between 1949 and 1992 and during 5 November (in 1961)–7 April (in 1991) 14 were reported, of which two were at Milford-on-Sea on 11 January 1984 and five singletons were dead or died shortly after being found.

Post-BoH (1993–2015) 35 were recorded during 30 October (in 2001)–1 January (in 2007) in October (1), November (26), December (7) and January (1). Of those, five occurred on 18 November 1995 and a passer-by found another, alive in a ditch in Lower Pennington Lane, on 5 December 2009. Sixteen, split equally between birds that flew east and west, were reported at Hurst Spit.

Guillemot *Uria aalge*
Common, a spring and autumn passage migrant and summer and winter visitor
'Resident, nesting in the cliffs of the Island, but not on the mainland. Col. Hawker frequently sailed across to see the cliff birds between the Needles and Freshwater and used a special contrivance of "'bell, string and flag' to make them fly off the cliff." They are frequently washed ashore on the beach during autumn and winter, but it is rare to see a living bird in the harbour. Coles however saw a single bird about the end of May 1911, swimming about and diving in the pool on the harbour side of the hatches during the ebb tide' (K&C).

Considering the large numbers that nested on the Freshwater and Needles cliffs immediately post-K&C, they were presumably overlooked or under-recorded in NW Solent waters. The Isle of Wight breeding population apparently declined during the 1940s and during 1951–1980 it was unusual to see a healthy Guillemot in Hampshire, when an average of only eight per year were reported (BoH). A 50 per cent increase in the national breeding population during 1985–1987 (Lloyd 1991) was doubtless reflected in an increase in reports of Guillemots in Hampshire during 1981–1992, but improved observer coverage was probably also a contributing factor (BoH). A total of at least 117 were reported in the NW Solent during 1958–1992. No fewer than 63 of these occurred in winter, of which December accounted for 23 with a day-maximum of ten that flew west on 23rd in 1990. Spring, summer and autumn reports totalled 54 individuals, of which 35 occurred during March–June and 19 during July–October; day-maxima were seven that flew east on 7 May 1988 and six on 22 July 1967. Beached corpses totalled 16, of which seven were oiled; the last of these was reported in late February 1990.

Post-BoH, the Guillemot was more often recorded. A total of 767 individuals occurred, ie 307 in winter, 341 in spring, 53 in summer and 66 in autumn. Day-maxima were 40 on 3 February 2002, 50 on 14 May 2010 (a record county day-total) nine on 5 June 2004 and six on 6 September 2007. At least 15, of which the last was reported in early December 2009, were visibly oiled.

Black Guillemot *Cepphus grylle*
Rare, a spring vagrant; the nearest breeding colonies are in southern Ireland and Anglesey.
'An occasional winter visitor – once in the Crimean winter off Yarmouth' (K&C).
Two records: adults in summer plumage, ie on 11 May 1989 and 12 May 2010, were reported at Hurst Spit.
The Hampshire total to 2015 was three individuals.

Sooty Tern *Sterna fuscata*
Rare, a summer vagrant; it breeds in tropical and sub-tropical zones of the Atlantic, Indian and Pacific Oceans
One off Hurst Spit on 17 June 1961 was the first for the county.
The Hampshire total to 2015 was two individuals; the other involved a long dead corpse.

Little Tern *Sternula albifrons*
Common, a summer resident and spring and autumn passage migrant
'A spring and autumn migrant to the coast. There is a colony on the Chesil Bank at Langton Herring. Coles has seen a specimen hawking up and down over Sturt Pool in the autumn and has also picked up a dying specimen after a gale in the grounds of his present residence at Milton' (K&C).
It is unclear when breeding first occurred on the NW Solent, though a major colony was in existence on Hurst Spit immediately before, during and immediately following, the 1939–45 War. Up to 50 pairs were present during the late 1930s, at least 13 (nests) in 1940 and 16 pairs in 1948. The colony was subject to increasing disturbance during the 1950s/early 1960s when numbers fell from about 30 pairs in 1951 to some 12 pairs during 1957–1959, all nests failed in 1961 and the site was deserted by 1966. Meanwhile, pairs were found breeding in the Lymington Estuary, with five nests in 1949 and a reference of 'up to 25 pairs in recent years' were presumably included in a total of 35–40 pairs between Lymington and Hurst Spit in 1947. The NW Solent breeding population was monitored annually during 1966–2012, peaked at 105 pairs in 1981, but was as low as four pairs in 2011; unfortunately, 25 pairs in 2012 reared no young.
The Little Tern was a prominent spring migrant through the NW Solent. First arrivals were usually in April, though one was at Hurst Spit on 24 March 1957. Between 1968 and 1992, a grand total of 3,926 flew east during 7 April (in 1974 and 1985)–14 June (in 2012). The most prolific year was 1976 when no fewer than 631 occurred, of which 428 in April included 254 on 27th and 203 in May, of which 73 were on 6th.
Autumn gatherings included 90 off Pennington Marshes on 4 August 1975 and 100 off Oxey Marshes on 24 July 1973, though both totals probably included breeding residents; the latest of four October records was at Oxey Marshes on 21 October 1991.
Post-BoH, a further 1,629 that included a spring-maximum of 233 in 1994 and a day-peak of 114 on 10 May 1993, flew east during 2 April (in 2004)–8 June (in 2012). Early arrivals occurred on 2 April 2005, 3 April 1998 and 5 April 2006. Autumn gatherings were unexceptional; one of 55 at Pennington Marshes on 17 July 2010 was probably composed of summer residents. The last of three October individuals occurred on 8 October 1995.

Gull-billed Tern *Gelochelidon nilotica*
Rare, a spring and summer vagrant; its world distribution is virtually cosmopolitan, but a decline in British occurrences was probably due to reductions at German and Danish colonies
Four records: singletons at Hurst Spit on 5 July 1966 and at Pennington Marshes on 27 May 1972 were the third and eighth county records, one spent the day feeding and loafing at Pennington Marshes/Oxey Lake on 11 July 1982 and one off Hurst Spit on 12 May 1994. Some questioned the 1982 record, yet about a dozen observers saw it, often at close range, as it foraged over lagoons inside the seawall.
The Hampshire total to 2015 was 15 individuals.

Caspian Tern *Sterna caspia*
Rare, a summer vagrant; its breeding range is virtually cosmopolitan, but British records are probably from the Baltic Sea population, which winters in tropical West Africa
Two records: one at Milford-on-Sea on 22 June 1974 and one that flew west at Normandy Farm on 28 July 2013, were the first and fourth county records.
The Hampshire total to 2015 was four individuals.

Whiskered Tern *Chlidonias hybridus*
Rare, a spring vagrant; it breeds discontinuously from W Europe to E Siberia, sub-Saharan Africa (where those that breed in Europe spend the winter) S Asia and Australia
Three records: one at Hurst Spit on 12 May 1970, one that flew east at the Spit on 13 May 1972 and one that flew east at Hurst Spit/Normandy Farm on 6 May 2008, were the first, second and eighth county records.
The Hampshire total to 2015 was 11 individuals.

Black Tern *Chlidonias niger*

Common, a spring and autumn passage migrant; it breeds in Europe, north and central Asia and N America and winters in tropical Africa and central and north S America

Few records were traced for the first half of the twentieth century, though singletons were reported at Keyhaven on 1 May 1935 and in The Solent, west of Lymington, on 27 July 1948, but seven were at Keyhaven on 22 July 1959 and ten on 10 September 1960. Black Terns, subsequently found to be regular spring migrants, were presumably previously undetected or unrecorded. Between 1961 and 1992, 2,100 flew east at Hurst Spit during 11 April (in 1979)–16 June (in 1970) with a day-maximum of 400 (a record county day-total) on 1 May 1965; other spring-maxima in excess of 100 occurred in 1971, 1974, 1980 and 1989. Of 12 June reports, all were singletons other than doubletons on 30th in 1961 and 23rd in 1977.

One thousand and seventeen logged during 1 July (in 1975)–3 November (in 1984) included an autumn-maximum of 97 and a day-peak of 54 on 17 August; in 1980, but at Pennington Marshes 64 flew west on 1 September 1987 and 26 flew west on 1 October 1982.

Post-BoH, 650 flew east during 19 April (in 1998)–17 June (in 2006) with a season-maximum of 95 between 23 April and 14 May, in 1994 and a day-maximum of 75 on 10 May 1993. In autumn, 474 individuals included a season-maximum of 119 in 2001, of which 46 occurred on 18 August.

White-winged Black Tern *Chlidonias leucoptera*

Rare, a spring and autumn visitor; it breeds in E Europe and winters in inland tropical Africa

Some ten individuals have occurred, ie juveniles at Hurst Spit on 11th and 18 August 1963, on 6 September 1992 and 11 September 2010 and at Keyhaven–Normandy Farm on 28 September and 4 October 1971, on 12th and 13 August 1973 and 25 August 1979, where also, adults were reported on 29 May 1972, on 21 September 1980 and on 3 June 1991 and a second-summer on 18 May 1992. Those in 1963, 1971 and 1972 were the third, eighth and ninth county records.

The Hampshire total to 2015 was 35 individuals.

Sandwich Tern *Sterna sandvicensis*

Common, a summer resident, spring and autumn passage migrant and has occurred in winter

This bird first nested in Hampshire in 1954 when ten pairs bred between Hurst Spit and Lymington. At that time the combined Scottish and English population was estimated at 1,750 pairs, an apparent decline from 3,520 in 1946, though Cramp *et al* (1974) cautioned that trends were difficult to assess as colonies tended to shift because of excessive disturbance or habitat change.

The NW Solent colonies were also very mobile, with highly variable fledgling success. Those at Keyhaven during 1955–1959 included up to 80 pairs that raised about 50 young in 1957. During 1960–2009, a total of 2,673 pairs attempted breeding between Hurst Spit and Sowley; ten-year averages were 33 pairs, 47 pairs, 49 pairs, 45 pairs and 92 pairs respectively. Breeding pairs exceeded 200 in 2006 (224) and 2007 (205) though both years were unproductive and it is doubtful if any young were reared. Losses were due primarily to fox-predation, high spring-tide washouts and in the early years, to egg thieves.

Discussing Hampshire as a whole, Cohen wrote that Sandwich Terns had been reported 'from 1935 … in nearly every year on both passages.' It was certainly a regular spring passage migrant on the NW Solent post-1955. A total of 7,365 reported during 17 March (in 1981 and 1992)–31 May (in 1976) included season and day-maxima of 1,357 and 277 during 17 April–17 May and on 23 April, in 1978 respectively. Higher numbers recorded at watch points in the east of the county probably also included some of those that had passed south of the Isle of Wight.

Other than 200 that flew west through Hurst Narrows on 21 September 1980 and a gathering of 80 at Pylewell on 26 August 1991, those on autumn passage were unremarkable in a county context. One on 19 October 1987 was the latest of three singletons in that month; none were reported during November–February.

Post-BoH, 7,157 (mostly observed from Hurst Spit) flew east during 10 March (in 2008)–31 May (in 2000). Annual and day-maxima were 848 (during 22 March–13 May, of which 178 occurred on 24 April) in 2009 and 220 at Keyhaven on 29 July 2001 respectively. Winter records during 1996–2012 involved 21 individuals in November (12), December (4) and February (5).

Common Tern *Sterna hirundo*
Common, a summer resident and spring and autumn passage migrant; has occurred in winter

'A spring and autumn migrant to our coast. There is a large colony of some thousands nesting on the Chesil Beach at Abbotsbury in Dorsetshire, which is no doubt the headquarters of those, which visit our neighbourhood. Hawker mentions this species in his bag of "various"' (K&C).

Common Terns were first reported breeding on the NW Solent in 1948, when 7–12 pairs nested. It became an established summer resident during the early 1950s, at a time when the Black-headed Gull colony, which presumably afforded increased protection from predators, was also rapidly expanding. A grand total of 1,048 pairs that included 148 pairs in 1967, were recorded during 1951–1969. During 1970–2009, a total of 5,263 pairs nested, ten-year averages being 99 pairs, 42 pairs, 156 pairs and 228 pairs respectively. Numbers fluctuated between as few as 11 pairs in 1984 and up to 371 pairs in 2006. As with other NW Solent breeding tern species, fledgling rates were often poor, due principally to spring-tide washouts and predation. Most nested on cheniers (shingle and shell spreads on saltmarsh) or in Sea Purslane *Halimione portulacoides*, but a few pairs, usually in single-figures, but up to 20 pairs in 1997, also nested on islands in Normandy Farm lagoon, eg five pairs in 1995.

Common Terns were noted on spring passage in 1956, when 108 flew east on 21 May. With the exception of three (one of which was possibly an Arctic Tern) at Hurst Spit on 27 March 1989, first arrivals during 1967–1992 were usually in the first half of April, the earliest being 3 April (in 1973 and 1974). During 1966–1991, a total of 49,068 that flew east included a season-maximum of 6,204 between 15 April and 31 May 1978 and monthly day-peaks of 2,625 on 20 April 1983 and 3,530 on 3 May 1974. Other spring-maxima in excess of 4,000 were 5,933 in 1974, 4,453 in 1980 and 4,000 in 1983.

The largest autumn day-counts at Hurst Spit were 1,275 on 31 August 1963 and at least 2,000 that flew west through the Narrows on 21 September 1980; the latest was a juvenile at Hurst Spit on 28 October, in 1984.

Post-BoH, one on 12 March 2006 (Hampshire's earliest by eight days) was one of six NW Solent March records. A total of at least 45,685 that flew east at Hurst Spit during 12 March (in 2006)–9 June (also in 2000) included a season-maximum of 5,916 during 28 March–1 June, in 2008 and a day-peak of 2,500 on 6 May 2006. Other spring-maxima in excess of 4,000 were 5,471 in 2006 and 4,033 in 2012.

Autumn-peaks included a gathering of 330 off Pennington Marshes on 14 August 2011, 807 that flew east at Hurst Spit during 22 August–25 September 1999 and 400 that flew west on 27 August 1997. November singletons were noted at Hurst Castle on 9th in 2005 (a first-winter) and at Keyhaven on 1st and 6th, in 2011.

Roseate Tern *Sterna dougallii*
Scarce, has bred, a spring and autumn passage migrant

Nesting occurred on a number of occasions, with young seen or suspected, in at least eight seasons. As with other tern species, breeding-season losses were due to predation, high spring-tides and to egg thieves. Adults, accompanied by single juveniles, though not necessarily reared locally, were observed at Hurst Spit on 24 September 1985 and 1 October 1991.

This bird was not recorded on the NW Solent until 1955 when five flew west at Hurst Spit on 4 September; the first Hampshire report was just six weeks earlier. The next occurred in 1956, when two early migrants flew east at Hurst Spit on 15 April (Cohen) though Hampshire's earliest was given as 17 April (HBR 2011) — but see also **post-BoH** below. Roseate Terns were regular NW Solent spring migrants during 1969–1992. At least 33, mostly at Hurst Spit during 1 May (in 1978)–19 May (in 1972 and 1985) included seven that flew east on 3 May 1969 and five on 1 May 1978; also, two flew west off Pennington Marshes on 23 June 1979.

At least 13 that were considered to be autumn migrants, occurred during 22 July (in 1982)–6 October (in 1985) in July (1), August (3), September (6) and October (3).

Post-BoH, 84 migrants during 16 April (in 2006)–16 September (in 2004) included 34 that flew east at Hurst Spit during 17 April (in 2011)–8 June (in 2002) and a day-peak of four on 4 May 2003; also, two flew east on 3 August 2001.

Arctic Tern *Sterna paradisaea*
Common, a spring and autumn passage migrant

'A spring and autumn migrant to the coast, but less common than the last, from which it is hardly distinguishable when on the wing' (K&C).

Though presumably once much overlooked, particularly pre-1992, an expanding army of observers equipped with modern telescopes and up-to-date identification information, has since rectified the NW Solent situation. The first post-Second World War records were April singletons at Hurst Castle, on 27th in 1947 and 30th in 1955 and seven that flew east at Hurst Spit on 1 May 1956. During 1980–1992, a further 62 individuals occurred, of which 28 were during 4 April (in 1987)–20 May (in 1984 and 1985) and included four on 23 April 1984 and on 9 May 1991. The remaining 34, during 9 July (in 1983)–28 October (in 1984) included a total of ten on three dates during 13 September–3 October, in 1992, of which six were juveniles on the former date.

Post-BoH, about 200 documented records related to 647 individuals, of which 474 occurred during 9 April (in 2009 and 2012)–20 May (in 2007) with a season-maximum of 137 during 21 April–13 May 2006 and a day-maximum of 56 on 24 April. Four other day-counts exceeded 20 individuals, in late April 2008 and in May 2004 and 2012. It was less frequent on autumn passage, when during 11 July (in 2000)–15 November (in 2006) season and day-maxima were 25 during 21 July–3 October 2012 and ten (two adults and eight juveniles) on 10 September 1994 respectively.

Sabine's Gull *Xema sabini*
Scarce, an autumn and winter visitor, often following south-westerly gales and has occurred in spring; it has a circumpolar breeding distribution, but winters at sea off Namibia and South Africa

'A rare accidental visitor. Coles shot a specimen among the phalaropes at Sturt Pond on October 21st 1891. This bird was shown to the late Mr Howard Saunders, who wrote in the Field shortly afterwards; "It is a thoroughly adult bird; in fact, among a somewhat large series in my collection, there is only one specimen which shows a trifle less black on the outer web of the sixth primary. The hood, characteristic of summer plumage, has now given place to dusky black markings on the nape, while, as Mr Coles observes, the primaries are abraded, especially their tips. Reverting to the occurrence of adults in the British Islands, I may mention that only two examples are known to me. Immature birds are of not infrequent, though irregular occurrence, but Mr Coles may be congratulated on the acquisition of a third adult British specimen." Another specimen was killed on the 13th of the same month at Bournemouth since that date the bird has been recorded almost yearly from various parts of the coast, owing, no doubt, to the greater interest taken in the study of ornithology. A beautiful specimen in immature plumage may be seen in Mr Hart's Museum at Christchurch, obtained on September 26th, 1886. The bird should be looked for in the autumn season, especially after heavy gales' (K&C).

Sabine's Gull & Black-headed Gull. Sturt Pond

The above was the first to be recorded in Hampshire; perhaps we should add that Saunders was the foremost tern and gull expert of the day. No more were reported in local waters until 1954 when, though observed from Warden Point on the Isle of Wight, an adult was in Hurst Narrows on 28 November. The first NW Solent juvenile was found on Sturt Pond on 12 September 1970; it remained between Hurst Spit and Pennington Marshes until 11 October. The next four records involved five juveniles, all in September, at Pennington Marshes on 28th in 1975 and on Sturt Pond on 25th, two at Pennington Marshes on 26th and Hurst Castle on 27th, all in 1981. Interestingly, the records in 1970, 1975 and 1981 all more or less coincided with the arrival of dowitchers, two of which were specifically identified as Long-billed, in the immediate locality. On 15/16 October 1987, a gale of remarkable force tracked rapidly from the Bay of Biscay across southern England, bringing with it large numbers of Sabine's Gulls and other pelagic species (see Hume & Christie 1989). Some 120–140 Sabine's Gulls occurred in Hampshire, of which Hurst/Pennington Marshes' share consisted of seven (five adults) on 17 October, 50 (40 adults) on 18 October and 36 (24 adults) on 19 October; another adult occurred at Pennington Marshes on 14 November. Also a juvenile was off Hurst Castle on 8 October 1988 and single adults were on flooded fields at Keyhaven on 20 December 1989 and at Hurst Spit on 19 August 1990. Those in 1954, 1970, 1975 and 1981 constituted the second, fifth, sixth and eighth–tenth (11th individual) county records.

Post-BoH (1993–2015) a further 17 individuals, of which six were adults, were recorded between Milford-on-Sea/Hurst Spit and Pennington Marshes during 22 August (in 1998)–6 May (in 2007) in August (2), September (6), October (3), November (3), December (1), January (1) and May (1). All reports involved singletons, with the exception of doubletons in 2008, ie on 7 September (both adults) and 7 October (both juveniles) and two juveniles during 19–28 September, in 2011.

The Hampshire total to 2015 was 163 individuals.

Kittiwake *Rissa tridactyla*
Common, an all-season visitor, most often following westerly gales
'A regular winter migrant. This bird formerly nested in the Isle of Wight, but has not done so for many years past and the record of an egg found on the Culver Cliff in 1903, proves to be a mistake' (K&C).

Few were reported during the first half of the twentieth century until 15 flew east at Hurst Spit on 20 December 1956. A Kittiwake 'wreck', many of which were victims of massive marine oil-spills at that time, occurred on the southern and western shores of Britain in early 1957. In Hampshire, it was most marked in the west of the county where at least 40 were at Hurst Spit on 9 February. Kittiwakes were recorded almost annually during 1960–1992. Significant spring movements at Hurst Spit included 480 during 24 March–20 May 1979, of which 259 occurred on 25 March and 108 that flew east on 5 May 1984. Few were recorded in summer, but 20 flew west at Hurst Spit on 22 June 1968 and others included adults at Pennington Marshes on 3 June and at Oxey Marshes on 12 July, in 1986 and eight adults that flew east on 10 June 1989.

It was not until early October that significant numbers, often storm-driven, were usually reported. At Hurst Spit, day-totals in excess of 100 on six occasions, included 400 that flew west on 15 October 1971 and 151 that flew west on 24 October 1981.

Winter occurrences were relatively infrequent, but 40 were off Hurst Spit on 16 January 1984, 259 flew east through Hurst Narrows on 19 January 1986 and 90–100 flew east there on 24 February 1990.

Post-BoH, Kittiwakes apparently became more numerous in NW Solent waters. A total of about 5,800 were accounted for, of which 2,065 occurred during March–mid-June, 14 during mid-June–31 July, 257 during August–October and 3,462, most of which flew west, during November–February. Three-figure day-totals were reported on at least eight occasions, mostly in winter, with day-maxima of 900 that flew west on 8 November 2001 and 829 that flew west on 8 April 2005.

It is pleasing to report that very few oiled Kittiwakes were reported during the initial decade of the twenty-first century. However, other contaminants involved in recent English south coast marine-pollution incidents, resulted in the deaths of large numbers of other seabird species.

Black-headed Gull *Chroicocephalus ridibundus*
Common, a resident, spring and autumn passage migrant and winter visitor
'The most abundant of our gulls, to be seen in the harbour at all seasons, but not nesting in the parish. The largest nesting colony in our district is at Rempstone on Poole Harbour and there are smaller gulleries between Hern and

Ringwood, on the Newtown River in the Isle of Wight and (as we have been recently informed) near the mouth of the Beaulieu River. It must be remembered that at the season when this bird is most numerous in our harbour it is in its winter plumage and has lost the characteristic chocolate-coloured feathers of the head from which it is named. Hawker apparently condescended to shoot gulls and gives elaborate directions in his "Instructions to Young Sportsmen" as to the best means of obtaining them, adding that "though scarcely eatable in any other way they make an excellent substitute for 'giblet soup.'" All gulls are protected in Hampshire all the year round, under the Wild Birds' Protection Act' (K&C).

The Black-headed Gull, particularly in the breeding season, is the most characteristic and well-known seabird of the west Solent. It is commonly accepted that it first nested at Keyhaven between 1905 and 1913, most likely during latter years (see K&C above). The Keyhaven colony was certainly in existence in 1927 (Campbell 1979), was at least 50 pairs strong in 1938 (Hollom 1940) and was described as 'large' by 1951 (Cohen). A survey in 1957 revealed almost 500 pairs at Keyhaven and more than 900 pairs at Tanners Lane and those colonies increased to a combined 4,000 pairs by 1958. Further expansions occurred during the 1960s/1970s. At least 5,000 pairs included 3,000 pairs that nested between Hurst Spit and the west bank of the Lymington River in 1968 and 8,000 pairs between Keyhaven and Pitts Deep in 1972. Colonies were highly mobile and subject to considerable annual, or even daily, fluctuation. Those on Keyhaven/ Pennington Butts saltings subsequently declined to some 600 pairs by 1991, due principally to habitat loss resulting from sea-level rise and to flooding during tidal back-up on the westward flowing ebb. At that time, of a Hampshire total of 14,500 pairs, 6000 nested between Hurst Spit and Pylewell Lake. Together with those in Kent and Dorset, the English South Coast then supported 1.5 per cent of the world's breeding population.

The saltmarsh showed signs of dieback in the early 1950s, since when the seaward edge has exhibited an accelerating rate of erosion. Known as Oxey Island, a small section of rapidly eroding saltmarsh close to the seawall, supported up to 150 pairs of Black-headed Gulls, as well as a significant Little Tern colony, during the 1970s; it had all but disappeared a decade later. Increases in Langstone Harbour (an additional 1,600 pairs) and on the NW Solent, where there were some 9,000 pairs in 2003, were possibly due to relocation of birds displaced from the Beaulieu Estuary. The NW Solent breeding population, however, fell from 7,738 pairs in 2010 to 4,050 pairs in 2015.

Mankind has a long history of harvesting seabirds, their eggs and young. Unsurprisingly, Black-headed Gull colonies on accessible saltmarsh, such as that on the NW Solent, were also exploited. Local fishermen and others from Southampton, Poole and elsewhere, particularly post-1945, commercially harvested the Keyhaven and Lymington colonies. There were no restrictions on the duration of the egg-harvest season pre-1966 and others, casually obtaining a few eggs for the table, extended the collecting season. Though considered by some as a ruse whereby lower prices were negotiable with local fishermen, dealers implied that in May of each season, large numbers of eggs were imported into Britain from the European mainland.

Though the practice imposed some disadvantages, available evidence suggests that egg harvesting probably saved the NW Solent colonies from extinction, particularly since the 1950s when the saltmarsh breeding sites became increasingly vulnerable to high spring-tide flooding. Daily egg removal over a period of four or more weeks (only newly-laid eggs are permitted for sale) delayed the onset of incubation and thus the gull population retained a much closer and protracted affinity to the breeding site than otherwise might have been the case. In the absence of egg removal, birds were incubating full clutches well before the end of April. Following the onset of incubation, further developing eggs degenerate, after which Black-headed Gulls are unable to produce additional eggs that season (Weidmann 1956). As a consequence, gulls had little or no incentive to remain on the breeding grounds following losses by early-season disasters, or return the following year. On the nearby Beaulieu Estate, the Needs Ore gullery (at one time the largest in Britain with 20,000 pairs) was deserted following early season spring-tide inundation, during the first spring of egg-harvest prohibition. The suggestion that the presence of Peregrines was the principal cause of site desertion was unconvincing.

A ban on egg harvesting across selected sections of the NW Solent saltmarshes was imposed by Natural England (the Government's advisor on nature conservation) in 2010. The ban was designed to protect a small population of breeding Mediterranean Gulls (qv) among the long-established gullery on the west bank of Lymington River. Unfortunately, Black-headed Gulls deserted that site in the wake of early-season spring-tide inundation and predation. For instance, very few young fledged in 2012 (washed-out) or in 2013 (heavy and prolonged fox-predation) no young were reared in 2014 (1,500 pairs deserted early in the season) and the site was abandoned in 2015. It is instructive to contrast breeding success on nearby Pylewell saltings where gull egg harvesting by responsible and experienced collectors was allowed to continue. At least 3,200 pairs reared numerous young in 2012 and 2013 and about 4,850 and 4,050 pairs did so in 2014 and 2015 respectively. A study, commissioned by Natural England, and intended to highlight the pros and cons of egg harvesting, was inconclusive.

Outside the breeding season, a regular spring easterly passage occurred at Hurst Spit, where the largest day-total of 5,250, composed largely of adults, flew through Hurst Narrows on 6 April 1957; insignificant movements were recorded at other seasons.

Winter roosts were a feature of Keyhaven and Lymington Rivers, where January four-figure counts included 3,000 in January 1974, 3,173 in 1978, 4,000 on 14 February 1982 and 26 February 1983, 2,264 in 1983 and 5,260 (of a Hampshire total of 46,443) in 1993, the fifth national BTO Survey of Roosting Gulls. Other concentrations included 1,900 at Efford Rubbish Tip on 5 January 1987.

Juveniles from Hampshire colonies dispersed mainly into southern England, though some wintered as far afield as France and Iberia. Some reared in Hampshire later nested in other counties and vice versa. The breeding population was mainly resident, though numbers were augmented in winter by arrivals from further north in Britain and the Continent (BoH).

Little Gull *Hydrocoloeus minutus*

Common, a spring and autumn passage migrant and winter visitor, a few occurred in summer; it breeds in northern Eurasia and north-east N America and winters south to southern Europe and northern US

'A rare occasional visitor during the winter months. Coles has little doubt that he saw a bird of this species among other gulls off the shingle beach in a heavy gale on February 7th 1912. Fifteen examples are recorded from the Hampshire coast in Kelsall and Munn's Birds of Hampshire' (K&C).

Until the early 1950s, Little Gulls were no more than scarce passage migrants, particularly in autumn, along the coasts of south-east England. An increase, detected in the 1940s in eastern Scotland, then on English coasts was such, that by the 1970s, annual-totals of several hundreds, reported both on the coast and inland, were linked to the expansion of the breeding population around the Baltic Sea (Hutchinson & Neath 1978).

With this background, it was no surprise that numbers increased on the NW Solent. An adult was at Keyhaven on 1 November 1953, but no more were reported until 1960 when 12 were seen during 27 August–2 November, of which eight were storm-driven on 9 October. Easterly spring migration was detected in the mid-1960s and became an almost annual Hurst Spit event where during 1966–1992 a total of 750 was recorded, mostly during late April–mid-May. By far the heaviest movement occurred on 3 May 1974 when 315 were logged. June/July reports were relatively unusual, eg singletons were at Keyhaven on 14 June 1966, in Oxey Lake on 24 June 1968, at Pennington Marshes during 25 May–2 June 1986 and on 24 July 1983 and at Hurst Spit on 19 July 1991.

It was also a regular autumn visitor and some 60 individuals, included six on 27 August and seven on 1 September, in 1988. Many of those seen in late autumn were as a result of gales. During 1961–1992, some 85 were noted and those associated with the 'Great Storm' of October 1987 included day-maxima of 16 on 17th, 18 on 18th and 29 on 19th.

It was an infrequent winter visitor; 33 individuals included day-maxima of seven on 13 December 1981 and eight on 24/25 December 1989.

Post-BoH, of a recorded 2,348 individuals, 1,215 logged during 4 March (in 2012)–18 June (in 2011) included 102 on 20 April 1999. Little Gulls remained scarce July visitors: those reported included two, which summered at Keyhaven during 16 July–21 August 1994, a juvenile at Pitts Deep on 28th in 1995, a first-summer on 24th in 2003 and a first-summer that frequented Keyhaven Marshes Fishtail during 5 June–late August 2010.

Three hundred and eighty-nine, reported during 1 August (in 1996)–31 October (in 2004 and 2010) included 85 that flew east on 21 October 2004. A total of 741 during 1 November (in 1998)–28 February (in 2002) included westerly November movements at Hurst Spit of 319 on 12th in 1994, 103 on 30th in 2009 and a massive 1,107 (a Hampshire day-maximum) in calm weather, but poor visibility, on 11th in 2013.

Laughing Gull *Larus atricilla*

Rare, a winter vagrant; it breeds in eastern N America and winters south to Brazil

A singleton on Salterns Eight Acre Pond on 20 November 2005 was considered the same individual that was found at Gosport during 5–13 November and on 11 December, at Hill Head on 7 November and at Fareham on

22 November. A first for the county, it coincided with an unprecedented influx of more than 50 individuals into Britain and Ireland.

The Hampshire total to 2015 was two individuals.

Mediterranean Gull *Larus melanocephalus*
Common, a resident and spring and autumn passage migrant

This gull was first reported on the NW Solent in 1966, when an immature was at Normandy Farm/Oxey Lake on 17 September. Just two years later, nesting occurred for the first time in Britain, when a pair reared two young on the Beaulieu Estuary. During 1972–1992, it was recorded almost annually on the NW Solent, in all months other than August, October and November. A total of 49 individuals was reported in January (4), February (1), March (4), April (18), May (12), June (1), July (4), September (4) and December (1). Thirty-one were adults, some of which held territory in Black-headed Gull colonies and others also remained for considerable periods, eg singletons during mid-February–end of April 1987 and during January–end of March 1991.

Post-BoH, as sightings in Hampshire continued to increase, nesting occurred on the NW Solent in 1994 (a pair nested unsuccessfully) in 2003 (two pairs — fledged juveniles were seen) in 2005 (two pairs laid eggs, but no young reared) and in 2007 (five pairs — outcome unknown). Juveniles that were reported in late August 2005 and in late July 2006 were presumably reared elsewhere. A developing breeding population that expanded from 23 pairs in 2008 to 66 pairs in 2012 was largely unsuccessful (qv).

Poor NW Solent breeding performance was attributed to the presence of licensed gull-egg collectors, so Natural England imposed a ban on egg harvesting across the Mediterranean Gull site, on the west bank of Lymington River, in 2010. The net result was increased and repeated fox-predation, as well as losses from high, spring-tide washouts. Subsequently only 11 young (some of which, ironically, were on areas where egg harvesting was allowed to continue) were reared from 108 breeding attempts during 2011–2013, no young were raised in 2014 and only three pairs were located between Hurst Spit and Lymington in 2015.

Mediterranean Gull

Outside the breeding season, Mediterranean Gulls were reported annually during 1993–2000, with a season-maximum of 12 individuals in 1997. At Hurst Spit, a small easterly movement during 2001–2005 included 35 during 3 March (2004)–7 May (2002) with a spring-maximum of 20 during 3 March–26 April 2004. During 2006–2012, influxes included 342 to the Oxey Marshes' foreshore on 6 March 2011 and 300 on 4 May 2012. Adults in a group of 86, of which only 13 were first-year and second-year birds, at Pennington/Oxey Marshes' foreshore on 24 March 2007, presumably dispersed into breeding colonies (not necessarily in Hampshire) as by 22 April only five remained. In autumn, 372 were on newly ploughed land at Keyhaven on 1 October 2011 and 100 (an exceptional winter-count in Hampshire) were at Sowley on 11 January 2009.

Two colour-ringed birds at Keyhaven on 24 August 2009 were from France and the Czech Republic.

Common Gull *Larus canus*
Common, has bred, a spring and autumn passage migrant and a winter visitor

'A regular autumn and winter visitor, but not by any means as common as the Black-headed and Herring Gulls and not nesting nearer than the borders of Scotland' (K&C).

Breeding was first proved in Hampshire in 1991, when two pairs nested, of which one on the NW Solent laid eggs, though the outcome was unknown. Adults were also found during the summer in NW Solent gull colonies on five other occasions during 1968–1992.

Though certainly under-recorded on the NW Solent during 1950–1992, it was most frequently reported in spring, mostly on diurnal passage, but occasionally at night, eg over Salterns on 15/16 March 1984. At Hurst Spit, 543 that flew east during 12 March (in 1984)–13 May (in 1982) included 193 on 8/9 April 1961; also, 50 were present on 17 February 1991.

Post-BoH, one or two pairs annually frequented the gull colonies and breeding was successful on at least four occasions.

It was most frequently observed during January–May. Of 5,284 that flew east during 1 January (in 2007)–31 May (in 2001 and 2012) the annual-peak was 697 during 6 February–22 May 2004, of which 308 occurred on 20 March. Other annual maxima in excess of 500 were 503 during 6 February–11 May 2011 and 502 during 8 February–17 May 2002 and day-count maxima were 150 at Tanners Lane on 21st and 31 March 2008.

Ring-billed Gull *Larus delawarensis*
Rare, a spring and winter vagrant; it breeds in S Canada/N US and winters south to Caribbean

Two records: a first-winter at Pennington Marshes on 9 April 1988 (the tenth occurrence in Hampshire) and an adult at Sturt Pond on 19 December 1998. The first British record was as recent as 1973, but during 1981–1992, between 30 and 100 were recorded annually.

The Hampshire total to 2015 was 41 individuals.

Ring-billed Gull

Lesser Black-backed Gull *Larus fuscus*
Common, a spring and autumn passage migrant and winter visitor

'A scarce resident. A few birds have nested for many years past among the Herring Gulls in the Isle of Wight and we hear from Mr Isaacs, the pier-master at Alum Bay, who has the cliff-birds under his supervision, that the breeding colony of this species has much increased of recent years' (K&C).

It was not proved to breed on the NW Solent though a territorial pair was present in early June 1989.

Available data during 1963–1992 indicated that this bird was predominately a spring passage migrant. Of 260 individuals, at least 213, reported during 17 March (in 1991)–14 May (in 1982 and 1988) included 30 at Keyhaven on 13 April 1970 and 50 that flew east at Hurst Spit on 4 May 1974. The autumn day-maximum was only 12 on 15 October 1968 and the winter day-peak a mere eight on 1 December 1963.

Post-BoH, single pairs nested in 1993 (outcome unknown) in 2006 (one young reared) 2007 (two young) a territorial adult was present in 1994 and a pair in 2002.

Of a total of 615 individuals, spring migrants included 224 in March (180), April (25) and May (19) of which 51 flew east at Hurst Spit during 12–20 March 2004 and the day-maximum was 26 that flew north on 13 March 2008.

Of 255, reported during August–November, the day-maximum was 200 that flew south over Pennington Marshes on 29 October 2006.

An additional 136 during November–February included 30 adults at Efford Rubbish Tip on 27 February 1994 and 64 between Hurst Spit and Sowley on 10 January 1999.

Herring Gull *Larus argentatus*
Common, has bred, a spring and autumn passage migrant and winter visitor

'An abundant resident, but not nesting on the Hampshire mainland. This is the most common of the larger gulls which frequent our harbour, its principal breeding stations being on the cliffs of Freshwater and Culver, in the Isle of Wight and with the exception of a small colony of the Lesser Black-blacked Gull, is the only gull which nests there. Young birds of the first year offer a remarkable contrast to the adults, their plumage being mottled all over with brown. It has been proved that in captivity the full plumage is acquired by the fifth year, but it is highly probable that in a wild state the change is more rapidly completed' (K&C).

The first recorded nesting in Hampshire was on shingle in Beaulieu Estuary in 1938, but no more breeding occurred in the county until a pair nested on Keyhaven/Pennington saltmarshes in 1950; also, a pair nested at Keyhaven in 1968. The Herring Gull was presumably under-reported on the NW Solent during the 1950s/early 1960s as available data for 1963–1992 showed it to be numerous in winter and also a spring passage migrant. At least 1,618 that flew east at Hurst Spit during 21 March (in 1971)–16 May (in 1974) included a day-maximum of 604 on 9 April 1979. Large numbers were attracted to Efford Rubbish Tip where the recorded counts included 1,400 on 16 February 1977, 1,300 on 31 December 1966 and 1,000 on 13 January 1974 and on 25 January 1984.

Post-BoH, one or two pairs continued to breed on the saltmarshes in most years and in 2007 a pair attempted to nest at Hurst Castle.

Relatively few were recorded on spring passage at Hurst Spit where monthly day-maxima included 296 on 22 March 1998, 275 on 30 April 2000 and 661 on 8 May 2000. Gatherings in the low hundreds remained at Keyhaven/Pennington Marshes into June/July, eg 350 on 28 June 2006 and 272 on 18 July 2000. Numbers increased from August and in winter, when at Keyhaven/Pennington Marshes up to 1,000 occurred on 24 August 2006 and on 24 October 2000 and at Efford Rubbish Tip where there were 3,000 on 23 January 2004 and 5000 (a record Hampshire gathering) on 16 November 2004.

Yellow-legged Gull *Larus michahellis*
Scarce, an all-season visitor

The first for the NW Solent were single adults at Keyhaven and Efford Rubbish Tip in July and September, in 1985. An additional ten individuals (all adults other than a third-winter in January 1986) were reported during 1986–1991 in January (3), July (2), August (1), September (3) and October (1).

Post-BoH, a further 88, of which 25 were adults and 63 juveniles or immatures, were recorded in January (8), February (10), March (3), April (5), May (5), June (2), July (20), August (20), September (4), October (4), November (4) and December (3); up to six (an adult and five juveniles) occurred in July 2003.

Caspian Gull *Larus cachinnans*
Rare, a spring, autumn and winter vagrant; it breeds in central Asia, but is expanding its range westwards into eastern Europe

Just five were reported, ie first-winters at Keyhaven/Pennington Marshes on three dates during 25 September–5 October in 2002, on 8 December 2003, on 21 March 2004 and 10 March 2010 and a third-winter at Normandy Farm on 29 December 2011.

The Hampshire total to 2015 was 40 individuals.

Iceland Gull *Larus glaucoides*
Rare, a spring, autumn and winter visitor; all records referred to nominate race *glaucoides* that breeds in Greenland and winters mostly in Iceland

The first reports for the NW Solent were in 1970, ie one that flew east at Hurst Spit on 4 May and one at Milford-on-Sea on 11 October. A further 19 individuals (all singletons except for two which flew east at Milford-on-Sea on 29 April 1998) were reported during 21 October (in 1994–6 May (in 2008) in October (1), December (1), January (5), February (3), March (3), April (5) and May (1). The most recent were juveniles that flew west at Milford-on-Sea on 8 February 2014 and 5 December 2015.

The Hampshire total to 2015 was 101 individuals.

Glaucous Gull *Larus hyperboreus*
Scarce, a spring, autumn and winter visitor that has remained into summer; it has a circumpolar distribution, its nearest breeding grounds are in Iceland and Spitzbergen

The first for the NW Solent (and Hampshire) were two near Lymington on 24 May 1941 (Davies 1941); they were erroneously dated as 1921 (Cohen & BoH). Further NW Solent records involved 28 individuals (four adults) during 19 August (in 1987)–10 May (in 1976) in August (1), November (1), December (3), January (8), February (4), March (4), April (5) and May (2). All were singletons, other than two (one first-winter, one second-winter) that flew west at Milford-on-Sea on 25 January 2009. One in third-year plumage in Hurst Camber/Keyhaven River during 23 April–18 June 1961 returned during the three following winters and was last recorded on 29 February 1964.

The Hampshire total to 2015 was at least 117 individuals.

Great Black-backed Gull *Larus marinus*
Common, has bred, a spring and autumn passage migrant and winter visitor

'A scarce winter migrant. Hawker writes on January 28th 1847, "I had the luck to get the very bird I had long tried … a huge saddle-back gull, that was blown by the raging tempest into the marsh close by; he measured 5ft 3in from tip to tip of wing. I once killed five at a shot of these monsters when a youth and a lieutenant in the 14th Dragoons, but had never killed one since the olden time." The late Mr Stonehouse, of Milford, bought one of these birds from a fisherman about the year 1899 and took it to Kelsall, who presented it to the Winchester College Museum and Coles has seen the bird from time to time in this district in stormy weather' (K&C).

Hawker's bird of 1847 is possibly the first reference for the NW Solent. Single pairs nesting on the Keyhaven/Pennington saltmarshes in 1950 and 1951 appear to be the first breeding records for Hampshire. Single territorial pairs on the saltmarshes during 1994–1996 did not breed; neither did a territorial pair on a Lymington rooftop in 2003 or a pair on the saltings in 2004. In 2005, however, one saltmarsh pair raised three young and two pairs reared four young on Lymington buildings; up to three pairs (in 2009) nested successfully on the saltmarshes during 2006–2010.

A total of 463 spring migrants logged during 5 March (in 2012)–30 April (in 2009) included 51 that flew east at Hurst Spit on 24 April 2009. Summering records involved 821 individuals in June/July and included day-maxima of 100 on 30 June 1984 and 125, most of which were immature, on 18 July 2002.

In autumn, 282 individuals reported during August–October included 50 on 10 September 1959, 40 on 30 October 2002 and 32 that flew east at Hurst Spit on 23 September 2012.

Most occurred in winter when, of a total of 871 individuals reported during 1966–2012, 64 flew east at Hurst Spit on 10 January 2001 and the day-maximum was 126 on Efford Rubbish Tip on 27 December 2002.

Feral Pigeon *Columba livia*
Common, a resident, particularly in built-up areas
Feral Pigeons excite little interest amongst most birdwatchers, so were poorly recorded and very little information was available. A few counts of groups of up to 100 in Milford-on-Sea in the late 1990s, suggest that such numbers were probably commonplace in urban areas.

Stock Dove *Columba oenas*
Common, a resident and a spring and autumn passage migrant
'A resident, but not common. It is remarkable that Hawker only includes one bird of this species in his bag and we have no means of discovering when the species began to breed in our cliffs, but about the year 1894, Coles found a strong colony existing in the rabbit holes on the east side of Barton Court. It was no doubt the institution of the golf-links on the edge of this cliff, which led to the dispersion of this colony, the nesting ground being harried by the caddies. A single pair nested in Becton Bunny about five years ago and there may be a few pairs on the Milford side of the Bunny, but we have no direct evidence on the point at present. The bird breeds sparingly in hollow beeches in the Forest. This bird must not be confused with the Rock Dove, which is not a native of this county and may always be recognised by the conspicuous white feathers on the rump' (K&C).

During the CBC, the Stock Dove was encountered at Normandy Farm in 1982 and 1997/98, but was absent from Salterns. A different situation emerged on the Keyhaven/Oxey grazing marshes, where up to 50 were often recorded during late April–August in the 1970s/1980s. During the Atlas Survey, breeding was considered likely at Keyhaven, Lisle Court and Pitts Deep, and during 2008–2010, at Pennington Marshes.

Spring migration was seldom recorded, but 20 flew east with Woodpigeons on 7 March 2003. The only autumn records of note during 1953–1992 were recorded at Pennington Marshes in October 1976, where 121 flew south-west on 24th and 222 flew south-east on 31st.

By far the largest NW Solent concentrations occurred during winter and spring. A gathering of 550 at Sowley Farm on 27 April 1986 was the largest flock ever recorded in Hampshire at that time, but a flock of 400 at 'Sowley' on 27 December 1965 was possibly outside the recording area. Other counts in excess of 100 included 112 at Keyhaven in late December 1967, 300 at Pennington/Oxey Marshes on 2 March 1975 and 400 at Keyhaven on 3 January 1990.

Post-BoH, migrant flocks that occurred during mid-October–mid-November were recorded moving to and from all points of the compass, eg 121 flew west on 15 November 1998, 22 flew north-east on 11 November 1999, 40 flew south on 9 November 2005 and 165 flew south–south-west on 5 November 2005. Stock Doves were regular visitors at Normandy Farm/Salterns, where 20 were reported on 9 November 2005 and 90 flew west on 29 October 2006. Peak numbers at Sowley included up to 500 on 2 February 2003 and 300 on 5 November 2004.

Woodpigeon *Columba palumbus*
Common, a resident, spring and autumn passage migrant and winter visitor
'Common resident. Hawker's game bag only included twenty, which is a surprising fact considering the abundance of the species at the present day, when the numbers of resident birds, already sufficiently plentiful, are largely increased by an influx from the Continent during the winter months' (K&C).

During the CBC, Normandy Farm's breeding population peaked at 17 pairs in 1996 and up to 16 pairs during 1997–2000, while at Salterns three or four territories comprised the usual breeding complement.

By far the largest numbers occurred during mid-October–late November and the day-maximum of 3,170 flew south–south-east at Keyhaven in two hours after first light on 7 November 1981. A total of 3,000 that flew east at Oxey Marshes on 18 November 1985 was the only other reported four-figure day-count.

Post-BoH, an autumn-maximum of c.16,000 during 13 October–7 November 2005, included a day-peak of 14,300 on 23 October; other day-counts in excess of 3,000 were 8,000 that flew west in 20 minutes during the early morning of 14 November 2007, 7,150 at Pennington Marshes on 23 November 2010 and 9,000 at Keyhaven/Manor Farm on 26 November 2011. Those that passed during very short periods shortly after first light, offer credence to the theory that such early morning concentrations are composed of birds that leave nocturnal roosts.

Collared Dove *Streptopelia decaocto*
Common, a resident and spring and autumn passage migrant
The first for the area were reported at Keyhaven, where a single pair bred during 1964–66 and two or three pairs nested in 1967, by which year they also colonised Milford-on-Sea, Lower Pennington and Lymington. During the CBC, single pairs nested at Normandy Farm in four seasons during 1983–1991 and were present in two others; breeding was unconfirmed at Salterns, but individuals were present in eight seasons during 1976–1999. During the Atlas Survey, breeding was confirmed or considered likely at Lower Pennington, Waterford and Lisle Court.

At Keyhaven, flocks of up to 36 were recorded on 18 September 1967 and c.170 on 28 August 1970 and 7 October 1973. A group of 200 at Pennington/Oxey Marshes during autumn 1974 remained until 2 March 1975 and 130 were still there on 8 March.

Post-BoH, a pair nested at Salterns Marshes in 2009. Collared Doves excited few birdwatchers, which possibly explained why the largest reported groups were of only 51 individuals at Keyhaven on 2 October 1997 and 63 on 20 September 2003.

Small numbers were often recorded in circumstances suggestive of dispersal, albeit possibly of a local nature. Of a total of 29 that flew north or east, nine occurred at Hurst Spit and 20 at Salterns/Normandy Farm during 14 March (in 1976) –15 June (in 1988). Also, singletons were noted at Hurst Castle (where it was seldom encountered) on 10 March and on 24 May, in 2005 and five flew east at Iley Point on 10 May 2008. Other than two that flew east on 27 September 1995, autumn movements were undetected.

Unlike Woodpigeons and Stock Doves, Collared Doves were seldom observed feeding on NW Solent saltmarshes or foreshore.

Turtle Dove *Streptopelia turtur*
Formerly common, it is currently a scarce summer resident and spring and autumn passage migrant
'Regular summer migrant, arriving at the end of April or beginning of May and departing in September or October. The smallest of our pigeons and easily recognised by its purring note' (K&C).

Turtle Doves nested annually, often in leggy gorse on the Keyhaven grazing marshes, during the 1960s/1970s; at least two pairs did so at Iley Point in 1969. During the CBC, a combined Normandy Farm/Salterns population of up to three pairs, nested in 1976, but breeding ceased at Salterns in 1979 and at the Farm in 1990. During the Atlas Survey, breeding was considered likely at Waterford and Lisle Court; up to four pairs at 'Sowley' during that period were probably outside the recording area.

Spring arrivals were noted at Hurst Spit on 3 May 1980 (6) and 14 April 1981 (1) and at Normandy Farm (4) on 19 May 1991.

Flocking began in late June, eg 29 at Keyhaven Marshes on 23rd in 1976, but larger groups sometimes occurred, eg 74 at Keyhaven on 17 July 1977 and 110 that equalled the county record, at Vidle Van Farm on 29 August 1968. At Salterns, 12 were seen to leave a nocturnal roost at dawn on 23 August 1974 and six were at Keyhaven on 17 September 1990. There were just six October records, the last of which were singletons on 10th in 1981 and 1992. One at Oxey Marshes on 8 February 1975, the first for Hampshire in that month, had probably over-wintered; what must have been the same individual was recorded in exactly the same field on 8 March. Given the time of year, the possibility of Oriental Turtle Dove *S. orientalis* was considered at the time, though any hopes that it might be that species were soon dashed.

Post-BoH, none were proved to nest on the grazing marshes and the only mid-summer records occurred in June 2002, ie a male in song at Keyhaven on 19th and probably the same individual on 22nd.

During 1993–2009, only c.17 individuals were reported in spring between 5 April (in 1993 — one over Lymington and the earliest for the NW Solent) and 31 May (in 2003 — one at Keyhaven Marshes). Those included singletons at Hurst Spit on 23 April 2008 and on Keyhaven seawall on 23 May 2009, the only NW Solent report for the year.

In autumn, c.11 individuals during 21 August (in 2005) –28 September (in 2006) included two on 11 September 2000. None were reported on NW Solent during 2010–2012.

In his book *The Birds of Sussex* (1891) Borrer wrote: 'It is very fond of salt and may often be observed in little flocks on the salt-marshes.' However, unlike Woodpigeons and Stock Doves, this bird was seldom observed on NW Solent saltmarshes or foreshore.

Ring-necked Parakeet *Psittacula krameri*
Scarce, a resident; introduced to Britain from Africa/India, the original feral populations were in Kent and London

A singleton that flew east at Keyhaven on 25 August 1984 was probably the same individual reported in Milford-on-Sea on 26 April; it was one of at least ten in Hampshire during that year (BoH). This bird occurred regularly at a Milford-on-Sea feeding station in 1991, when one was also reported at Pennington Marshes on 18 August. **Post-BoH**, it was recorded at Normandy Farm/Lymington, though no more than eight individuals, which included up to seven at Lymington during September–December 2002, were recorded in any single year to 2007. The many records of birds observed at Lower Pennington/Normandy Farm during 2008–2012 probably involved no more than two or three individuals. It is worth noting that the larger Alexandrine Parakeet *P. eupatria* was also seen in the area, eg singletons during 18 August–21 September 1991 and on 3 May and 6 June 1992, so some reports of Ring-necked may have in fact referred to this species, or even hybrids between the two.

Great Spotted Cuckoo *Clamator glandarius*
Rare, a spring vagrant; breeds S Europe, Middle East and Africa (migratory at northern and southern parts of range)

The first and the only Hampshire record to 2015, was a first-summer individual at Keyhaven/Pennington Marshes during 2–17 April 2000.

Great Spotted Cuckoo.
Pennington Marshes

Cuckoo *Cuculus canorus*
Common, a summer resident and spring and autumn passage migrant

'Regular summer migrant' (K&C).

It was unknown whether a juvenile in the vicinity of Hurst Lighthouse during 22–31 July 1966, was hatched there, but successful breeding occurred at Keyhaven/Pennington Marshes in 1969, 1973 and 1979 and they were particularly numerous in the Lower Woodside area in 1978. During the CBC, breeding was confirmed at Normandy Farm in seven seasons and at Salterns in five. During the Atlas Survey, breeding was considered likely at Sturt Pond, Waterford, Lisle Court and Pitts Deep.

Cuckoos were sometimes observed arriving off The Solent, eg singles at Keyhaven Marshes on 24 April 1982 and on 5 June 2004, or off the sea at Hurst Spit, eg one on 8 May 1981.

Post-BoH, breeding occurred at Normandy Farm in 2006 and 2011 and was likely in 2007–08 and 2010, up to three territories were occupied on Pennington/Oxey Marshes in 2003 and a juvenile was on Keyhaven Marshes on 4 August 2010.

Earliest spring arrivals involved singles at Normandy Farm on 31 March 1996 and at Iley Point on 6 April 2009. Individuals in the vicinity of Hurst Castle included one on 11 June 2003. The latest was one at Milford-on-Sea on 3 October 1996.

Yellow-billed Cuckoo *Coccyzus americanus*
Rare, an early winter vagrant; it breeds in N America, C America and Caribbean and winters in S America

A singleton at Pennington Marshes on 6 November 1976 was seen by just three lucky observers. It was the third county record and prompted a large (for the time) but unsuccessful twitch, during the following day.

The Hampshire total to 2015 was four individuals.

Barn Owl *Tyto alba*
Formerly common, now a scarce resident

'Resident and fairly common. The most valuable of its family, its food consisting almost entirely of rats and mice, a fact which appears now to be generally recognised by our landowners and farmers. Also known as the White or Screech Owl' (K&C).

A pair reared young in a dead elm tree, close to Salterns, in 1974 and 1975, during which they were frequently observed hunting over Pennington, Oxey and Salterns Marshes. The Hawk Trusts' organised national censuses during 1982–85 revealed a marked decline since 1932, the date of the first national survey. The coastal fringe of the New Forest, however, still supported 10–15 pairs per 10 km square, as dense a population as anywhere in Britain. During the CBC, none nested at Normandy Farm or Salterns, but during the Atlas Survey, breeding was confirmed at Lower Pennington and Pennington Marshes and was considered likely at Waterford and Lisle Court.

From at least the early 1960s, Barn Owls hunted regularly over Keyhaven/Pennington Marshes and as many as five, in close proximity, were quartering Manor Farm on mid-winter mornings.

Post-BoH, pairs nested close to Normandy Farm and Salterns in 1993 and 1995, on the Farm during 2003–05, but failed to rear young in 2007; a second pair bred at nearby Salterns in 2005 and a pair bred successfully close to the grazing marshes, west of Lymington, in 2012.

Snowy Owl *Bubo scandiacus*
Rare, a spring vagrant; breeding range circumpolar above tree line, mainly on Arctic tundra, but bred in Shetland 1967–75

One was on Pennington Marshes on 14 March 1965, but as Snowy Owls were known to have been commonly imported around that time (Harber *et al* 1966) the possibility exists that it was an escape. What was presumably the same individual was seen on the Isle of Wight on 28 March.

There were just two other Hampshire reports of this magnificent Arctic owl.

Little Owl *Athene noctua*
Formerly common, now a scarce resident

'A south European species that was introduced to the New Forest district about thirty years ago and has recently nested in the Parish of Milton' (K&C).

Little Owls frequented the Keyhaven/Normandy Farm grazing marshes and presumably the coastal strip between Lymington and Colgrims, from at least the 1950s. They were occasionally seen at Hurst Castle, eg singletons on 24 November 1957, 22 October 1960 and throughout 1963. During the CBC, they were present on Normandy Farm in 1989 but breeding was confirmed only at Salterns, where single pairs nested in the Creek Cottage salt-barns in 1986 and during 1993–1995, where they were also recorded in 1984 and 1996–1998). During the Atlas Survey breeding was confirmed at Lower Pennington, Waterford and Lisle Court and considered likely at Sturt Pond and Pitts Deep.

Post-BoH, the population declined, but one was recorded at Hurst Castle on 13 November 1998. An upward trend in the Little Owl Hampshire population was detected at the turn of the twenty-first century and two or three were at Pennington Marshes in 2001, while breeding was confirmed or considered likely at Keyhaven/Oxey Marshes during 2002–2012.

Tawny Owl *Strix aluco*
Common, a resident
'Resident, nesting in the big woods. May be distinguished from the Barn Owl by its prolonged and melancholy hoot. The most common owl in the New Forest, where it may be heard hooting, even at mid-day' (K&C).

Tawnys remain the commonest of the NW Solent's breeding owls; it was found throughout the recording area and nested in and around the settlements of Milford-on-Sea, Keyhaven, Lymore and Lymington, as well as in the countryside. A favoured site in the 1960s was the overgrown garden of the derelict, Harewood House, where a nest contained young in May 1969. During the CBC, it was recorded only on Normandy Farm in 1999. It was clearly under-recorded during the Atlas Survey, when breeding was considered likely at Lower Pennington and Lisle Court.

Post-BoH, though it did not breed within the Keyhaven/Oxey grazing marshes' boundary, breeding was confirmed in the Pennington Marshes tetrad during 2003–05, at Waterford in 2006 and was considered likely at Pennington Marshes and Lisle Court during 2008–2010.

Long-eared Owl *Asio otus*
Rare, a summer, autumn and winter vagrant
'Resident, nesting in the New Forest, especially in plantations of fir' (K&C).

There were only four records during 1950–2015, ie one at Salterns on 1 October 1989, two at Keyhaven on 31 December 1991 and singletons in 2013, at Hurst Castle on 21 June and at Normandy Farm during 10–25 September.

Short-eared Owl *Asio flammeus*
Common, a spring and autumn passage migrant and winter visitor
'A winter migrant, may be met with in most years in the open fields and on the marshes along the coast. Often called the Woodcock Owl, as it arrives about the same time as that bird' (K&C).

Short-eared Owl. Oxey Marsh

Short-eared Owls occurred on the Hurst/Lymington coast in 29 winters during 1953–1992; three or more individuals were noted in three winters and numbers peaked at seven on 29 December 1981 (BoH). Records for 1958–1992 revealed occurrences, other than June and July, in all months. Spring migrants, all singletons, occurred in the vicinity of Hurst Spit on 30 March 1971, 29 April 1978 and 1 May 1990 and others at Salterns on 9 May 1975 and (a corpse) on 21 April 1982, on Keyhaven/Pennington Marshes on 25 May 1979, 14 May 1984 and 6 May 1985.

The earliest autumn migrants occurred at Normandy Farm on 6 August 1987 and at Keyhaven on 7 August 1988 and two were at Pennington Marshes on 29 August 1982; one flew south towards the Isle of Wight on 8 November 1970.

Post-BoH, at least three individuals occurred in May, ie on 7th in 2005, and on 4th in 2010 and another that remained during 27 April–5 July in 2012; other out-of-season individuals occurred on 6 June 2002 and 19 July 1998. Numbers were at particularly low ebb in Hampshire during 1997 when the sole records for NW Solent were singletons in January and November. The earliest autumn return to the marshes during 2008–2012 was on 28 September 2011.

Nightjar *Caprimulgus europaeus*
Rare, a spring and autumn passage migrant; has occurred in summer
'Regular summer migrant, a harmless and interesting bird, whose prey consists entirely of winged insects' (K&C). Post-1945, Nightjars were 'heard at Milford-on-Sea on summer evenings' in 1948, but it is unknown whether they were within the current NW Solent recording area. During the Atlas Survey, breeding possibly occurred at Lisle Court.

Excluding the above Atlas record, but including those during 1993–2015, 19 individuals, all singletons unless otherwise stated, occurred during 2 May (in 1969)–22 September (in 1974) in May (4), July (2), August (3) and September (10). Selected records, singletons unless otherwise stated, are as follows: hawking insects, around Keyhaven Coastguard Cottages on the evening of 18 May 1967 and over the sea at Hurst Spit on the evening of 2 May 1969, Lower Pennington Lane on 15/16 September 1987, two over the sea at Hurst Spit on the evening of 10 May 2001, a singing male (2300 hrs BST) on Pennington Marshes on 13 July 2004 and Avon Water reedbeds on 15 July 2007, the latter possibly an early autumn migrant, as Nightjars, particularly first-brood juveniles, vacate breeding sites as early as mid-July (BWP).

Swift *Apus apus*
Common, a summer resident and spring and autumn passage migrant
'Regular summer migrant, nesting in the roofs of the cottages near Vidley Van Farm' (K&C).

During the Atlas Survey, breeding considered likely only at Waterford, but was probably overlooked elsewhere in the recording area.

It occurred as a regular spring passage migrant. Day-totals of 300 or more, observed from single watch points, were relatively unusual, but 825 flew north at Hurst Spit on 13 May 1978. Peak numbers occurred in July and August, particularly during or following thunderstorms or similarly humid weather, eg on 6 July 1966 when 1,000 flew south over Hurst Castle and 1 August 1972 when 2,000 were over Keyhaven/Pennington Marshes. The latest usually occurred during September, but one was at Pennington Marshes on 8 October 1979.

Post-BoH, the first spring arrivals usually appeared during the third week of April; the earliest, though unexceptional for Hampshire, was one that flew north at Hurst Spit on 16 April 2005; at least five day-counts in excess of 300 included 1127 that flew east on 4 June 2012 and 923 on 27 April 2001.

Most departed by mid-September, but October records were singletons at Normandy Farm on 7th in 2000 and at Hurst Spit on 30th in 1999. A sole November record was one at Keyhaven on 15th, in 2006. Watched at length by about 20 observers, many of whom were well acquainted with Swift identification, so a 'defective observation' scenario (see Marr 2003) was unlikely.

Alpine Swift *Apus melba*
Rare, a spring vagrant; it breeds in mountainous regions from Iberia/Maghreb east to central Asia/Himalayas and other races in Afrotropics, Madagascar and India, those that breed in the Alps and southern France winter in sub-Saharan Africa
Two records: singletons over Salterns on 21 March 1990 and Normandy Farm on 3 May 2004 were the sixth and eighth county records.

The Hampshire total to 2015 was 13 individuals.

Alpine Swift

Kingfisher *Alcedo atthis*
**Common, a resident, spring and autumn passage migrant and
winter visitor**
'Resident but most frequently to be seen about Keyhaven
and Sturt during the winter months' (K&C).
A pair fed two fledglings at Sturt Pond on 1 September 1956 and this bird
occasionally nested in Pylewell Park where breeding was confirmed during the
Atlas Survey.
There are few more exotic sights in the British bird-world than that of a
Kingfisher. It was known principally as a wintering bird on the NW Solent post-
1952 when day-totals of up to five or six were often reported. Observations
that possibly involved individuals from farther afield included singletons that flew out of sight from Pennington
Marshes towards the Isle of Wight on 12 February 1978 and on 14 October 1979.

Kingfisher

Post-BoH, individuals reported after mid-April, eg those at Normandy Farm/Salterns during 16 April–28 June 2006,
were possibly from close-by breeding sites; the winter day-maximum was seven in December 2003. Post-2008 data
indicated a decline in the NW Solent wintering population, eg at Normandy Farm, monthly bird-day totals in 2008
of 68 in January, 15 in July and 74 in November, declined in 2009 to totals of just 37, ten and 16 respectively. On the
entire Hurst/Lymington coast, bird-days in 2013 totalled only five in January, 1 in July and 3 in December.

Bee-eater *Merops apiaster*
**Rare, a spring vagrant; it breeds from Iberia/Maghreb east into central Asia and from Mesopotamia east to
Chinese border and also, in small numbers, in southern Africa, those that breed in Europe winter in
sub-Saharan Africa**
The sole NW Solent report involved one, heard in flight over Keyhaven, on 28 April 2013.
The Hampshire total to 2015 was 31 individuals.

Hoopoe *Upupa epops*
**Rare, an all-season visitor, breeds across central and south Eurasia, most European nesters winter in
sub-Saharan Africa**
'A rare visitor from the south of Europe. Mr Jury, when at Rookcliffe saw a bird of this species on the lawn in
November 1904, being mobbed by sparrows. He was able to approach to within a few yards of it. The County of
Hampshire appears to be specially favoured by visits from this bird, since the authors of the "Birds of Hants" have
collected no less than 51 records of single birds and nine of pairs' (K&C).
During 1955–2015, ten individuals were recorded between 27 March (in 1955) and 3 September (in 1968) in March
(1), April (2), May (3), June (1), July (1), August (1) and September (1). Of these, singletons remained in a Milford-
on-Sea garden during 27 March–4 April 1955, at Keyhaven during 15 July–3 August 1958 and one flew in off the sea
at Milford-on-Sea on 9 May 1987.
The Hampshire total, 1950–2015, was 250 individuals.

Wryneck *Jynx torquilla*
Formerly a common summer resident, it is now a spring and principally, an autumn passage migrant
'Regular summer migrant, but in varying numbers. Last year (1912) its scarcity was marked' (K&C).
The Wryneck was a summer visitor to all parts of Hampshire, though not equally common everywhere and perhaps
more plentiful along the South Coast (K&M). It was well known to countrymen and was given many local names,
such as Barley Bird, Weet Bird and Snake Bird. It was also known by Hampshire, Sussex and Surrey woodmen as the
Rinding Bird, on account of its arrival in spring when the bark strippers were at work (K&M).
A major decline occurred during the first half of the twentieth century; by the 1950s it had all but disappeared as a
Hampshire breeding bird.
On the NW Solent, one was at Lymington during 18–26 March 1946, but no more were reported until 1968. During
1968–1990 nine (six at Keyhaven and singletons at Milford-on-Sea, Normandy Farm and Oxey Marshes) occurred
during 20 August (in 1985)–13 October (in 1990) in August (2), September (6) and October (1).

Post-BoH (1993–2015) 27 were reported in August (4), September (20) and October (3) all between 18 August (in 2012)–18 October (also present on 19th, in 2015).

Green Woodpecker *Picus viridis*
Common, a resident

'Common resident, one of the most beautiful and characteristic birds of the county' (K&C).

It was resident at Milford-on-Sea and Keyhaven from at least 1948. During the CBC, single territories were occupied in three seasons at Normandy Farm and single territories in five, at Salterns, though two juveniles close to Salterns Cottage on 10 July 1977 were probably hatched outside the census plot. During the Atlas Survey, breeding was confirmed or considered likely at Lower Pennington, Pennington Marshes, Waterford, Lisle Court and Pitts Deep.

Post-BoH, there were four territories in the Pennington Marshes tetrad in 2003 and 2004, three in 2005 and one in 2008. One that made repeated attempts to head out to sea at Hurst Spit on 26 July 2008 finally returned to the shore.

Great Spotted Woodpecker *Dendrocopos major*
Common, a resident and autumn passage migrant

'Resident, but not so common as the last' (K&C).

A pair nested immediately west of Oxey Farmhouse in 1976. During the CBC, breeding was not proved either at Normandy Farm or at Salterns, but during the Atlas Survey was confirmed or considered likely at Lower Pennington, Waterford, Lisle Court and Pitts Deep.

The British population is predominately sedentary, though some from Fenno-Scandinavia arrive in Great Britain in winter (Wernham *et al*). However, during 1971–1992 there was evidence that movement (into or from within the county) took place. At least 21 were recorded on the grazing marshes or moved along the line of the seawalls during 18 September (in 1977)–7 November (in 1975) and which included two on Normandy Farm on 26 September 1980 and singletons that flew east at Pennington Marshes on 17 October 1975 and south towards the Isle of Wight from Pennington Marshes, on 27 September 1987.

Post-BoH, one or two territories were occupied in the Pennington Marshes tetrad during 2003–2005 inclusive.

A juvenile that flew south along Hurst Spit on several occasions on 24 July 2012, always returned towards Sturt Pond while under observation. An additional 31 individuals during late August–late October, included up to four at Keyhaven Marshes on 10 September 2005 and at least nine during 9–18 September 2010.

Lesser Spotted Woodpecker *Dendrocopos minor*
Scarce, a resident

'Resident, but commonly overlooked, owing to its habit of frequenting high trees, such as elms and poplars' (K&C).

Breeding was confirmed during the late 1960s on the periphery of the recording area, ie in woodland surrounding Newlands Manor (Milford-on-Sea).

During the CBC, though this bird did not breed on Normandy Farm or at Saltern during the CBC, it was not uncommon in that area during 1974–1992, when singletons were often found in the numerous small, dead or dying elms lining the lanes, eg in July 1974, February and June 1977, September and November 1978, August 1979, November 1981 and May 1985. On 15 July 1985, one among Broad Bean plants in Normandy Farmhouse garden, was presumably eating blackfly *Aphis fable sp*. During the Atlas Survey, breeding was considered likely at Lower Pennington and Lisle Court, but was probably overlooked in adjacent tetrads.

Others were reported at Keyhaven in October 1978 and September 1989, at Pennington Marshes in September 1985 and at Pylewell/Pitts Deep in August 1981 and 1989.

Post-BoH, just 11 records included confirmed breeding, west of Lymington, in 2005. Most were recorded in winter, but three autumn individuals included one on a patch of moss on shingle at Hurst Castle on 1 September 2000 and another that flew from Keyhaven towards Hurst Castle, but returned, on 16 October 2008.

Kestrel *Falco tinnunculus*
Common, a resident and spring and autumn passage migrant.

'Resident and by far the most abundant of the Hawk tribe, nesting in woods and sea-cliffs. As we write this we can see a beautiful trained bird, sitting on her block on Coles lawn, probably the last representative from the eyrie formerly existing on Barton cliff, from which she was taken by a lad in July 1905. She is a great pet and perfectly tame with those who know her and will fly readily to the lure. In certain circumstances this species will take young game birds, but as a general rule it feeds upon mice, insects and occasionally small birds and must therefore be considered highly beneficial to the agriculturist. The destruction of this bird is now forbidden all the year round by the County Council's order under the Wild Birds Protection Act (1880) and it is much to be hoped that this order will always be strictly enforced' (K&C).

During 1967–1991, at least two or three pairs bred regularly on the periphery of the grazing marshes between Keyhaven and Normandy Farm. Nests were in holes in trees, in nest-boxes and in a conifer. During the Atlas Survey, nesting was considered likely at Sturt Pond and Lisle Court.

Kestrels were also spring and autumn passage migrants. On 11 September 1922, a loose group of 14 flew high to the east at the Lymington end of the marshes. The observer, Moreau (1923) wrote: 'They were clearly travelling in company and their method of progression was exactly similar to that which I have observed among the hordes of Lesser Kestrels migrating northwards through Egypt in spring against the prevailing N.W. or northerly winds, that is, the birds had attained a considerable height and, with wings thrown forward and tails expanded to their fullest extent, soared in a series of curves and with hardly a single wing-flap, steadily on their way against the wind.' Also, singletons were reported arriving off the sea at Hurst Spit, eg on 28 March 1976, 24 April 1978 and 25 April 1984, on 12 May 1982 and 7 April 1991. In autumn, one flew out to sea on 15 September 1974 and four (singly) flew north on 14 September 1975. Others that moved east and west, close to Milford beach, were probably of local origin and those observed crossing The Solent towards and from the direction of the Isle of Wight, were of unknown provenance (see Sparrowhawk and Buzzard).

Post-BoH, at least two pairs nested in 1999 and 2003, but not always successfully, in the vicinity of Salterns and Normandy Farm.

Red-footed Falcon *Falco vespertinus*
Rare, an early summer and autumn vagrant; it breeds in eastern Europe to central Siberia and winters in southern Africa

Two records: a male at Milford-on-Sea on the late date of 2 October 1964 and an adult female at Salterns on a more typical date of 4 June 1979.

The Hampshire total to 2015 was 59 individuals.

Merlin *Falco columbarius*
Common, a spring, summer (occasional) and autumn passage migrant and winter visitor

'Regular winter migrant, chiefly frequenting sea-coast and open country in pursuit of larks and small waders. We read in Hawker's Diary, under date Jan 26th 1842, that he "made a most brilliant shot at a Merlin Hawk that flew over me as swift as an arrow and though at least fifty yards, I cut him down as dead as a stone with snipe shot"'(K&C).

Singletons were reported on the NW Solent during the winters of 1956/57 and 1957/58 and during 16 October–10 December 1960, but records became more frequent from the mid-1960s. During 1967–1992, some 500 reports between 11 August (in 1984) and 7 May (in 1981) involved at least 98 individuals in August (13), September (18), October (26), November (11), December (5), January (6), February (5), March (7), April (5) and May (2). May records in Hampshire were exceptional (C&T) but no records for that month could be traced for the period 1950–1980 (Clark 1980). A majority involved singletons, but doubletons were recorded on many occasions, with a day-maximum of three (two females/juveniles and a grey male) on 3 January 1976. Over-wintering that frequently occurred on the NW Solent post-late 1960s followed a similar pattern to that recorded at another Hampshire coastal site, but in contrast at a third well-watched locality, though one or two appeared regularly each winter during the 1950s, this bird became much less frequent there by the end of that decade and only two were reported between 1963 and 1972 (BoH). That site's habitat and available potential prey items were apparently stable (Billett 1965) which suggested that the absence of the Merlin there was perhaps due to the demise of individuals from within a specific breeding area, rather than an overall population decline.

On the NW Solent, the Merlin was often observed to commute between Hurst Castle and the Isle of Wight, particularly during autumn and winter.

Post-BoH, this bird continued to winter regularly between 1992/93 and 2011/12. In excess of 1060 records referred to at least 120 individuals during 30 July (in 2005, the earliest Hampshire return)–15 May (also in 2005) in July (1),

August (4), September (28), October (32), November (14), December (6), January (1), February (2), March (12), April (13) and May (7). As during pre-1993, most reports involved singletons, but two were recorded on many occasions and three were at Keyhaven on 29 October 1995 and in the vicinity of Hurst Castle on 25 October 2005. It was considered by some to be less frequent on autumn passage during 2008–2012, though a greater number of records were submitted than during the previous five years.

Hobby *Falco subbuteo*
Common, a spring and autumn passage migrant; those that occurred during summer were probably close-by breeders

'Scarce summer migrant, arriving about the middle or end of May and occasionally nesting in the New Forest. Coles formerly possessed a specimen, which was taken at Keyhaven in June 1891' (K&C).

During 1966–1992, while noted as a spring passage migrant and a summer visitor, the Hobby was predominately an autumn passage migrant on the NW Solent. About 34 were reported during 12 April (in 1987)–10 June (in 1984) of which at least 16 arrived off the sea at Hurst Spit in April (3) and May (13) with a day-maximum of four on 3 May 1980. Of some 53 individuals, which occurred between 24 June (in 1972, 1974 and 1988) and 8 October (in 1988 and 1990) two flew west through Hurst Narrows on 3 October 1976 and singles flew south at Pennington Marshes on 28 September 1982 and at Hurst on 21 August 1992. As Hobbies often hunt several kilometres from their nests, those reported between mid-July and mid-September almost certainly included adults in pursuit of prey to feed to dependent young.

Post-BoH, some 400 records during 29 March (in 2001)–19 October (in 2007) involved at least 300 individuals. About 67 spring arrivals at Hurst Spit and off The Solent included day-maxima of three on 1 May, in 2004 and 2011. Autumn day-maxima were three on 4 September 1999 and 15 September 2007 and four on 30 August 2008. A very late individual over Milford-on-Sea on 31 October 2006, was outside the recording area.

Peregrine *Falco peregrinus*
Common, a resident, spring and autumn passage migrant and winter visitor

'Resident, nesting in the Isle of Wight and not infrequently to be seen at Keyhaven. This bird is "the Falcon, *par excellence*, of those devoted to the ancient sport of hawking," a sport still practised in this country, but with difficulty. The establishment of the Old Hawking Club, which has successfully carried on to the present generation the tradition of the palmy days of falconry, is still maintained at Lyndhurst. In this neighbourhood the Peregrine preys principally upon wild-fowl, seabirds and pigeons and well deserves the protection now given it by law, which has enabled the young to fly in safety after many years of persistent egg-robbery' (K&C).

Up to four pairs nested on the Isle of Wight during the 1920s/1930s (Ratcliffe 1980) and presumably often visited the Keyhaven area; documented occurrences included one on 11 September 1922, two on 10 September 1936 and one on 19 September 1937. Loss of breeding populations during the 1939–1945 War and from the effects of organochlorine pesticides between 1956 and 1961 resulted in desertion of all previously occupied sites close to Hampshire (BoH).

During 1962–1992, some 55 individuals occurred, 13 of those prior to 1979, in which year the HBR reported almost twice as many in Hampshire compared with 1978. Peregrines became increasing frequent on the NW Solent post-1986 and up to three were present during winter 1986/87.

Peregrine

Post-BoH, the Peregrine was as numerous as it had ever been and more than 1,200 records were submitted for the NW Solent. Successful breeding occurred twice within the recording area, but failed at the egg stage during a third attempt.

Golden Oriole *Oriolus oriolus*
Rare, a spring vagrant; it breeds in continental Europe and eastwards into Asia, but is a rare nester in Britain, occasionally in Hampshire, it winters, mainly south of the equator, in Africa

'Rare summer migrant. Miss Melvill saw a male bird in a field near Dr Harris' house on March 19th, 1901 and two other observers have seen the bird in a neighbouring parish' (K&C).

A male in song at Sowley Pond on 9 May 1984 was about 50 m outside the recording area. Three other reports

were: one at Keyhaven Marshes on 7 May 1986 and two in 2013, ie one at Pennington Marshes during 27–29 April and one, in off the sea at Hurst Spit then out towards the Needles, on 3 May.
The Hampshire total between 1950 and 2015 was 64 individuals.

Red-backed Shrike *Lanius collurio*
Rare, a spring, summer (occasionally) and autumn passage migrant, formerly a common summer resident
'Regular summer migrant, arriving in May and commonly known as the Butcher Bird' (K&C).
Red-backed Shrikes probably nested in the Waterford area of Lymington during the mid-1940s. In 1946, though no nest was found, a pair frequented Normandy Farm and Lane from 14 May and throughout June and another was seen close to the Coastguard Cottages in Kings Saltern Road.
The only records during 1950–1992 were: a first-winter at Salterns during 28 September–3 October 1975, a first-winter at Keyhaven/Pennington Marshes during 17 September–2 October 1983, a female at Normandy Farm on 24 May 1988 and a first-winter at Pennington Marshes during 20 September–3 October 1992.
Post-BoH (1993–2015) six singletons occurred as follows: Keyhaven/Pennington Marshes on 1 October 1995, Pennington Marshes on 3 September 2003, juvenile at Keyhaven/Oxey Marshes during 24 August–10 September 2006, female at Normandy Farm on 9 June 2007, Keyhaven/Pennington Marshes during 27 September– 11 October 2008 and at Lower Pennington Lane on 16 August 2009.

Great Grey Shrike *Lanius excubitor*
Rare, an autumn/winter passage migrant/visitor; those wintering in Britain probably originate from Fenno-Scandia
A flurry of records on the grazing marshes during 1965–75, possibly included the first documented NW Solent report, ie one at Pennington Marshes in late 1965. Overall, however, it was of less than annual occurrence and a total of ten (possibly up to 14) singletons arrived during 3 October (in 1968)–31 March (in 1968). One that remained during 1 January–31 March 1968, 3 October–31 December 1968 and 31 October 1969–6 January 1970 may have involved the same individual.

Great Grey Shrike

Post-BoH, it became less frequent. Two occurred in 1998, ie one at Pennington Marshes on 10 October and one that flew off The Solent at Keyhaven Marshes on 15 November; the only other report was of one at Keyhaven during 30 October–1 November 2007. The pattern of diminishing occurrences over the last decade mirrored that for Hampshire and Britain.

Woodchat Shrike *Lanius senator*
Rare, a spring vagrant; it breeds from Spain and Morocco to Iran and winters in the northern Afrotropics.
The only NW Solent report of one at Keyhaven on 12/13 May 2012 was the seventh county record.
The Hampshire total to 2015 was eight individuals.

Magpie *Pica pica*
Common, a resident

'Resident, but not so common as the Jay' (K&C).

This bird was heavily persecuted on the NW Solent immediately following the 1939–1945 War, eg 65 were shot at Milford-on-Sea in two days early in 1947. It regularly nested on the grazing marshes, where its bulky, domed nests, often situated in low thorn trees and visible even to the untrained eye, presented easy targets to those who wished to destroy them. However many species may have benefited from reduced Magpie populations as they are on constant watch for birds' eggs and together with Crows, may have also predated gulls and waders breeding on the saltmarshes.

During the CBC, one or two pairs nested regularly at Normandy Farm and at Salterns, but up to three pairs were occasionally present, with a maximum of four pairs at Normandy Farm in 2000. Outside the breeding season, the largest flock reported during 1959–1992 was 19 on Keyhaven Marshes on 24 October 1987.

Post-BoH, at least 30 were around Keyhaven on 22 September 1998 and one was at Hurst Castle, where it was an unusual visitor, on 11 April 2001.

Jay *Garrulus glandarius*
Common, a resident and spring and autumn passage migrant

'A common resident chiefly confined to the big woods' (K&C).

Though data were lacking, Jays presumably frequented the vicinity of the grazing marshes throughout the first half of the twentieth century. During the CBC, breeding took place at Normandy Farm in three seasons (1983/84 and 2000) and at Salterns in two (1998/99). During the Atlas Survey it was under-recorded, but breeding was confirmed at Sturt Pond and was considered likely at Lower Pennington, Waterford, Lisle Court and Pitts Deep.

In spring, 80 that flew north at Keyhaven/Pennington Marshes during 21 April (in 1984)–9 June (in 1967) included 50 during 6–24 May 1984, of which 24 occurred on the first date. Those detected inland, provided further evidence of movement into and through Hampshire.

In autumn, at least 110 individuals flew over the grazing marshes during 1967–1992. These included a day-maximum of 25 on 30 September 1983, an autumn in which a very large influx took place into Great Britain and which was attributed to a failure of the acorn crop both in this country as well as on the Continent (John & Roskell 1985).

Post-BoH, Jays occurred regularly in autumn and influxes during 22 September (in 1998)–28 October (in 2001) involved at least 100 individuals that included 59 at Keyhaven during 8–23 October 2005 and a day-peak of 22 that flew east, at Salterns/Normandy Farm on 15 October 2005. A heavy immigration in 2012, the most substantial in Hampshire since 1983, was apparently undetected on the NW Solent.

Jackdaw *Corvus monedula*
Common, a resident, a spring and autumn migrant and a winter visitor

'A common resident, nesting in the cliffs on the west side of the parish' (K&C).

Jackdaws apparently increased in Hampshire from about the 1920s, but though nesting commonly elsewhere throughout the recording area, Cohen commented that they had not nested in the Hordle cliffs since 1940. Regular morning and evening movements took place across The Solent during the latter half of the twentieth century, though Cohen recorded only Rooks similarly crossing The Solent.

National CBC data indicated increases during the 1970s/1980s, but were undetected in Hampshire. During the CBC, one territory was occupied at Normandy Farm in 1977 and two pairs nested at Salterns in 1983–1985. During the Atlas Survey, breeding was confirmed at Sturt Pond, Pennington Marshes, Waterford and Lisle Court and was likely at Pitts Deep.

Few data of feeding or roosting flocks were available, though at least 1,000 were on Manor Farm on 17 November 1984 (not 17 December as given in the Hampshire Bird Report).

Post-BoH, though comparative NW Solent data were lacking, the Jackdaw increased in the south-east region of England by more than 60 per cent during 1995–2010.

Rook *Corvus frugilegus*
Common, a resident

'A common resident in Milford parish' (K&C).

The Rook presumably remained a common resident on the NW Solent throughout the first half of the twentieth century. They regularly crossed The Solent between October and March, a movement first noted as long ago as the late 1940s (Cohen). Up to 500 flew to the mainland over Hurst Castle on 7 January 1952, while an earlier observation included a 'concourse' of Rooks that flew over Pennington Marshes and across The Solent towards Yarmouth on 26 June 1947. There were few additional data of this behaviour, but 800 were on Vidle Van Farm on 21 September 2003, 2,000 at Carrington Farm fields on 4 December 2009 and 500 there on 16 January 2011. A Milford-on-Sea rookery adjacent to the Sea Road Car Park contained 46 nests in March 2010.

Carrion Crow *Corvus corone*
Common, a resident
Carrion Crow numbers were depressed in the early twentieth century when it was a scarce resident, its numbers being kept down by the keepers' (K&C).
As with other members of the crow family, Carrion Crows increased during the 1914–18 war, a trend that continued through 1939–45 until the late 1940s; it also increased threefold between 1962 and 1988 (Marchant *et al* 1990). During the CBC, one or two pairs nested at Normandy Farm and also at Salterns. A breeding density of about six pairs per 100 hectares across the entire Keyhaven/Lymington grazing marshes in 1989 was about the county average. During the Atlas Survey, breeding was confirmed at Sturt Pond, Lower Pennington and Waterford and considered likely at Lisle Court and Pitts Deep. The Carrion Crow's British population is mainly sedentary, thus singletons that arrived off the sea at Hurst Spit on 24 April and 3 May 1982 were most likely of local origin.
Post-BoH, a pair attempted to build a nest on a gantry at Hurst Lighthouse in 2006 and nine flew off the sea at Hurst Spit on 21 April 1996.
It was sometimes numerous around Keyhaven, where largest gatherings were of feeding groups on Efford Rubbish Tip and on the saltings off Saltgrass Lane. On the former site up to 234 were present on 23 September 2004 and about 100 were on Keyhaven saltings on 12 June 2001.

Hooded Crow *Corvus cornix*
Rare, a spring, summer and winter visitor
'Regular winter migrant, frequently seen at Keyhaven, where it preys largely upon shell-fish and dead and crippled wild-fowl' (K&C).
It became less common in the county during the first half of the twentieth century and since 1951 only four singletons were reported on the NW Solent, ie at Pennington Marshes during 1–22 March 1968, on Manor Farm on 26 January 1985 and at Keyhaven on 29 April 1996 and on 6 June and 6 July, in 2000.
The Hampshire total, 1950–2015, was 43 individuals.

Raven *Corvus corax*
Common, a resident
'The Raven was occasionally seen at all seasons of the year, but less frequent than formerly, as there is now (1912) only a single bird remaining at the breeding station in the Isle of Wight' (K&C).
The majority of those reported in the Keyhaven area during the first half of the twentieth century probably involved those then nesting on the Isle of Wight. Occurrences during 1951–1992 involved singletons that flew from the Isle of Wight to Hurst Castle on 27 April 1958, south over the Castle on 17 September 1960, at Pennington Marshes on 8 December 1964, at Hurst Spit/Milford-on-Sea during 5–12 December 1970 (not November as reported in the Hampshire Bird Report) and at Keyhaven on 13 April 1974.
Post-BoH, the Raven re-occupied its former Hampshire breeding range and thus sightings became more frequent on the NW Solent. At least two pairs (display was recorded in early March) were present in 2006. A pair, apparently unsuccessfully, attempted to build a nest in 2007, but two adults, accompanied by a food-begging juvenile, were later observed in the same locality on 10 June and a pair was observed collecting nest material at Keyhaven in January 2009.
They were recorded annually during 1998–2012, with up to two during 1998–2000, five in 2002 and ten on 26 January 2008.

Goldcrest *Regulus regulus*
Common, a resident, spring and autumn passage migrant and winter visitor

'A common resident. The smallest British bird, which has much increased owing to the fashion of planting those coniferous trees that it inhabits' (K&C).

Though it remained a resident throughout the recording area, few data on which to assess its breeding status were available. During the CBC, one territory was occupied in 1985 and birds were also present in four additional breeding seasons at Normandy Farm and in eight at Salterns. During the Atlas Survey, breeding was confirmed at Sturt Pond and considered likely at Lower Pennington, Waterford and Lisle Court.

This bird usually attracts the attention of ornithologists as a spring and autumn passage migrant, when it is often to be found among the extensive gorse-brakes and thorn and bramble scrub along the seawalls and on the grazing marshes. Spring migration often occurred during mid-March–early April and a significant arrival was noted at Keyhaven/Pennington Marshes on 26 March 1974.

Goldcrest

In autumn, the first sometimes appeared in late September (particularly on 22 September 1982) but were more often encountered in late October, eg at Normandy Farm on 23rd in 1983 and on 18th in 1988.

Post-BoH, four territories were occupied in 2009, ie two at Normandy Farm and two at Salterns. Up to ten individuals were recorded around the Farm during December 2008.

Firecrest *Regulus ignicapilla*
Scarce, a spring and autumn passage migrant and winter visitor

Seventeen individuals, all singletons except for doubletons at Keyhaven on 27 December 1982 and at Normandy Farm on 9 January 1983, were recorded on the NW Solent during 1961–1992, in January (2), March (3), April (2), October (4), November (2) and December (4).

Post-BoH, c.84 individuals were reported, of which 34 during March–May, included three at Keyhaven on 5 April 2002 and on 11 March 2011.

One was in song on 9 July 2012. Twenty-seven, most of which were singletons that occurred during August–November, included two on 13 October 1996. An additional 22 during December–February included four at Pennington Marshes in December 2009 and 25 on January 2011.

Firecrests were not known to nest in Britain until 1961 (Adams 1966).

Blue Tit *Cyanistes caeruleus*
Common, a resident and autumn passage migrant

'Common resident' (K&C).

During the CBC, breeding occurred annually at Normandy Farm where two–six pairs nested and at Salterns where two-eight pairs bred. During the Atlas Survey, breeding was confirmed at Sturt Pond, Keyhaven, Lower Pennington, Pennington Marshes, Waterford, Lisle Court and Pitts Deep.

Large numbers occurred in the vicinity of Keyhaven/Hurst Spit in 1949, where 150 at Keyhaven were in Common Reed *Phragmites australis* on 20 November and 100 in Cordgrass *Spartina sp* at Hurst Castle on 27 November. Other notable reports at Hurst included 17 on 17 November 1956, 28 that attempted to leave northwards against a strong NW wind on 16 December 1957 (an irruption year) and 13 on 28 September 1963. Records from the mid-1960s revealed the Blue Tit to be a common autumn passage migrant. Significant influxes included 65 at Sowley shore on 30 November 1974, groups of up to 56 inside the seawalls on 19 September 1976, when birds were encountered all along the marshes and in autumn 1983 when 'large numbers' were on Keyhaven/Pennington Marshes on 20 September and 20 October and more than 100 on 30 October.

Post-BoH, a combined 13 pairs nested at Salterns/Normandy Farm in 2009.

Noteworthy records included one that flew in over Hurst Narrows and landed on rocks around the Castle, before heading north towards Keyhaven on 11 April 2001, two on Milford beach and 11 that flew high over Iley Point (Keyhaven Marshes) in groups on 12 March 2003 and one that flew in off the sea at Hurst Spit on 22 March 2009.

Great Tit *Parus major*
Common, a resident

'Common resident' (K&C).

During the CBC, breeding occurred annually at Normandy Farm where the population usually numbered one or two pairs, but increased to four pairs in 2000; at Salterns the usual complement of two or three pairs increased to four pairs in 1990. During the Atlas Survey, breeding was confirmed at Sturt Pond, Keyhaven, Lower Pennington, Pennington Marshes, Waterford, Lisle Court and Pitts Deep.

Unlike the situation at another Hampshire coastal locality where, up to 1991, one or two were noted on autumn passage, none on the NW Solent even hinted at immigration.

Coal Tit *Periparus ater*
Common, a resident

'Common resident. Seems to prefer the neighbourhood of pines and other conifers' (K&C).

During the CBC, it was absent from Normandy Farm, but was recorded at Salterns in 1977/78. During the Atlas Survey, breeding was confirmed at Sturt Pond and Lisle Court and considered likely at Lower Pennington, Waterford and Pitts Deep.

Records suggestive of immigration involved singletons that associated with Blue Tits, eg at Normandy Farm on 19 October 1975, at Keyhaven on 19 October 1975, at Salterns on 15 October 1977 and at Normandy Farm on 7 October 1985. Also, two were at Pennington Marshes on 18th and 20 September 1977 and at Normandy Farm on 30 September 1983, where three were reported on 30 September 1991.

Post-BoH, one territory was occupied at Pennington Marshes in 2010. Otherwise, Coal Tits were present at Normandy Farm in all months, other than May and October, in 2006 and 2008 and at Oxey Marshes/Normandy Farm in 2009.

At Hurst Spit, three flew east off the sea on 26 September 2008 and two did likewise the following day.

Willow Tit *Poecile montana*
Rare, a resident

During the Atlas Survey, breeding was confirmed only at Pitts Deep, but others, possibly outside the recording area included singletons at Sowley in November 2000, August 2001 and March 2007.

Marsh Tit *Poecile palustris*
Common, a resident

'Common resident. In this bird the black plumage is confined to the crown of the head and the throat and there is no white spot at the back of the head, as in the last [Coal Tit]. This brief description will enable the observer to distinguish between this species and the preceding' (K&C).

During the CBC, it was absent from both Normandy Farm and Salterns. During the Atlas Survey, breeding was confirmed at Lisle Court and considered likely at Sturt Pond and Pitts Deep.

The only records for the grazing marshes during 1966–1992, but where it was possibly under-recorded, were singletons at Keyhaven during 31 July –8 August in 1970, at Pennington on 22 May 1977 and at Keyhaven on 20 October 1983.

Post-BoH, a pair nested at Normandy Farm in 2009 and one territory was occupied at Pennington Marshes in 2010. The few additional documented records that involved just seven individuals in January, June, July and November, were perhaps indicative of the dramatic decline in southeast England during 1995–2010, the reasons for which were unclear.

Bearded Tit *Panurus biarmicus*
Scarce, a resident, spring and autumn passage migrant and winter visitor
After an absence of 63 years, Bearded Tits resumed breeding in Hampshire in 1966 (Duffin 1991): on the NW Solent single pairs nested in 1981 and 1989 and two pairs did so in 1990–92 inclusive.

In January 1965, a male was present on 21st and five, of which three were males, on 23rd. Thereafter they were of annual occurrence and a total of 436 individuals were recorded in January (50), February (54), March (36), April (9), May (1), July (1), October (152), November (97) and December (36). The day-maximum was 40 on 15 October 1972 and other notable double-figure counts included 14 on 4 February 1967, 23 on 21 October 1972, a group of 14 that flew south-east over Pennington Marshes' Butts on 2 November 1973, 30 on 13 October 1974, 26 on 13 November 1988 and 25 on 24 October 1989.

Post-BoH, single pairs nested (probably successfully) in 1999; breeding may have occurred in 2001 and was annual during 2002–2012 when three pairs were present in 2002 and twelve juveniles were seen on 1 June 2007. Autumn day-maxima included 32 on 27 September 2002, 30 on 30 September 2000 and 24 on 29 October 2001. Flocks were observed performing pre-migratory irruptive behaviour during late September–late October. Those included 28 on 30 September 2002, eight on 26 September 2006 and others on at least five other occasions during 12 October (in 2000)–7 November (in 2005) the latest date on which such behaviour was reported. Wintering groups usually numbered fewer than ten, but at least 12 were at Keyhaven on 14 November 2012.

Short-toed Lark *Calandrella brachydactyla*
Rare, a spring vagrant; breeds in Iberia/Maghreb east to China, European nesters winter in Africa
The sole record involved one at Normandy Farm lagoon on 18 May 2010.

The Hampshire total to 2015 was two individuals.

Woodlark *Lullula arborea*
Scarce, a spring and autumn passage migrant and winter visitor
'Scarce resident, chiefly seen in winter in Milford parish, but nesting in the New Forest' (K&C).

During 1950–1992, Woodlarks were scarce visitors on spring and autumn passage and in winter and just eight individuals were reported as follows: one at Pennington Marshes on 14 December 1978, three that flew towards the Isle of Wight from Pennington Marshes' seawall on 9 January 1982, one that flew north-east in off the sea at Hurst Spit on 12 March 1983, one at Salterns on 7 October 1985, one that flew off the sea at Hurst spit on 9 May 1988 and one that flew west at Pennington Marshes on 15 October 1989.

Post-BoH, individuals were in song on 26 March 2008 and on 14 October 2009 and an additional 66 were recorded in January (12), February (14), April (2), August (1), September (5), October (26), November (3) and December (3). Day-maxima involved groups of 11 (following heavy snowfall) at Tanners Lane on 3 February 2009 and eight that flew east in similar conditions at Oxey Marshes/Normandy Farm on 6 January 2010. Other notable reports were of four that flew east at Pennington Marshes on 4 October 2003 and four on 14 October 2006.

Skylark *Alauda arvensis*
Common, a declining resident, spring and autumn passage migrant and winter visitor
'Very common resident in Milford parish' (K&C).

During the CBC, occupied territories at Normandy Farm fluctuated between three (in 2000) and 19 (in 1990) while at

Bearded Tit

Salterns, up to three territories were occupied, in 1991. A national decline in Skylark populations, attributed to the severe winter of 1981/1982 and changes in farming practices, was reflected in the Hampshire CBC indexes (BoH). During the Atlas Survey, breeding was confirmed at Hurst Castle (it last nested there in 1996) Sturt Pond, Keyhaven, Pennington Marshes and Waterford and was considered likely at Lower Pennington, Lisle Court and Pitts Deep.

The Skylark occurred as a diurnal passage migrant in autumn and early winter, but particularly during cold weather. Spring migrants were seldom recorded, eg during 1960–1992, just 16 (12 that flew north and four that flew west) were reported at Hurst Spit/Keyhaven, ie six on 17 March 1967, two on 29 March 1975, four (west) on 5 March 1977 and singletons on three dates during March 1996 and on 5 May 1996.

Autumn day-maxima rarely exceeded 100, but heavier movements included 585 that flew north-west over Keyhaven on 16 October 1960 and 72 that flew west–north-west over Pennington Marshes on 24 October 1981. The largest movements occurred during or following heavy snowfall, eg 20,000 moved west/north-west at a rate of 5,000 per hour from first light until midday on 1 January 1979 and 4,000 flew west/north-west in four hours over Pennington Marshes/Salterns on 27 January 1979. Notable grounded concentrations were of 430 at Hurst Spit on 6 January 1963, 800 at Pennington Marshes on 9 January 1971 and 800 on Normandy Farm on 23 January 1979.

Post-BoH, breeding occurred at Waterford (up to 11 males on territory at Normandy Farm in 2011) Salterns (a pair in 2010) Pennington/Oxey Marshes (27 territories in 2004) Pennington Marshes (five pairs in 2009 and 2011) and at Keyhaven Marshes (five pairs in 2009 and 2011).

Autumn migrants reported at Hurst Spit and the marshes during 1993–2012 totalled 2,300 individuals, with day-maxima of 180 on 7 November 1998 and 121 that flew north on 31 October 2007. Heavier movements occurred in winter when 710 flew east on 6 January 2010 and 1,800 flew west on 2 December 2010. Gatherings included a roost of 400 on Keyhaven saltmarshes on 19 December and at least 450 at Keyhaven on 21 December 2010.

Shore Lark *Eremophila alpestris*
Rare, an autumn passage migrant and winter visitor; those on passage and wintering in Britain originate from Fenno-Scandia and western Russia

The first Shore Larks recorded in Hampshire were five at Pennington Marshes on 31 October 1955, but no more were reported on the NW Solent until winter 1969/70, when three at Hurst Spit during 10 December–7 April (one remained until 16 April) was the fifth county record. Another occurred at Keyhaven on 14 December 1978.

Post-BoH, three reports, all of which may have related to the same birds, occurred during November 1998, ie seven at Hurst Spit on 12th (the largest group recorded in the county) two there on 13th and one at Pennington Marshes on 15th. Others were one at Milford-on-Sea/Hurst Spit during 16–21 October 2003 and two at Keyhaven on 13 October 2009.

The Hampshire total to 2015 was 45 individuals.

Sand Martin *Riparia riparia*
Common, has bred, a spring and autumn passage migrant

'Common summer migrant. We are afraid that the large colony on the Barton cliff has been seriously disturbed by the golf caddies but there is another large settlement in the sand-pit to the north of Lymington station' (K&C). Sand Martins were opportunistic breeders and suitable, but temporary, sand-faces within the Efford gravel extraction/landfill site, were sometimes occupied by small colonies, eg 30 pairs in 1968 and 12 pairs during the late 1990s; colonies in Hordle coastal cliffs were outside the recording area.

During 1966–1992, a predominately northerly, but unremarkable, spring passage was recorded during 11 March (in 1977)–6 June (in 1981); peak migration occurred during 8–21 April.

Autumn passage was usually evident by early July and continued until 9 November (in 1983). Peaks occurred during the last week of August and included 600 that flew over Keyhaven on 24 August 1971. Alas, documented records do not reflect just how common an early passage migrant this species was, at least in the 1970s. On some days in late July and early August, Sand Martins moved westwards over The Solent and through Hurst Narrows in a continuous stream, but because this was such a familiar sight (1000s must have been involved on some days) it was inadequately documented.

Post-BoH, spring passage was reported during 8 March (in 1997)–6 June (in 2006); day-maxima rarely attained 50, but 280 flew north on 1 April 2001.

Migration took place during 13 June (in 2010)–26 October (in 1997). Clear-cut peaks occurred during 8–14 July and 9–15 September, though day-maxima were reported on 26 August 1995 (700) and on 5 July 2003 when 259 flew north-east. Day-maxima of 100 or more on four September dates during 2008–2012 included a peak of 920 at Pennington Marshes on 9 September 2011.

Sand Martins that roosted in the Avon Water reedbeds attained a maximum of 3,000 on 1 September 1995. This number was equalled at a Hampshire site in mid-July 2000, but only once surpassed, when 3,500 were at another locality in early August 1977 (BoH).

Swallow *Hirundo rustica*
Common, a summer resident and spring and autumn passage migrant, has occurred in winter

'Common summer migrant. According to general observation in the south of England this bird appears to be here in diminished numbers this season, 1912' (K&C).

K&M cite one 'as late as 7 December in the neighbourhood of Lymington', but do not give the year, but another was also at Lymington on 14 December 1938.

Swallows.
Salt barns by Creek Cottage

The Swallow nested at suitable sites throughout the recording area. Fluctuations during the CBC mirrored the national situation when at Normandy Farm, one pair nested in 1977, seven pairs in 1978, none in 1988 and only a single pair during 1994–2000. At Salterns two or three pairs usually nested, with four pairs in 1980, but none bred in seven seasons between 1987 and 1998. During the Atlas Survey, breeding was confirmed at Hurst Castle, Sturt Pond, Keyhaven, Lower Pennington, Pennington Marshes, Waterford and Lisle Court and was considered likely at Pitts Deep. A single territory was occupied at Hurst Castle in 1996 and two were occupied in 1999.

Swallows did not normally arrive before the first week of April, but of five March records during 1955–1992, the earliest were singletons on 12th in 1977 and 1988. Few accounts of more than 200, passing a watch-point on a particular day, were submitted; the maximum was just 300 that flew north at Hurst Spit on 7 May 1980.

Swallows were more numerous on autumn passage. The largest counts, at Pennington Marshes, were 3,000 that flew east on 12 September 1984 and a noteworthy 5,000 on 6 September 1985; the latest was one at Salterns on 23 November 1979. Mid-winter records were unusual and were confined to singletons at Milford-on-Sea on 13 December 1970 and at Keyhaven on 14 December 1986.

Post-BoH, two pairs nested at Normandy Farm in 2000, 2002 and 2004, while at least one pair did so during 2005–07.

March arrivals became more frequent and a total of 60 were reported. The earliest of those occurred on 15th in 1998, the highest count was 12 on 29th, in 2010, but the largest spring-count of all was 300 at Pennington Marshes on 9 May 2012.

In autumn, c.10,000 at Tanners Lane on 4 October 2000, 3,000 at Keyhaven/Pennington Marshes on 12 September 2010 and 10,000 that flew over Hurst Spit on 16 September 2011, were the heaviest autumn day-counts reported in Hampshire during those years.

House Martin *Delichon urbicum*
Common, a declining summer resident and spring and autumn passage migrant, has occurred occasionally in winter

'Common summer migrant. The scarcity of this species this year (1913) is even more noticeable than the last' (K&C). Four Hampshire avifaunas, published between 1905 and 1993, cited few NW Solent House Martin data, but 'some thousands' were at Lymington on 9 November 1896 (K&M).

The following account was derived from personal records, those of Keyhaven colleagues and those published in Hampshire Bird Reports. House Martins nested in small numbers at Keyhaven in the 1960s, eg two pairs on the Old Post Office in 1967. During the CBC, none nested at Normandy Farm or at Salterns. During the Atlas Survey, breeding was confirmed at Sturt Pond, Keyhaven, Waterford, Lisle Court and Pitts Deep.

Unexceptional spring passage on the NW Solent between 1962 and 1992, occurred during 9 April (in 1988)–31 May (in 1978); 100 flew north at Hurst Spit on 11 May 1982.

Autumn migration was noted during 31 August (in 1975)–26 November (in 1967) with a day-maximum of c.2,000 at Keyhaven on 29 September 1974.

Post-BoH, diurnal spring migration was reported during 24 March (in 1996)–3 June (in 2006) with a day-maximum of just 44 that flew north-east on 10 May 1993

Autumn migration was predominately in an easterly or southerly direction and occurred during 12 August (in 2006)–8 November (in 1997). Two peaks were detected, ie during 15–21 September and 29 September–5 October, with a day-maximum of 5,000 on 21 September 2002.

Red-rumped Swallow *Cecropis daurica*
Rare, a spring and autumn vagrant; it breeds in Iberia/Maghreb east to Japan (other races India/Afrotropics) and European nesters winter sub-Saharan Africa

A juvenile over the Avon Water at Keyhaven on 10 October 2005, was the fourth Hampshire record and one of only three in autumn in Britain, that year. Another was at Lower Pennington on 18 April 2014, the earliest spring occurrence for the county.

The Hampshire total to 2015 was 13 individuals.

Cetti's Warbler *Cettia cetti*
Common, a resident

The first for the NW Solent was a male in song during 24 March–21 April 1974. It was the fourth Hampshire record; the first for the county and for Britain, having occurred at Titchfield Haven during 4 March–10 April 1961.

The only other recording area report during the 1970s was a male in song at Keyhaven during 31 October–3 November 1976. Territorial males became regular at Keyhaven/Lymington during the 1980/90s: one in 1982, two in 1983 and 1986, four in 1988, 1989 and 1991, five in 1985, 1987 and 1991 and eight in 1984 and 1990.

Cetti's Warbler

With the exception of 1991, when coverage was considered to be incomplete, these data are considered reasonably accurate. During the CBC, none were recorded at Normandy Farm or Salterns, but one was at Salterns on 7 October 2000. During the Atlas Survey, breeding was confirmed at Keyhaven and considered likely at Lower Pennington.

Post-BoH, the Cetti's Warbler remained an established and increasing resident, with at least 15 breeding territories in 1994, 1997 and 2006. A singing male at Milford-on-Sea in 2005 was just outside the recording area.

Long-tailed Tit *Aegithalos caudatus*
Common, a resident and autumn passage migrant
'Common resident. Col. Hawker has this note in his Diary (Jan 1st 1833): "Found in the garden (at Keyhaven) the nest of a 'long-tailed Dick', with three eggs"' (K&C).

During the CBC, up to two pairs nested in three seasons on Normandy Farm and single territories were occupied at Salterns in six seasons. During the Atlas Survey, breeding was confirmed at Waterford and considered likely at Sturt Pond, Lower Pennington, Pennington Marshes, Lisle Court and Pitts Deep. Summer gatherings seldom exceeded single-figures, but 20 were at Salterns on 7 July 1980.

Long-tailed Tit

Larger flocks were sometimes encountered in autumn, eg 50 on Normandy Farm on 15 October 1982 and 24 there on 11 October 1985. British Long-tailed Tits were predominately sedentary and the following occurrences perhaps indicate dispersal: 15 arrived from south at Hurst Castle on 6 November 1959, ten high-fliers along Keyhaven Marshes' seawall on 11 October 2003 and others on 20 September 2008 and 20 on 25 October 2003.

Pallas's Warbler *Phylloscopus proregulus*
Rare, a winter vagrant; it breeds in Siberia and winters in SE Asia
The first for Hampshire, at Milford-on-Sea on 23 November 1974, occurred during an era when this beautiful *Phylloscopus* was still a real rarity; another in a Lymington garden on 15 January 2005 (the fourth for the county) was outside the recording area.

The Hampshire total to 2015 was nine individuals.

Yellow-browed Warbler *Phylloscopus inornatus*
Rare, an autumn and winter vagrant; it breeds in Siberia and winters in SE Asia
Three records: singletons were at Lower Pennington during 1–4 December 1999, at Salterns/Normandy Farm during 7–14 October 2007 and at Pennington Marshes on 25 October 2008. Two in Milford-on-Sea (along the Danes Stream) in October 2014 were outside the recording area.

The Hampshire total to 2015 was 104 individuals.

Wood Warbler *Phylloscopus sibilatrix*
Rare, a spring vagrant, though nesting in the New Forest
'Regular summer migrant abundant in the big woods of the Forest and passing through this parish on migration. Slightly larger than the two preceding [Willow Warbler & Chiffchaff] and distinguished by the tremulous character of its song, which frequently terminates with a few clear whistling notes, resembling those of the Nuthatch' (K&C).

The only subsequent record appears to be one at Keyhaven on 12 May 2001.

Common Chiffchaff *Phylloscopus collybita*
Common, a summer visitor, spring and autumn passage migrant and winter visitor
'A regular summer migrant. One of the earliest summer visitors, arriving about the middle of March and making itself known by the note from which it derives its name' (K&C).

Post-1966, there were no breeding season records for the grazing marshes until 20 May 1972, when an apparently unmated male was in song at Salterns. During the CBC, none were proved to nest until 1989, when one territory was occupied on Normandy Farm, but up to four pairs nested there in 1998 and in 2000 and at Salterns in 1995.

Spring passage took place during early March–late April. March records occurred in at least 15 seasons, but two at Salterns on 6 March 1977 had possibly over-wintered. The peak immigration period was during 5–18 April, when significant day-maxima included up to 20 at Keyhaven on 13 April 1972; however, an arrival of about 40, took place in the vicinity of Hurst Castle on 24 April 1990.

Autumn passage, during which a notable influx of at least 25 individuals occurred at Hurst Castle on 15 September 1963, took place during late August–early October, with the peak during 26 September–2 October.

Post-BoH, the Chiffchaff occurred frequently in spring, with significant numbers arriving much earlier than pre-1992. First arrival dates were during 22–28 March, with a day-maximum of 30 on 28 March 2004.

Autumn passage, though most evident during 12–18 September, occurred from the second week of August until the middle of October; the highest day-count was 60 on 4 October 2010.

Siberian Chiffchaff *Phylloscopus collybita tristis*
Rare, a winter vagrant; it breeds in Fenno-Scandia and Russia
One record: a singleton was at Keyhaven (Manor Farm) on 18 December 2008. Since 2009 a further 11 individuals have occurred elsewhere in Hampshire.

Willow Warbler *Phylloscopus trochilus*
Common, a declining summer visitor and spring and autumn passage migrant
'Regular summer migrant, arriving the first week in April. Though in appearance scarcely to be distinguished from the last [Chiffchaff], it is easily recognised by its soft and pleasing song' (K&C).

More numerous as a breeding species than the Chiffchaff, it occurred throughout the recording area. During the CBC, up to 12 territories (in 1995) were occupied at Normandy Farm and up to seven (in 1975) at Salterns; a combined maximum of 18 territories was occupied in 1985 and 1995. During the Atlas Survey, breeding was confirmed or considered likely at Sturt Pond, Keyhaven, Lower Pennington, Lisle Court and Pitts Deep.

The earliest of four March records during 1966–1992 was on 23rd in 1977, though first arrivals occurred more often during the first week of April. The peak week for immigration, which continued during the first week of May, occurred during 8–14 April, the most memorable falls being of 150 at Sturt Pond/Keyhaven on 14 April 1972 and at least 100 that arrived off the sea at Hurst Spit on 3 May 1980.

Autumn passage, during mid-July–mid-September, was apparently much less pronounced, but peaked during 15–21 August; the latest individual occurred on 10 October 1981.

Post-BoH, spring passage included a dozen first arrivals in March, of which the earliest was on 17th in 2001. The peak week for migration, which involved almost a third of the spring bird-day total, was during 8–14 April. The autumn migration peak, which accounted for about a fifth of the autumn bird-day total, occurred during 8–14 August; the latest was on 24 October 2001.

Blackcap *Sylvia atricapilla*
Common, a summer visitor, spring and autumn passage migrant and winter resident

'Regular summer migrant' (K&C).

During the CBC, single territories were occupied in most years on Normandy Farm (but two in 1998) and two were occupied at Salterns in 1996/97.

Due to the presence of wintering birds, first spring migrant arrival dates were difficult to assess, but during 1966–1992 included one at Keyhaven on 2 April 1990. A very large fall on 30 April 1976, also involved Whitethroats.

A protracted autumn migration took place during mid-July–late October, with the last at Normandy Farm on 3 November 1981. Wintering individuals, eg a male at Oxey on 20 December 1999, were often observed in gardens.

Blackcap

Post-BoH, the earliest spring arrivals were apparently in March, the earliest one on 12th in 2005; others were reported during 15th–27th. The highest spring-counts occurred in April, ie eight at Normandy Farm on 16th in 2011 and nine at Sturt Pond/Pennington Marshes on 28th in 2012.

Apparent increases occurred in the grazing marshes' breeding population in the early years of the twenty-first century, when up to 11 territories were occupied at Keyhaven/Pennington in 2003 and 14 territories in 2004, while at Normandy Farm, four territories were occupied in 2007 and 2011.

The autumn migration was unexceptional; one at Lower Pennington on 19 November 1993 was probably a late passage migrant. Wintering individuals were reported at Milford-on-Sea on 30 November 2004 and in Normandy Lane on 23 December 2005.

Garden Warbler *Sylvia borin*
Common, a summer visitor and spring and autumn passage migrant

'Regular summer migrant' (K&C).

During the CBC, one territory was occupied at Normandy Farm in 1996 and individuals were present at Salterns in 1985. During the Atlas Survey, when it was probably overlooked in many tetrads, breeding was considered likely at Waterford.

The earliest spring arrival during 1966–1992 was one on 12 April 1978.

During the late 1960s/70s, they were particularly numerous at Keyhaven during early August–early September; the latest was at Normandy Farm on 15 October 1975.

Post-BoH, but when it was under-recorded during the breeding season, one at Pennington Marshes on 9th and 19 June 2012, provided the only indication of nesting.

The earliest spring arrival was a singleton at Keyhaven on 25 April 1993 and others were reported during 5 May (in 2004)–24 May (in 2003).

Thirty-one individuals were reported during 29 July (in 2008)–10 October (in 1993) of which 18 occurred in August, with a day-maximum of four at Keyhaven Marshes on 30th, in 1998.

Barred Warbler *Sylvia nisoria*
Rare, an autumn vagrant; it breeds central Europe and eastwards to Kazakhstan and winters mostly in Kenya and Sudan

There were just two reports of this robust and rather long-tailed warbler, both of which involved singletons in first-winter plumage, ie at Keyhaven on 7 October 1990 and Pennington Marshes on 24 September 1997; they were the third and fifth county records.

The Hampshire total to 2015 was 11 individuals.

Lesser Whitethroat *Sylvia curruca*
Common, a summer visitor and spring and autumn passage migrant
'A regular summer migrant, preferring gardens, shrubberies and copses' (K&C).

Several pairs nested at Milford-on-Sea in 1946 and regularly between Lymington and Keyhaven during 1966–1992; breeding was confirmed at Keyhaven Marshes during 1967–69 inclusive and in 1974. During the CBC, up to two territories were occupied in nine seasons at Normandy Farm and up to two in 1984 and 1992/93 at Salterns. During the Atlas Survey, breeding was considered likely at Sturt Pond, Keyhaven, Lower Pennington, Pennington Marshes and Waterford.

In only three years were first arrivals reported prior to the last week of April, the earliest being on 16th in 1981. The spring-peak occurred during the second week of May, though day-totals of grounded individuals were modest and did not exceed five.

Autumn passage often began in late July and continued until late September. Peak numbers usually occurred during 22–28 August and included day-maxima of 20 at Salterns on 23 August 1974 and 20 at Keyhaven on 27 August 1978. Passage decreased after mid-September and four October reports included one, the latest for Hampshire at that time, on 21 October 1971.

Post-BoH, nesting occurred at Pennington Marshes, where a pair and three young were reported on 7 June 2001 and where up to four territories were occupied in 2004; also single territories were occupied at Normandy Farm in at least three seasons during 2001–2007.

First spring arrivals, the earliest of which was on 14 April 2009, were reported between 15th and 21 April in seven seasons, all earlier than during the previous three decades. Peak numbers occurred in late April/early May, with a day-maximum of seven, grounded in foggy conditions at Keyhaven, on 22 April 2009.

The autumn-peak occurred during 29 August–4 September, the day-maximum being six on 29 August 2008; the latest was a singleton on 15 October 1995.

Whitethroat *Sylvia communis*
Common, a summer visitor and spring and autumn passage migrant
'Regular summer migrant, chiefly found along hedgerows' (K&C).

The Whitethroat was a common summer visitor at Keyhaven/Lymington until the late 1960s. A solitary record of a male at Sturt Pond on 1 May 1967, when spring passage at Hengistbury Head (then in Hampshire) was also reported as poor (HBR 1967) was perhaps indicative of the impending British Whitethroat population crash of 1969 (see Winstanley *et al* 1974). At least one territory, however, was occupied at Iley Point in 1969, two pairs nested at Salterns in 1974, but at least 12 males held territories on Keyhaven/Pennington Marshes in 1976. During the CBC, up to seven pairs nested (in 1996) at Normandy Farm and up to nine pairs (in 1993) at Salterns: a combined total of 13 pairs bred in 1996. During the Atlas Survey, breeding was confirmed at Sturt Pond, Keyhaven, Lower Pennington, Pennington Marshes, Waterford and Lisle Court and was considered likely at Pitts Deep.

The earliest arrivals during 1966–1992 were on 14 April (in 1979 and 1980) while spring passage peaked during 22–28 April. Day-maxima did not exceed 15 individuals, though 'large falls' at Keyhaven on 26 April 1968 and 30 April 1976 presumably involved greater numbers.

The bulk of the autumn passage occurred during mid-August–late September; a distinct peak during 26 August–2 September included c.100 at Keyhaven on 31 August 1992 and the latest was a singleton on 16 October 1971.

Post-BoH, territories on the grazing marshes between Keyhaven and Normandy Farm declined from 65 in 2004 to 36 in 2005; at least ten territories were at Oxey Marshes/Normandy Farm in 2007.

Spring migration occurred much earlier and at least eight individuals, five of which were reported on 3/4 April, arrived during the first week of April (none pre-1992); largest day-counts were in 2002 with 40 on 23 April and 50 on 7 May.

Though the bulk of the autumn migration occurred during 19 August–9 September, it was more protracted than pre-1992 and at least seven individuals were reported during October, the latest on 20th, in 2001.

Dartford Warbler *Sylvia undata*
Common, a resident, passage migrant and winter visitor
'A rare resident. This bird certainly inhabits the furze-brakes of Barton and Becton and doubtless occurs in similar places in Milford-on-Sea. It may be described as a small dark warbler with a very long tail, but is easily overlooked on account of its secretive habits and the density of the gorse bushes, which it frequents' (K&C).

Dartfords were reported at Keyhaven/Pennington Marshes prior to and following 1939–45, ie in the breeding season of 1938 and in December/January of the savagely cold winter of 1946/47. During a period of steady increase in the Hampshire population, Dartford Warblers were again reported in winter during the 1950s, eg one at Pennington Marshes on 3 December 1955 and a pair at Keyhaven on 4 November 1956.

A male was in song in April/May and two at a second locality during late July–early December, in 1975. At one of the NW Solent 1975 sites, nesting probably occurred in 1977 but was not confirmed until 1980. Adults and young were reported at a third locality in 1986, while at least 10 males/pairs were located during May 1991.

Autumn reports included two at Pennington Marshes on 15 October 1961 and three that remained until the end of the year, at Keyhaven on 4 October 1971. During the following two decades, Dartfords were often found on the grazing marshes in autumn/winter, though no day-count exceeded three.

Post-BoH, breeding was proved or considered likely in every season during 1999–2012, with a maximum of ten territories in 2012.

The marshes' autumn/winter day-maximum was ten on 27 October 2010. At Hurst Castle, where it was rarely reported, singletons were found on 28 March 1993, 11 November 20011 and 21 October 2007.

Grasshopper Warbler *Locustella naevia*
Scarce, a spring and autumn passage migrant
'Regular summer migrant, seldom seen but recognised by its curious reeling note, resembling that of a grasshopper. This bird appears to have decreased somewhat in numbers in this neighbourhood, during the last few seasons' (K&C). Grasshopper Warbler numbers continued to fluctuate in Hampshire; there were noticeable declines in the 1970s (BoH). Breeding was not proved on the NW Solent post-1966, where it was recorded only as a spring and autumn passage migrant. Forty individuals were reported during 15 April (in 1971) –12 May (in 1973), but its skulking nature meant that it was certainly much overlooked, particularly in autumn. Eighteen reported during 27 July (in 1969)– 23 September (in 1989) included four individuals at Keyhaven during 13 August–17 September 1988.

Post-BoH, about 39 individuals reported during 11 April (in 2009)–3 May (in 2001) included four on 20 April, in 2004 and 2009. In autumn 49 individuals, included day-peaks of seven at Sturt Pond on 19 August 2003 and eight at Pylewell on 22 August 2004 during 29 July (in 2000)–21 September (in 1999).

Savi's Warbler *Locustella luscinioides*
Rare, a spring vagrant; it breeds in Iberia/Maghreb, eastwards to central Asia and winters in sub-Saharan Africa
The only report concerned a male in song at Keyhaven on 6 May 1989.
The Hampshire total to 2015 was 35 individuals.

Melodious Warbler *Hippolais polyglotta*
Rare, an autumn vagrant; it breeds in France, Spain, Italy and north-west Africa and winters in tropical West Africa
Two records: September singletons occurred at Keyhaven on 2nd/3rd in 1961 and at Hurst Castle on 25th/26th in 1965; they were the first and fourth county records.
The Hampshire total to 2015 was 17 individuals.

Aquatic Warbler *Acrocephalus paludicola*
Rare, an autumn visitor; it breeds E Europe to fringes of Western Palearctic and winters in W Africa
Aquatic warblers are not only skulking but in serious population decline. It is thus not surprising that there were just six records for the NW Solent, none more recent than 1989, ie at Keyhaven on 27 August 1969, 22 August 1970, 30 August 1973, 7 September 1980 and 20 September 1981 and a first-winter at Pennington Marshes on 19 August 1989. The Pennington bird was found just inside the seawall at high tide and thus was suspected of having been washed off the saltings.
The Hampshire total to 2015 was 85 individuals.

Sedge Warbler *Acrocephalus schoenobaenus*
Common, a summer visitor and spring and autumn passage migrant

'Regular summer migrant, very common in the reed beds of Sturt and Keyhaven' (K&C).

Given the above assessment, it is possible that the Sedge Warbler became less common on the NW Solent during the second half of the twentieth century. Habitats may have become less suitable as this species is now known to favour the drier edges of poorly developed reeds (Thomas 1984). It was, however, a common breeder in Hampshire until massive declines in the British population, caused principally by a series of drought years in one of its main wintering areas in West Africa, occurred in 1969 and during the 1980s. Available data for the NW Solent were too fragmentary for comparison with its early-1900s breeding status. During the CBC, up to three pairs nested (in 1986) at Normandy Farm and up to two pairs (in 1989) at Salterns. During the Atlas Survey, breeding was confirmed at Keyhaven and Waterford and considered likely at Lower Pennington and Pennington Marshes.

The earliest spring arrival was one at Keyhaven on 2 April 1978; the day-maximum was eight at Keyhaven/Pennington Marshes on 18 April 1968 and migration peaked during 15–21 April. It was sometimes recorded at Hurst Castle, eg a singleton on 27 May 1979.

The latest autumn reports included singletons on 9 October 1983 and 23 October 1988.

Post-BoH, it continued to breed in modest numbers, with seven pairs at Keyhaven/Pennington Marshes and one pair at Normandy Farm, in 2005. The earliest arrival was on 3 April 2004 and the day-maximum was 12 on 25 April 2005.

It was more noticeable in autumn. The peak week for migration was during 29 August–4 September with the day-peak of 25 at Keyhaven on 31 August, in 1992. Other notable counts included 16 on 7 September 2012 and 15 on 3 August 2007 and 2 August 2009; the latest was a singleton on 14 October 1999.

Marsh Warbler *Acrocephalus palustris*
Rare, a spring and autumn vagrant

Three records, ie one in spring and two in autumn. The spring report involved a male in song at Keyhaven on 19 May 1935 (Whitlock); other than two pairs said to have bred in the south-east of the county in 1907 (Cohen) this was the only other Hampshire record during the first half of the twentieth century. A singleton at Keyhaven on 1 October 1989 was the tenth county record since 1950 and another was at Keyhaven on 31 August 1992. The Hampshire total, 1950–2015 was 23 individuals.

Reed Warbler *Acrocephalus scirpaceus*
Common, a summer visitor and spring and autumn passage migrant

'Regular summer migrant. We have no certain knowledge of the nesting of this bird in the parish, but it must pass through it on migration, as it builds in the reedbeds of all the larger Hampshire and Wiltshire rivers' (K&C).

During the second half of the twentieth century it became commoner than the Sedge Warbler on NW Solent and nested in reedbeds at Sturt Pond and Avon Water. During the CBC, up to five territories were occupied (in 2000) at Normandy Farm and up to seven (in 1999) at Salterns. During the Atlas Survey, breeding was confirmed at Sturt Pond, Keyhaven, Pennington Marshes and Pitts Deep and was considered likely at Lower Pennington, Waterford and Lisle Court, though no population estimates were available. Up to 58 territories, however, were on the grazing marshes' lagoons in 2003 where, prior to the early 1990s, saline conditions inhibited establishment of suitable habitat. A total of 18 territories were occupied in 2010, at Oxey Marshes (1), Salterns (4) and Normandy Farm (13). Nesting also occurred on Bulls Saltern (Lisle Court) and elsewhere where suitable stands of Common Reed *Phragmites australis* occurred.

The earliest spring arrival was on 19 April 1982 and the latest in autumn was on 6 October 1984.

Post-BoH, early and late individuals were recorded at Keyhaven on 4 April 2008 and at Pennington Marshes on 23 November 2010, the second latest Hampshire record to date.

Waxwing *Bombycilla garrulus*
Rare, an occasional autumn and winter vagrant; an irruptive migrant from northern Fenno-Scandia and Siberia

The only records were as follows: one at Lymington on 28 December 1965 'and a few days before', one in Lower Pennington Lane on 13 November was probably the same as at Normandy on 1 December 1988, up to 85 at Lymington in 2005 during 25 January–25 March and on 8 May, one at Sowley shore on 25 October 2007 and six at Keyhaven on 25 December 2010.

Nuthatch *Sitta europaea*
Common, a resident
'Common resident' (K&C).

The Nuthatch regularly nested throughout the recording area though, unsurprisingly, was absent from the grazing marshes. During the CBC, none were recorded at Normandy Farm, but it occurred at Salterns in 1992. During the Atlas Survey, breeding was confirmed at Sturt Pond and Waterford and considered likely at Lower Pennington, Lisle Court and Pitts Deep.

Otherwise, singletons were recorded at Salterns on 15 September 1977, 27 August 1978, 28 July 1979 and two that flew over Normandy Farm, on 5 October 1983.

Post-BoH, the Nuthatch was recorded at Lower Woodside in October 2002 and breeding was considered likely at Waterford during 2005–2011 and at Lower Pennington in 2010. This bird's population greatly increased in south-east England during 1995–2010.

Treecreeper *Certhia familiaris*
Common, a resident
'Common resident' (K&C).

Treecreepers regularly nested throughout much of the recording area, though were absent from the grazing marshes. During the CBC, it was present, but did not breed, at Salterns in 1978, 1989/90 and 1992. It was probably overlooked during the Atlas Survey when breeding was considered likely at Lower Pennington and Pitts Deep, but confirmed only at Lisle Court. Up to 1992 the only additional records were singletons at Salterns on 3 October 1974, 16 March and 15 July 1981 and at Normandy Farm on 22 February 1984.

Post-BoH, breeding was confirmed or considered likely at Lower Pennington in 2010 and at Waterford in 2006–09 and 2011/12.

Wren *Troglodytes troglodytes*
Common, a resident
'Common resident. The local name of Cutty, being akin to the Welsh cwt, bob-tailed, was doubtless used in Hampshire before the Saxon conquest' (K&C).

During the CBC, up to 15 pairs nested (in 1993) at Normandy Farm and up to 10 pairs (in 1983) at Salterns. Though not strictly comparable to the CBC data, 39 territories were occupied at Oxey Marshes/Salterns/Normandy Farm in 2009. No record was indicative of migration and no data were available on which to assess the strength of the wintering population.

Starling *Sturnus vulgaris*
Common, a resident, autumn passage migrant and winter visitor
'Abundant resident' (K&C).

NW Solent Starling data were fragmentary. During the CBC, up to a combined total of 12 pairs, ten of which were on the Salterns plot and two on Normandy Farm, nested in 1978. The population subsequently declined and from 1987 only one territory, at Salterns, was occupied. It also nested at Hurst Castle, where up to seven pairs were present during the 1990s.

During autumn, 210 flew north-west at Hurst Spit on 12 October 1980, but a day-maximum of c.1,000 flew north at Hurst Castle on 24 October 1981 (cf Redwing).

It was most numerous at reedbed roosts, eg on the Avon Water at Keyhaven, where Starlings were present from late June and throughout the autumn/winter; at least 2,000 were there during 14–19 September 1987.

Post-BoH, autumn movement from the direction of the Isle of Wight was often detected, with a day-maximum of 2,190 on 15 November 2001. At the Keyhaven roost, significant estimates were 5,000 in mid-November 2002, 10,000 in early January 2009, but up to 20,000, in late December 2010.

Rose-coloured Starling *Pastor roseus*
Rare, a summer and autumn vagrant; it breeds from south-eastern Europe to central Asia and winters mostly in the Indian sub-continent
Five records: adults were at Keyhaven during 26 August–3 September 2001 and at Oxey Marshes on 10 June 2007, juveniles at Pennington Marshes during 23–28 September 2007 (possibly present from 21 September) and at

Keyhaven/Pennington Marshes on 2/3 October 2011. An adult over Keyhaven Marshes (Fishtail lagoon) on 22 June 2014 was seen earlier that day in a Milford-on-Sea garden.

The Hampshire total to 2015 was 24 individuals.

Ring Ouzel *Turdus torquatus*
Scarce, a spring and autumn passage migrant and occasionally in early winter

'An occasional visitor in spring and autumn' (K&C).

It occurred less than annually on the NW Solent during 1959–1992. Just 15 individuals were reported, of which six occurred during 28 March (in 1976)–19 April (in 1975) and nine during 25 September (in 1977)–5 November (in 1988). Other than one at Normandy Farm on 17/18 October 1988 and two at Keyhaven on 5 November 1988 (a year in which 65 were recorded in Hampshire) all were one-day singletons.

Post-BoH, five individuals were recorded during 13 March (in 2007)–22 April (in 2000).

They occurred more frequently in autumn. During 25 September (in 2001)–31 October (in 2005) at least 28 individuals included one on 25 September 2001 (the earliest NW Solent return) one that flew east at Hurst Spit on 14 October 2003 and 14 during 7–31 October 2005 (of which five on 16th coincided with an influx of Blackbirds) and a day-maximum of nine on 22nd.

Blackbird *Turdus merula*
Common, a resident, spring and autumn passage migrant and winter visitor

'Common resident. This species is subject to albinism and several pied specimens have occurred in Milford-on-Sea' (K&C).

During the CBC, breeding populations peaked at 14 territories at Normandy Farm in 1984 and 12 at Salterns in 1985. Notable spring influxes occurred in mid-March 1971 and 1984 and were detected on the grazing marshes on many autumn dates, during mid-October–early November in 1974/75 and in 1978–1984 inclusive. Significant nocturnal movements also occurred, specifically on the nights of 31 October/1 November and regularly during November, in 1974 and on 16/17 October 1981.

Post-BoH, 12 territories were occupied at Normandy Farm in 2008/09.

Notable influxes of up to 30–40 individuals, were reported at Normandy Farm on 2 November 1997 and on 12 November 2005, at Pennington Marshes on 7 October 2000, at Keyhaven on 31 October 2004 and at Tanners Lane on 11 October 2007 and 58 were on Keyhaven Marshes on 23 October 2012.

Fieldfare *Turdus pilaris*
Common, a spring and autumn passage migrant and winter visitor, particularly during cold weather; it breeds in north and central Eurasia and winters south to northern Africa

'Regular winter migrant, arriving about the same time as the last [Redwing] and sometimes remaining till May. Hawker's Diary for February 2nd, 1831, contains an account of a remarkable visitation of this bird. In flight and size it resembles the Missel Thrush, but may be distinguished by its note "chuck chuck' and the blue-grey colouring of its head and the lower part of its back' (K&C).

The influx to which K&C referred involved not less than 20,000 birds at Keyhaven/Westover during a SW hurricane and overwhelming snowfall; they had gone by the following day.

Post-1966, the largest influx was of a similar magnitude when 15,000 flew west at Sturt Pond on 7 February 1986. Other significant movements that involved day-counts in excess of 1,000 individuals were as follows: 2,500, of which 1,950 flew south/south-east over Keyhaven and 550 were grounded at nearby Efford, on 28 January 1979, 1,000 at Keyhaven on 17 February 1978 and 3,200 that flew west–south-west at Keyhaven on 10 February 1985. Few migrants were reported after the end of February and of 100 individuals recorded in March 60 occurred on 31st in 1975. The last spring passage migrants included 12 that roosted at Keyhaven Marshes on 14 April 1970, 60 at Oxey Marshes on 11 April 1975 and a singleton at Keyhaven on 27 April 1980.

The earliest autumn arrival was a 'small party' at Efford on 18 September 1971. October migration, included 50 that flew north at Milford-on-Sea on 12th, in 1972, 500 that flew north at Keyhaven on 22nd, also in 1972 and 38 that flew north at Hurst Spit on 12th in 1980. Nocturnal movement was recorded during October/November 1981, on 28/29 October 1983, 1/2 October 1984, 1/2 November 1986 and on one or two occasions during mid-December–mid-January. Additional, selected counts included 400 or more at Keyhaven on 27 November and 2 December, in 1991; also 30 flew south-west from Pennington Marshes at dusk on 18 December 1985.

Post-BoH, there were few documented spring records. Those usually occurred in March when one flew north at Hurst Castle on 29th, in 2002, seven roosted in trees at Keyhaven on 30th, in 2004 and (all at Normandy Farm), 30 on 12th in 2008, 12 on 22nd in 2009, up to seven on 19th in 2010 and 26 on 6th in 2011; the latest were nine at Keyhaven on 5 April 2002.

Autumn migration, from 13 October (in 2007) included day-totals of 80 at Normandy Farm on 15 November 1993, 51 that flew north at Hurst Spit on 20 October 2003 and 190 that flew east at Pennington Marshes on 7 November 2003. December day-totals rarely exceeded 20 individuals, but 50 roosted at Normandy Farm during 27 November–5 December 1993 and 110 did so at Keyhaven on 19 January 2000. The only substantial cold-weather movements occurred in February 1996 when c.2,000 flew east at Keyhaven on 7th, others arrived at dusk and dropped into trees, probably to roost and 540 flew west at dusk at Normandy Farm on 10th.

Song Thrush *Turdus philomelos*
Common, a resident, autumn passage migrant and winter visitor
'Common resident' (K&C).

A decline in the national population, initially detected in the 1940s, was particularly evident from the 1970s (Marchant *et al* 1990). During the CBC, up to two pairs nested (in 1981, 1983–1985 inclusive and 1989/90) at Normandy Farm and four pairs (in 1984) at Salterns.

Autumn nocturnal migration was recorded on 1/2 October 1978, during 3–17 October 1981 and on 17 September 1986. Song Thrushes were occasionally associated with Blackbird influxes, eg on 31 October 1978, 24 October 1979 and 20 October 1980.

Post-BoH, small numbers, eg 12 that flew south at Lower Pennington on 4 October, eight that flew south at Tanners Lane on 7 October 1998 and 24 that flew east or south during 19 October–2 November 2009 were reported during 4 October (in 1998)–21 November (in 2001). Cold-weather concentrations in excess of 50 included 54 at Keyhaven on 8 January 2003, while diurnal passage at Hurst Spit included three in off the sea on 31 December 1996.

Redwing *Turdus iliacus*
Common, a spring and autumn passage migrant and winter visitor; it breeds in northern Eurasia and winters south to southern Europe
'Regular winter migrant, arriving, by night, at the end of October or beginning of November' (K&C).

A massive cold-weather movement, the heaviest observed on the NW Solent, occurred on 6 February 1986 when c.14,000 flew east at Sturt Pond. Other than 380 in five groups that flew high south-east at dusk, at Salterns on 11 March 1981, spring passage post-1966 was unexceptional; the latest were 60 at Oxey Marshes on 11 April 1975. The earliest autumn arrivals were four on 29 September 1972, but a major influx occurred only a fortnight later when on 12 October, 4,500 flew in off the sea at Milford-on-Sea cliff-top. Other noteworthy counts were 900 that flew north-west at Hurst Spit on 12 October 1980 and 1,200 that included one flock of 1,000, which flew high to the north at Keyhaven Marshes shortly after dawn on 24 October 1981 (cf Starling).

Post-BoH, insignificant spring passages included a day-maximum of only 70 at Normandy Farm during 10–15 March 2005; the last was a singleton there on 1 April, in 2011.

Diurnal autumn passage was evident during 14 October (in 1994)–19 November (in 2006) with a day-maximum of 860, grounded in poor weather between Keyhaven and Normandy Farm, on 2 November 2005 and 275 were on the Farm three days later. Winter passage migrants included 200 that flew east at Pennington Marshes on 7 February 1996.

Mistle Thrush *Turdus viscivorus*
Common, a resident, spring and autumn passage migrant and winter visitor
'Common resident' (K&C).

During the CBC, a single pair nested at Normandy Farm during 1976–1985 and it was recorded there in 1999; at Salterns, one or two pairs nested during 1976–1987 and it occurred in 1988. Summer/autumn gatherings included 13 at Keyhaven on 10 August 1972 and 21 at Salterns on 23 June 1979.

Mistle Thrush

There was little evidence of autumn/winter movements, but five flew high westwards across Salterns on 19 October 1980 and one flew out over The Solent towards the Isle of Wight on 26 November 1983.

Post-BoH, two were at Normandy Farm throughout the breeding season of 2006 and a gathering of nine was recorded there on 13 July 2006. It became more frequent during late September (in 2001)–late November (in 2007) during which a total of 31 included day-maxima of 11 at Keyhaven on 5 November 2005 and seven at Milford-on-Sea on 24 November 2007; also 22 flew east at Normandy Farm on 6 January 2010.

Spotted Flycatcher *Muscicapa striata*
Previously common, a declining summer visitor and spring and autumn passage migrant
'Common summer migrant' (K&C).

Spotted Flycatchers nested at Keyhaven in the 1960s, when single pairs took up residence in Saltgrass Lane in 1966/1967, two pairs bred in the village in 1968 and a pair nested at Salterns in 1974. During the CBC, though breeding was unconfirmed, birds occurred at Normandy Farm in 1978, 1983 and 2000 and at Salterns during five seasons, but where successful breeding occurred in 1980 and 1981. During the Atlas Survey, breeding was confirmed at Waterford and considered likely at Lower Pennington and Lisle Court. The last report of breeding was in 1999 when a single pair reared two broods in Lymington town centre.

Spring passage was unexceptional; the earliest flew in off the sea at Hurst Spit on 2 May 1972 and two did likewise on 3 May 1980.

It was more numerous on autumn passage when first migrants usually appeared during the first week of August, with peaks in the last week of the month, ie 20 on 28th, in 1973 and at least 30 on 31st, in 1979; the latest was one at Keyhaven on 22 September, in 1970.

Post-BoH, there were just 31 records that involved 57 individuals, during the 20-year period post-1993, a reflection of the 50 per cent decline of the British population during 1995–2010 (Balmer *et al* 2013). Of nine spring individuals, singletons arrived off the sea at Hurst Spit on 11 May 1996 and on 1 May 2004. Other than an isolated record of one at Pennington Marshes on 2 July 2011, the remainder occurred during 11 August (in 2007)–4 October (in 1998) with day-peaks of four on 26 August and on 9 September 2007.

Robin *Erithacus rubecula*
Common, a resident, spring and autumn passage migrant and winter visitor
'Common resident' (K&C).

During the CBC, occupied territories at Normandy Farm fluctuated between one in 1976 and 1990 and seven in 1994 and 1999. At Salterns, three territories in 1978 increased to nine in 1983. Hampshire indices showed reductions in the overall county population following three cold winters during the 1980s and in 1991.

Post-BoH, singletons that arrived off the sea in March 2005, ie at Milford-on-Sea on 20th and flew north at Hurst Spit on 29th, hinted at immigration.

Counts of 20, 30 and 50 individuals at Keyhaven/Pennington Marshes on 23 August, 23 September and 20 October, in 2001 respectively, one on Hurst Spit on 30 October 2001 and at least seven, of which five moved off eastwards, on Hurst Spit on 23 October 2012, were indicative of autumn migration.

A count of 17 at Keyhaven/Pennington Marshes on 18 January 2001 indicated an influx.

Nightingale *Luscinia megarhynchos*
Formerly common, now scarce, a summer visitor and spring and autumn passage migrant

'Regular summer migrant' (K&C).

The Nightingale presumably remained a common and widespread summer visitor on the NW Solent, both prior to and following the 1939–45 War. Few specific data were available, though one was recorded 'singing all day within 50 yards of the Old Coastguard House' at Waterford on 1 May 1946 and it was described as 'very common' at Milford-on-Sea in 1948. Single pairs nested at Keyhaven in 1969 and at Pitts Deep during 1971–1975 and juveniles were recorded at Lisle Court. During the Atlas Survey, single territories were occupied at Salterns in 1974 and 1989 and nesting was considered likely at Lower Pennington and Waterford. Fledged juveniles at Keyhaven during 29 July–12 August 1968, 6 July–5 August 1970 and 7 July–16 August 1971 (two) were presumably reared close-by. Spring migrants occurred at Keyhaven during 19 April (in 1959)–30 April (in 1967).

In autumn, singletons were reported in August at Keyhaven, ie on 16th in 1978, on 19th in 1979 and 16th/17th in 1986 and at Normandy Farm on 2 September 1987.

Post-BoH, one territory was occupied at Salterns in 1996, where the male was in song on 8 April. Spring migrants detected during 8 April (in 1996, 2010 and 2011)–29 May (in 1999) included males in song at Keyhaven during 23 April–3 May 2000 and 3–23 May 2001.

Autumn migrants were confined to singletons at Pennington Marshes on 29 July 2007 and 6 August 2009.

Bluethroat *Luscinia svecica*
Rare, a spring and autumn vagrant; it breeds across the Palearctic from Iberia to East Asia (marginally Nearctic), those that breed in Spain, Germany and Scandinavia probably winter in the Sahel region of Africa and Arabia

Six records: singletons at Keyhaven on 30 August 1959, at Hurst Castle on 2 September 1961, immatures at Keyhaven on 2 September 1964 and 5th and 11 September 2007, a male, though speculation arose as to its exact racial identity, of the White-spotted race on Keyhaven Marshes on 11 April 2013 and a first-winter male along the Ancient Highway at Keyhaven on 26 October 2015, was photographed. Those in 1959 and 1961 were fifth and sixth county records.

The Hampshire total to 2015 was 31 individuals.

Pied Flycatcher *Ficedula hypoleuca*
Scarce, a spring and autumn passage migrant

Just 22 were reported during 1961–1992 of which four were in April (on 22nd in 1962, 24th in 1987 and on 17th and 23rd in 1988) and the remainder mostly in August; extreme dates were 31 July (in 1980)–22 September (in 1961).

Post-BoH, 18 individuals were reported of which the sole spring record was a female in off the sea at Hurst Spit on 21 May 2001. The remainder occurred during 29 July (in 2002)–28 September (in 1999): of note was a singleton that remained in Haven Boatyard (Waterford) for about a week from 17 August 2001 and three in a Lymington garden on 15 August 2002.

One ringed at Keyhaven on 10 August 1969 was found in Morocco on about 2 May 1970; it was the first recovery of a Hampshire-ringed Pied Flycatcher.

Black Redstart *Phoenicurus ochruros*
Scarce, a spring and autumn migrant and winter visitor

Occasional Hampshire winter records in the 1950s/early 1960s were mostly from Hurst Spit (BoH); nine such records during 1955–1960 occurred in January (1), February (2), November (3) and December (3). During 1961–1992, 47 individuals were recorded between 14 October (in 1961 and 1984) and 17 May (in 1972) in October (16), November (8), December (8), January (2), February (3), March (5), April (3) and May (2).

Post-BoH, with the exception of one at Pennington Marshes on 23 July 2010, an additional 82 were logged during 11 October (in 1995)–21 May (in 1994) in October (16), November (25), December (7), January (13), February (2), March (12), April (5) and May (2); the day-maximum was four on 17 November 1998. Long-stayers were at Hurst Spit during 12 November 1998–28 February 1999, 18 October 2001–10 January 2002 and 14 October (2002)–18 January 2003; of two on 24 November 2012, one remained into 2013.

Redstart *Phoenicurus phoenicurus*
Common, a spring and autumn passage migrant

'Regular summer migrant but chiefly seen on migration. The nearest nesting places, as far as we know, are in the New Forest' (K&C).

A recent estimate of the British breeding population of more than 100,000 breeding pairs (Musgrove *et al* 2013) was double that of Whinchat, though it is a less noticeable migrant on the NW Solent. Twenty-two individuals were reported in spring during 1966–1992, of which seven occurred during 29 April–5 May and one arrived off the sea at Hurst Spit on 3 May 1980; records spanned the period 10 April (in 1966)–20 May (in 1973).

It was more numerous on autumn passage, when during 18 July (in 1972)–22 October (in 1988) c.100 individuals were reported. A majority occurred during 2–8 September with a day-maximum of five on 5 September 1989. A singleton on 24 November 1989 was the latest on record for Hampshire at that time.

Post-BoH, 34 individuals were recorded on spring passage during 31 March (2001)–5 June (2006). The peak occurred during 15–21 April, with a day-maximum of eight on 17 April 2004. Return passage was in progress by 23 June (in 2007) and continued until 13 October (in 2005): most occurred during 26 August–1 September, a week earlier than during the previous two decades, with a day-maximum of 14 on 25 August 2001.

Whinchat *Saxicola rubetra*
Common, a spring and autumn passage migrant, one possibly over-wintered

'Regular summer migrant, but few remain to nest in this district. May be distinguished from the stonechat by the white stripe over its eye' (K&C).

Whinchat

The Whinchat nested in the New Forest until 1990, but there was no evidence that breeding occurred on the NW Solent, at least during the last six decades.

The British population was recently estimated at 47,000 breeding pairs (Musgrove *et al* 2013), but relatively few were observed on spring passage on the NW Solent. Other than one at Keyhaven on 9 March 1938 (possibly an over-wintering individual) and one 'near Lymington' on 14 June 1988, immigration was noted during 15 April (in 1966)–25 May (in 1985). At least 116 individuals reported during 29 April–5 May included a day-peak of 30 on 1 May 1990.

Migration during 14 July (in 1981)–13 November (in 1970) involved a minimum of 600 individuals. The autumn migration peak coincided with that of Redstart, ie during 26 August–1 September, though the day-maximum of 40 occurred on 9 September (in 1987); the peak October count was 15 on 2 October 1976.

Post-BoH, most of 52 noted on spring passage during 16 April (in 2001)–7 June (in 2001) occurred during 29 April–5 May; the day-maxima were five on 1 May 1993 and 29 April 2004.

Return migration, recorded during 12 July (in 1993)–8 November (in 1998) involved a minimum of 520 individuals. A majority occurred during 9–15 September and included a day-peak of 20 on 12 September 2002.

Stonechat *Saxicola torquatus*
Common, a resident, spring and autumn passage migrant and winter visitor

'A common resident, its numbers largely increased in spring. A conspicuous bird in all gorse breaks, especially the cock bird with its black head, white collar and red breast' (K&C).

The Stonechat is resident on the NW Solent between Milford-on-Sea and Colgrims, where eight pairs nested around Keyhaven in 1975, but fewer occur east of Lymington River. During the CBC, up to three pairs nested (in 1995) at Normandy Farm and two pairs (in 1994/95) at Salterns. It nested at Lisle Court in 1971–75, but was probably over-looked during the Atlas Survey, when breeding was confirmed only at Sturt Pond, Keyhaven and Pennington Marshes.

The few available autumn data included nine on Keyhaven/Pennington Marshes on 9 October 1983, 12 on 12 November 1989 and 12 or more on 8 October 1990.

Post-BoH, up to nine or ten pairs nested on the grazing marshes between Keyhaven and Normandy Farm in 2001/02.

Spring passage was insignificant, though March migrants at Hurst Spit included one, grounded in thick fog, on 18th in 2004 and three (one on 11th and two on 13th) in 2005.

In contrast, autumn passage was more noticeable, particularly during October, when the highest day-count was 45, of which at least 33 were at Keyhaven, on 20th in 2006. Observers who walk the coastal path from Keyhaven/Normandy Farm in mid-winter should expect to encounter at least a dozen individuals during the day.

Wheatear *Oenanthe oenanthe*
Common, a spring and autumn passage migrant and has occurred in winter

'Regular summer migrant, most conspicuous along the coast when returning southwards in autumn. Numbers may be seen along our cliffs, during August and September and easily recognised by the white patch over the tail' (K&C).

There was no breeding evidence for the NW Solent, but a male remained on Pennington Marshes during 10 May–8 June, in 1981.

With a large and widespread European population, the Wheatear is, perhaps unsurprisingly, the most numerous of the chats to traverse the area during both spring and autumn migrations. The first spring migrants appeared in March when extreme dates were 7 March (in 1991)–31 May (in 1981). A majority occurred during 5–11 April, but day-maxima, usually less than a dozen, peaked at 62 in the vicinity of Hurst Spit/Castle on 18 March 1963 and 42, along the Keyhaven/Pennington Marshes' seawall, on 2 April 1987. Migrants often arrived low over the sea from the south-west and at least 12 that included a group of six, did so on 14 April 1981. A male in song at Cut Bridge on 6 May 1971 soon moved on.

Return passage took place during 17 July (in 1969 and 1982)–17 November (in 1984); most occurred during 19 August–1 September, with day-maxima of 40 on 25 August 1984, but 40 also occurred on 9 September 1988.

Post-BoH, spring passage involved a reported 760 individuals, of which 140 occurred in 2001, during 4 March (in 2010)–31 May (2007). Two distinct peaks were detected, ie during 15–21 March and 19–25 April; the latter period included a day-maximum of 60 on 25th, in 2005.

No fewer than 2,200 individuals were logged during 9 July (in 2009)–14 November (in 1999 and 2011); the peak occurred during 19 August–1 September, with a day-maximum of 45 on 28 August 2010. Passage was particularly heavy in 2000 when 255 were recorded during 26 July–30 October; conversely only 20 were reported during 3 August–2 November in 1994. A female in Lymington on 3 January 1995 was the third Hampshire January record. Individuals showing the characteristics of the race *leucorhoa* — the Greenland Wheatear — which breeds in north-east Canada and the Faeroes, were reported during 2000–2012, eg two in late April, four during early–mid-May, singletons in mid-August and mid-September and five in October, of which three were on 17th in 2007. It must be noted, however, that birds which breed in Iceland and the Faeroes are intermediate between nominate *oenanthe* and *leucorhoa* (Vaurie 1959) while identification is not straightforward, even in the hand and especially in autumn (see Svensson 1992).

Dunnock *Prunella modularis*
Common, a resident and autumn passage migrant
'Very common resident' (K&C).

During the CBC, up to seven territories were occupied (in 1998) at Normandy Farm and up to five territories (in 1977) at Salterns. Following a series of cold winters during the 1980s/90s, county-wide decreases were not reflected on the NW Solent where Normandy Farm's breeding population remained at five pairs in 1981 and 1982, increased from three pairs in 1984 to five pairs in 1985 and from two pairs in 1986 to five pairs in 1987.

At Salterns, three pairs in 1981 were followed by a blank in 1982, though three pairs nested in four seasons during 1994–1999.

Post-BoH, autumn influxes at Keyhaven/Pennington Marshes were indicated by counts of 15 on 23 September 2001 and 25 on 8 September 2002.

House Sparrow *Passer domesticus*
Common, a resident and spring and autumn passage migrant
'Abundant resident' (K&C).

Few data were available, but this mainly sedentary species presumably remained a common resident on the NW Solent throughout the twentieth century. During the CBC, up to six pairs nested (in 1988) at Normandy Farm and 14 pairs (in 1976) at Salterns: the Farm's population declined to a single territory in 1999, though breeding had ceased at Salterns by 1988.

Other available 1950–1992 records involved a total of 23 individuals that flew over Hurst Spit during 22 September–22 October 1962; those included nine that flew east, from south, on 7 October and eight that flew east on 22 October.

Post-BoH, autumn gatherings at Keyhaven included 100 at New Lane on 6 August 2001 and 250, the largest flock recorded in Hampshire since August 1998, on 24 August 2011. Though possibly overlooked, they were uncommon in the vicinity of Hurst Castle/Spit, where a female or juvenile was present on 13 October 2001 and on the grazing marshes, where one flew north over Pennington Butts on 26 March 2003 and three (two females and a juvenile) were reported on Keyhaven Marshes on 13 July 2006.

Tree Sparrow *Passer montanus*
Scarce, a spring and autumn passage migrant and winter visitor
'Generally considered a resident species but we have no information as to its nesting in the parish' (K&C).

Few data were available post-1945, though it was considered scarce at Milford-on-Sea in 1946 and one near Lymington on 21 October 1952 was the first encountered by Cohen in that area in ten years watching. Though one or two occurred during April/May, nesting was not proved and the breeding status of this bird remained an enigma. As a predominately winter visitor, peak numbers occurred during 1976/77. Disregarding a flock of 120 at Sowley in January 1977 that was possibly outside the recording area, a gathering on Manor Farm (Keyhaven) increased from 60 on 31 October to 190 on 11 December and to 200 during 8–22 January, then decreased to 60 on 21 February and to 18 on 5 March; the last was a an isolated flock of 30 during 17–23 April. Others were 40 at Hurst Spit during cold weather on 9 January 1960, one at Tanners Lane on 13 January 1963 and eight on Pennington Marshes on 17 December 1967.

In autumn, singletons flew south-east at Hurst Spit on 22 October 1962, east at Keyhaven on 7 October 1972 and east at Pennington Marshes on 14 October 1979, while six flew east at Keyhaven on 14 October 1972 and 11 were grounded there on 12 October 1971.

Post-BoH, this bird became a rare visitor and the only reported NW Solent records were three at Keyhaven Marshes on 15 August 1998 and singletons that arrived from the north-west at Hurst Spit and landed in fields at New Lane on 23 October 2005, flew south-west over Salterns on 22 March 2010 and south-west at New Lane (Keyhaven) on 23 September 2011.

Yellow Wagtail *Motacilla flava flavissima*
Formerly common, has bred, a spring and autumn passage migrant
'Regular summer migrant, chiefly seen on the spring and autumn migration' (K&C).

The Yellow Wagtail, perhaps surprisingly, was rarely known to nest on the Keyhaven/Normandy Farm grazing marshes. Breeding occurred just thrice, post-1950, in 1966 when two pairs nested, one male of which showed characteristics of a Blue-headed Wagtail (qv) in 1968 when a pair nested at Pennington Marshes and in 1987 when a pair that fledged at least two young, was the sole NW Solent breeding record during the Atlas Survey. Those recorded during the CBC, in 1981 and 1983/84, were almost certainly transients. Unmated males were recorded on a number of occasions and included singletons at Pennington Marshes on 3 June 1977 and at Keyhaven Marshes during 7–13 June 1981.

As a regular spring passage migrant, it occurred during 31 March (in 1990)–31 May (in 1974), but the first usually arrived during the second week of April. With the exception of 32 that arrived off the sea at Hurst spit on 3 May 1980 (when an exceptional 97 were recorded at Titchfield Haven) day-totals rarely attained double-figures, eg 12 at Keyhaven on 16 April 1988.

Yellow Wagtail.
Oxey Marshes

Return passage began in July and peaked during late August– early September. Pre-roost gatherings often exceeded 100 and included 250 at Keyhaven on 2 September 1962, 200 on 3/4 September 1976 and 150 on 27 August 1990. Migrants that flew south over Hurst Castle included 230 on 27 August 1960, 150 on 10 September 1961 and 100 (in one flock) on 27 August 1971. A dozen October records, the last of which was at Keyhaven on 22nd in 1988, included a group of 12 on Pennington Marshes on 3rd in 1982.

There was one record that suggested wintering, ie one with Meadow Pipits at Keyhaven Marshes, during very cold weather, on 16 January 1985.

Post-BoH, breeding was not proved, but a female was on Keyhaven/Pennington Marshes during 5–22 June 2010. Spring passage took place during 21 March (in 1998 and 2003)–29 May (in 2007). The highest day-count involved 17 that flew east at Pennington Marshes on 19 April 1996, while the season-maximum, ie 39 that flew north at Hurst Spit during 15 April–6 May 2007, was a significant NW Solent spring-total.

High counts at Keyhaven/Hurst Spit in August were 112 that flew south on 1st in 2000, 134 on 25th in 1999 and 120 on 25th in 1998. Some 130 individuals were reported in October, of which no fewer than 49 occurred on 7th in 1998; the latest was a singleton on 1 November 1998.

Blue-headed Wagtail *Motacilla flava flava*
Rare visitor, a spring and autumn passage migrant, has occurred in summer
Individuals showing characteristics of this race (all males unless otherwise stated) were at Keyhaven/Oxey Marshes, ie in 1966 when paired with a female Yellow Wagtail, on 16 July 1970, on 7 May 1994, during 2–26 May 1995, on 30 July 1995, in song on 14 April 1996, on 7 September 1996, on 29 April and 10 May 1999, a female on 21 May 2000, on 20 May 2004 and two, in 2013, on 27/28 April, on 29 April and on 31 August.

Citrine Wagtail *Motacilla citreola*
Rare, an autumn vagrant; it breeds mainly Asia but increasingly west to Baltic States and central Europe and winters in Iran, the Indian sub-continent and south-east Asia

A first-winter at Pennington Marshes during 7-9 September 2003 was the fifth county record.

The Hampshire total to 2015 was five individuals.

Grey Wagtail *Motacilla cinerea*
Common, a spring and autumn passage migrant and winter visitor

'Regular autumn and winter migrant, so far as this parish is concerned, though nesting in many parts of the British Isles' (K&C).

There were no confirmed breeding records for the recording area, but during the Atlas Survey it possibly nested at Lower Pennington.

Those present in early March had possibly over-wintered, but five spring migrants flew north at Hurst Spit/ Normandy Farm during 17 March (in 1973)–24 April (in 1988) and one flew south on 1 May 1976. Others during April/May and suggestive of spring migration were at Keyhaven/Pennington Marshes on 20 April 1989, 16 May 1974 and 7 May 1978. Individuals in late June, eg at Salterns on 21st in 1977, on 30th in 1981, one that flew east over Normandy Farm on 18th in 1979, one at the Farm on 21st in 1980 and at Tanners Lane on 28th in 2006, were difficult to categorise, but were perhaps, indicative of post-breeding dispersal of the New Forest population.

Those that flew over the marshes in an easterly or south-easterly direction during 21 June (in 1976)–16 November (in 1988) included seven on 9 September 1973 and six flew north-east on 10 September 1979.

Two distinct peaks occurred, ie during 26 August–28 September and during 6–19 October, though other than 12 at Keyhaven/Pennington Marshes on 28 September 1982, day-maxima barely attained double-figures. Up to 12 at a Keyhaven roost on 12 January 1990, was the winter day-maximum.

Post-BoH, spring passage was confined to singletons that flew north at Hurst Spit on 7 March 2004 and on 7 May 2006 and grounded individuals at Oxey Marshes during 8–13 March 2006, at Normandy Farm on 1st and 16 April and on 24 May, in 2007 and two at Keyhaven on 5 June 2009, were also probably in that category.

Autumn migrants included 15 that flew east at Pennington Marshes on 9 September 2000 and 11, which included a group of nine that flew south on 28 August 2007. Many occurred during 2005, ie at least 39 flew south during 8 September–7 October. Other than 12 in a reed-filled ditch at Keyhaven on 12 January 1990, winter day-totals did not exceed two.

Pied Wagtail *Motacilla alba yarrellii*
Common, a resident, spring and autumn passage migrant and winter visitor

'Common resident. Large numbers of these birds arrive from the continent towards the end of March, but only a few spend the winter with us' (K&C).

Bred regularly within the recording area, eg in the Normandy Farm barns and on small vessels moored in Keyhaven harbour. During the CBC, up to two pairs annually nested at Normandy Farm and at Salterns.

This bird regularly occurred in modest numbers as a spring passage migrant and post-1960, grounded groups of up to 15 were frequently recorded with White Wagtails (qv). They were also sometimes reported in flight over the area, eg six flew in off the sea at Hurst Spit on 20 March 1976.

Autumn migration took place mostly during late September–late October, most notably on 7 October 1962 when 215 flew south-east at Hurst Spit.

Winter roosts, such as that at Keyhaven, usually held no more than 50 individuals.

Post-BoH, a mere 174, which included a day-maximum of ten on 1 March 2002, arrived off the sea during 1 March (in 2009)–23 April (in 2008).

The autumn day-peak was 315 that flew south-east on 3 October 2002. A season–maximum of 750 flew over the area during October 2003, of which no fewer than 200 flew east on 3rd. An autumn roost in greenhouses at Efford, peaked at 300 individuals on 3 November 1996, but no winter roost was reported.

White Wagtail *Motacilla alba*
Common, a spring and autumn passage migrant and also occurred in winter

'Summer migrant but we have no record of its nesting at Milford-on-Sea' (K&C).

The NW Solent was a favoured Hampshire spring locality. K&C were obviously familiar with this bird; also six males were reported at Keyhaven on 28 April 1936. During 1961–1992, passage took place between 13 March (in 1983) and 5 June (in 1967) when the peak migration period occurred during 15–28 April. Double-figure day-counts were attained in eight seasons and maxima (all in April) included 30 at Keyhaven/Pennington Marshes on 20th in 1966, 22 on 23rd in 1989 and a group of 21 on 17th in 1983.

Selected autumn records were three at Sturt Pond on 8 September 1991 and eight at Pennington Marshes on 11 October 1992.

Post-BoH, spring passage was reported during 5 March (in 1994 and 2008)–21 May (in 2008) and peaked in the same week (15–21 April) as pre-1992, though day-maxima were only 17 on 14 April 1996 and 16 at Keyhaven/Pennington Marshes on 15 April 1993.

Autumn migration occurred during 18 August (in 2000)–25 October (in 2005); experienced observers reported 22 on 23 September 1998.

Richard's Pipit *Anthus richardi*
Rare, a spring, autumn and early winter visitor; breeds Siberia east to Pacific
(remarkably, small numbers winter as far west as Middle East/Iberia/NW Africa)

Fifteen records (all singletons) occurred at Keyhaven/Pennington Marshes during 17 September (in 2005)– 9 March (in 2014) in September (5), October (3), November (6) and March (1). Those on 1 November 1969, on 14 October and 15–21 November 1970, on 3 November 1974, 1 October 1975 and 21 September 1980, were the third–fifth and eighth–tenth county records.

The Hampshire total to 2015 was 40 individuals.

Tawny Pipit *Anthus campestris*
Rare, a spring and autumn vagrant; it breeds Iberia/Maghreb north to the Baltic and east to China,
those that breed in western Europe winter in the Sahel region of Africa

Three records: one at Pennington Marshes on 3 September 1972 was the fifth county record and others were at Keyhaven on 1 June 2008 and at Keyhaven Marshes on 26 August 2010.

The Hampshire total to 2015 was 18 individuals.

Tree Pipit *Anthus trivialis*
Common but declining, a spring and autumn passage migrant

'Regular summer migrant. May be recognised by its habit of singing in the air, as it descends upon a tree or a telegraph wire' (K&C).

Few Tree Pipits were recorded on spring migration. Of 40 individuals during 23 March (in 1975)–5 May (1962) most were reported in April, though the day-maximum of eight occurred on 3 May 1980.

It was more frequent on autumn passage. During 19 July (in 1992)–22 October (in 1988) at least 445 were reported; those included 30 that flew south at Keyhaven on 16 August 1969 and 80 that flew south on 16 August 1971.

Post-BoH, by which time the active observer force had greatly increased, only 36 Tree Pipits were reported in spring, all during 19 March (in 2001)–13 May (in 2006) and of which a day-peak of nine occurred on 25 April 2006.

In autumn, 487 individuals were reported during 1 August (in 2005)–23 October (in 2006); no fewer than 65 departed south and south-east at Keyhaven/Hurst Spit on 14 August 2011.

A decline in numbers and range of the British breeding population since the Atlas was most pronounced in the south-east, central and northern regions.

Meadow Pipit *Anthus pratensis*
Common, a resident and spring and autumn passage migrant

'Common resident, largely increased by migration during March. Utters a similar song to the last, but usually rises from the ground and returns to it' (K&C).

The Meadow Pipit breeds on the grazing marshes, at one or two saltmarsh locations, around Hurst Castle and in the recording area's hinterland. During the CBC, it nested annually on Normandy Farm (maximum of 18 territories in 1976) and at Salterns (maximum of six pairs in 1992). During the Atlas Survey, breeding was confirmed at Hurst Castle, Keyhaven, Pennington Marshes and Waterford, but has now decreased as a breeding species throughout its NW Solent range.

A protracted spring movement often began in late February and continued into the third week of May. Migration watches during 1966–1992, revealed predominately northerly movements on a broad front. Day-counts of 200 or more included 300 on 2 April 1969, at least 312 that flew east on 31 March 1990 and 500 that flew north at Hurst Spit/Pennington Marshes on 7 April 1974. Grounded flocks seldom exceeded 50, though 100 were on Milford-on-Sea cliff-top on 12 March 1972 and an exceptional 250 at Normandy Farm on 8 April 1984.

During 1966–1992, a small autumn passage was evident, mostly during mid-September–mid-October, exceptionally into early November. The largest day-total was 250 that flew east at Salterns on 10 October 1979, while grounded flocks at Keyhaven/Pennington Marshes attained 500 in September and October 1974 on 29th and 6th (during SW/W gales) respectively, 300 on 28 September 1975 and 300 on 4 October 1982.

Post-BoH, the Meadow Pipit apparently became more numerous during spring and autumn migrations, though was probably under-recorded during previous decades. Spring-totals in excess of 1,000 were reported during at least 11 seasons, eg 6,453 were logged during 5 March–2 May 2012 and 4,250 during 10 March–1 May 2007, with a day-maximum of 1,900 that flew north at Hurst Spit on 10 April 2004. Autumn migration included season-maxima of 4,200 during 9 September–12 October 2004, of which 3,640 flew north at Hurst Spit on 24 September and 3,700 during 12 September–15 October 2010, of which 3,000 flew north on 12 September.

Rock Pipit *Anthus petrosus*
Common, a resident, autumn passage migrant and winter visitor

'Occasional visitor. No doubt this bird visits Milford-on-Sea occasionally in winter, as it nests commonly on the opposite shores of the Isle of Wight' (K&C).

The Rock Pipit traditionally nested in and around Hurst Castle, where at least eight pairs were resident in 1963, eight in 1970, up to seven during 1971–1983 and up to three during 1984–1992. One or two pairs also nested on the Milford-on-Sea cliffs, on Hurst Spit at Cut Bridge and occasionally in the Pennington Marshes' seawall.

It was also an autumn passage migrant and winter visitor, most numerous in the latter season, with day-maxima of 37 at Keyhaven/Pennington Marshes on 11 December 1977 and 32 at Sturt Pond/Hurst Castle on 19 December 1987.

Post-BoH, up to two pairs nested on Milford-on-Sea cliffs, one or two pairs between Milford-on-Sea and Cut Bridge and up to six pairs at Hurst. Also, two (an adult and a juvenile) were recorded at Tanners Lane on 3 July 2002.

Winter day-maxima included 21 at Milford-on-Sea/Hurst Spit on 13 December 1997, 21 Milford-on-Sea/Hurst Castle on 14/15 December 2000 and 25 at Pennington/Oxey Marshes on 26 October 2002.

Rock Pipits that showed characteristics of the Fenno-Scandian race *littoralis* — Scandinavian Rock Pipit — were rarely recorded in Hampshire prior to 1971. The first on the NW Solent was reported on 12 March 1993, followed by at least 43 during 1994–2012 between extreme dates of 29 November (in 2007) and 4 April (in 2005) and which included a day-maximum of eight on Normandy Farm on 21 February 2007. However, Svensson (1992) noted that racial variation was 'Clinal and slight' and that the two subspecies were 'often inseparable.'

Rock Pipit. Cut Bridge

Water Pipit *Anthus spinoletta*
Scarce, a spring and autumn passage migrant and winter visitor; it breeds locally in southern Europe and winters to south Asia

One on Pennington Marshes on 14 November 1951 was the first record for Hampshire (BoH). It was known in the county mainly as a spring passage migrant before observers became aware of its winter status. NW Solent totals were difficult to assess, but during 1957–1992 at least 47 were recorded during 27 October (in 1981)–21 April (in 1990) in October (2), November (1), December (1), February (3), March (12) and April (21). An additional seven at Keyhaven included at least two in spring.

Post-BoH, a greatly increased observer force reported 282 during 7 October (in 2005)–18 April (in 2004) in October (16), November (27), December (30), January (22), February (52), March (90) and April (45). The day-maximum was 15 on 25 March 2006 and other double-figure counts were 12 on 7 March 2009, 11 on 29 December 2001 and 9 February 2012 and ten on 24 March 2010.

Chaffinch *Fringilla coelebs*
Common, a resident, spring and autumn passage migrant and winter visitor
'Very common resident' (K&C).

The Chaffinch remained a very common resident. During the CBC, season-maxima were 16 pairs on Normandy Farm during 1985–87 inclusive and eight pairs at Salterns in 1987.

During 1960–1992, it occurred in unexceptional numbers as a spring, autumn and winter (cold-weather) passage migrant, eg 35 flew east at Salterns on 9 March 1980, 487 flew north-west at Keyhaven on 11 October 1980 and 40 flew north at Hurst Castle on 30 December 1962.

Post-BoH, ten males were on territory on Normandy Farm in 2010.

A modest spring passage during 10 March (in 2005)–25 April (in 2008) included light northerly movements at Hurst Spit, eg nine during 7th–24 April 2006 and ten on 25 March 2012.

It was more numerous on autumn passage. Twelve hundred and sixty migrants recorded over the marshes during 18 September (in 2005)–21 November (in 2010) included 557 during 29 September–28 October 2012 of which 207 that flew north on 23 October. Winter flocks included 87 at Lymore on 13 December 2001, 220 at New Lane on 15 November 2007 and 200 there on 28 November 2008.

Brambling *Fringilla montifringilla*
Common, a spring and autumn passage migrant and winter visitor; it breeds in northern Eurasia and winters south to southern Europe and central Asia
'Winter migrant, generally to be seen in large numbers when there is a heavy crop of beech-mast' (K&C).

Available data for 1954–72 revealed the Brambling as a frequent winter visitor, with maxima of 65 at Hurst in early January 1963 and up to 100 at Keyhaven on 21 February 1972. In the 1950s/1960s it was often found feeding on Iley Point foreshore with Chaffinches, Greenfinches, Yellowhammers, Cirl Buntings and Reed Buntings; up to 20 were there during late January–early February 1954.

It was scarce in spring, the latest being a singleton at Oxey Barn on 23 March 1974.

The Brambling was an autumn passage migrant during 8 October (in 1986)–24 November (in 1981), though the day-maximum was just nine on Pennington Marshes on 24 November 1981.

Post-BoH, singletons were on Normandy Farm on 4 April 2006 and 15 April 2008. It was again more numerous in autumn and early winter. Three hundred and thirty flew over Hurst Spit and the grazing marshes during 26 September (in 2006)–4 December (in 2011) of which an annual maximum of 88 that flew north during 26 September–2 November 2006 included 67 on 14 October. Off-passage October migrants included 19 at Keyhaven Marshes on 10 October 1998 and during December, up to 25 were in Lymore Lane fields on 22nd in 2001.

Greenfinch *Chloris chloris*
Common, a resident, spring and autumn passage migrant and winter visitor
'Very common resident' (K&C).

The Greenfinch remained a common resident, nesting throughout the recording area, though not around Hurst Castle. During the CBC, up to eight territories were occupied (in 2000) at Normandy Farm and up to four pairs (in 1977) nested at Salterns. It was grossly under-recorded during the 1950s/60s, the few available data included at least three breeding pairs in Keyhaven village in 1969, a flock of 15–20 at Keyhaven on 7 May 1956 and day-totals of 21 and 27 that flew north-west at Hurst Castle on 15 and 28 October 1960 respectively.

During 1975–1992, it was recorded mostly as an autumn migrant, when grounded flocks included up to 60 at Hurst Castle on 31 October 1977, 100 at Normandy Farm on 25 October 1983, 50 at Pennington Marshes on 6 November 1983 and 80 on Manor Farm on 3 November 1985.

Post-BoH, 12 pairs nested at Normandy Farm in 2010, 11 pairs bred at Oxey Marshes/Normandy Farm in 2009 and eight at Oxey Marshes in 2010.

A few diurnal spring passage migrants were reported, eg 19 flew north and nine south at Hurst Spit on four dates during 6 March (in 2004)–28 April (in 2006).

It was frequently observed in autumn and 1,122 were reported during 11 September (in 2009)–15 November (in 2003) of which 635 flew eastwards. Grounded flocks included 150 on Keyhaven Marshes' seawall on 2 December 1994, 200 on Pennington Marshes on 19 November 2010 and 350 in Lymore Lane fields on 10 November 2001.

Serin *Serinus serinus*

Rare, a spring and autumn visitor; it breeds in NW Africa, continental Europe, rarely in England and Asia Minor

Seven records involved probably six individuals, ie a male in song at Keyhaven then flew eastwards, on 2 May 1991, at Hurst Spit on 11 April 1999, east at Keyhaven Marshes on 20 October 2001, at Keyhaven on 11 July 2003, north at Milford-on-Sea on 10 May 2006 and one that flew east at Milford-on-Sea on 27 April 2007 was possibly the same as at Normandy Farm on 5 May.

The Hampshire total to 2015 was 45 individuals.

Goldfinch *Carduelis carduelis*

Common, a resident, summer resident, spring and autumn passage migrant and winter visitor

'Common resident and very largely increased during the past twenty years' (K&C).

Goldfinches regularly occurred in Keyhaven hamlet, at Salterns and throughout the NW Solent recording area during 1966–1992. The local breeding population was considered to be a component of the 80 per cent of the British stock that winters on the near continent. During the CBC, up to two pairs nested (1977, 1995 and 1998/99) at Normandy Farm and three pairs (in 1976, 1984/85 and 1993) at Salterns.

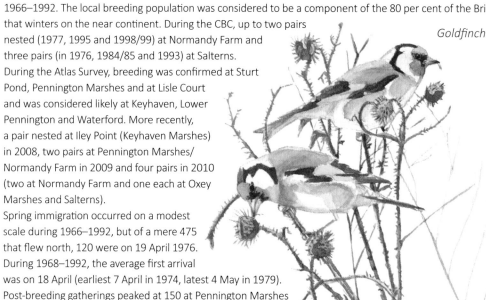

Goldfinch

During the Atlas Survey, breeding was confirmed at Sturt Pond, Pennington Marshes and at Lisle Court and was considered likely at Keyhaven, Lower Pennington and Waterford. More recently, a pair nested at Iley Point (Keyhaven Marshes) in 2008, two pairs at Pennington Marshes/ Normandy Farm in 2009 and four pairs in 2010 (two at Normandy Farm and one each at Oxey Marshes and Salterns).

Spring immigration occurred on a modest scale during 1966–1992, but of a mere 475 that flew north, 120 were on 19 April 1976. During 1968–1992, the average first arrival was on 18 April (earliest 7 April in 1974, latest 4 May in 1979). Post-breeding gatherings peaked at 150 at Pennington Marshes on 25 August 1984. Autumn passage, also unexceptional by Hampshire standards, involved only 2,650, most of which flew east, during 29 September (in 1980)–12 November (in 1983). The largest day-count was 525 on 13 October 1972, but 450 flew east at Normandy Farm in one hour on 17 October 1988 (cf Siskin). Grounded flocks included 100 at Lower Pennington on 2 October 1976 and Pennington Marshes on 21 September 1985.

Post-BoH, a grand total of 1,870, of which 334 flew north-east at Hurst Spit on 1 April 2001, were reported during 10 February (in 2008)–10 May (in 2008). Autumn/early winter passage was much heavier and 10,600 were reported during 13 September (in 1998)–30 November (in 2012) with a maximum day-count of 736 that flew south-west on 21 October 2007. The largest grounded flocks were 614 at Pennington Marshes on 10 October 2010 and c.1,000 feeding on hemp seed at Walhampton on 21 October 2010.

Siskin *Carduelis spinus*

Common, a spring and autumn passage migrant and winter visitor

'Winter migrant, but not common' (K&C).

There were just two spring records during 1966–1992, ie three on 4 April 1975 and one that flew west at Salterns on 8 March 1980.

A majority occurred in autumn when a total of 535 during 9 September (in 1986)–27 October (in 1974) included 120 (a day-maximum) that flew east in one hour at Normandy Farm on 17 October 1988. Few were recorded during winter, eg 27 at Pennington marshes on 21 December 1975 was the largest reported day-count.

Post-BoH, the Siskin was more frequently reported in spring and 94 during 5 March (in 2012)–22 May (in 2009) included 24 that flew north at Hurst Spit in April, ie 12 on 9th in 2004 and 12 on 5th in 2008.

In autumn/early winter, 3,890 individuals were reported during 23 August (in 2012)–18 November (in 2012) of which a season- maximum of 1,133 in 2008 included a day-peak of 165 in flight over Normandy Farm on 16 September; only five other day-counts exceeded 100. An additional 427 that included day-maxima of 50 at Keyhaven on 2 January 2006 and 47 at Normandy Farm on 4 November 2008 were reported during November–February.

Linnet *Carduelis cannabina*

Common, a resident, spring and autumn passage migrant and winter visitor

'Common resident, especially in the gorse-brakes along the coast' (K&C).

The few available NW Solent data for the first half of the twentieth century included a count of 100 on the marshes in September 1946. Post-1950, the breeding population appeared to be composed principally, if not entirely, of summer residents. During the CBC, up to 18 pairs nested at Normandy Farm in 1985/86 and up to five pairs at Salterns in 1992. During the Atlas Survey, breeding was confirmed at Hurst Castle, Sturt Pond, Keyhaven, Lower Pennington, Pennington Marshes, Waterford and Lisle Court and post-breeding gatherings included 100 at Keyhaven/Pennington Marshes in July 1967.

During 1955–1992, a total of 13,000 were reported, of which 2,000 during 20 March (in 1977)–17 May (in 1978) included a day-maximum of 341, which flew north–north-east on 19 April 1976.

In autumn, some 10,000 occurred between 13 August (in 1983) and 26 October (in 1991); of these, 9,100 that over-flew the marshes included 4,300 during 5–31 October 1992 and a day-peak of 2,250 that flew east on 12 October 1972. An off-passage flock of 300 was at Efford Rubbish Tip on 9 October 1976. Presumably much under-recorded in winter, just 125 that included 80 on Normandy Farm on 27 November 1973, were reported during November–February.

Post-BoH, breeding-season surveys indicated a decline, eg at Hurst Castle, where up to four pairs nested in the 1990s, just a single pair did so in 2007.

No fewer than 25,500 were reported in spring, of which 7,445 during 1 March (in 2012)–12 May (in 2006) included a day-maximum of c.1,000 that flew north on 11 March 2001.

An autumn-total of at least 6,200 flew over Hurst Spit and the marshes during 29 August (in 2003)–11 November (2007). A significant number, ie 810 that flew south–south-west, occurred during 2–31 October 2006, with a day-peak of 469 on 14 October 2007. Off-passage gatherings included c.1,000 on farmland on 3 October 1993.

Twite *Carduelis flavirostris*

Scarce, a spring and autumn passage migrant and winter visitor

The first for the NW Solent were three that flew east at Hurst Castle on 20 October 1958. During 1959–1992, 360 occurred during 3 October (in 1995)–17 March (in 1976) in October (17), November (94), December (51), January (176), February (9) and March (13).

Wintering occurred during 4 November 1974–9 April 1975 with day-maximum of 60 on 9 January 1975 and during 30 November 1975–25 January 1976 with a day-maximum of 50 on 17 January. A group of 13 on 17 March 1976 were probably newly-arrived passage migrants. Two on Normandy Farm on 28 December was the only late-year Hampshire record in 1986.

Post-BoH, 49 were reported during 3 October (in 1997)–9 March (in 1996) in October (6), November (23), December (3), January (14) and March (3). During the winter of 1997/98, records spanned 1 November–21 February with day-maxima of six on 1st and 3 November, that of 1998/99 from 27 November–23 January with a day-maximum of ten on 27 November and that of 1999/00 during 4 November–23 February with day-maxima of two on 4 November and 16 January. This bird became less frequent post-2003; the last was a singleton on 17 December 2009.

Lesser Redpoll *Carduelis cabaret*
Common, a spring and autumn passage migrant and winter visitor, also occurred in summer
'Resident, occasionally nesting, but constantly to be seen in flocks among the alders and birches in winter' (K&C). Post-1960, the Lesser Redpoll was predominately an autumn passage migrant and winter visitor and though not proved to nest on the NW Solent, a few also occurred in spring and summer. A total of 953 were reported during 10 July (in 1971)–7 June (in 1988) in July (2), August (2), September (76), October (575), November (264), December (10,) January (6), February (1), April (4), May (12) and June (1). Of the 653 in flight over the marshes, 429 occurred during October, of which 124 flew east during 5th–31st in 1972; day-maxima were 50 on 5 October 1971 and 50 that flew south-east on 9 November 1980. However, during a substantial easterly finch movement over Normandy Farm on 17 October 1988, only 19 were identified as Redpolls.
Post-BoH, 716 were reported during 18 September (in 2005)–10 January (in 2003) in September (18), October (461), November (226), December (9) and January (2). Of these, 144 flew east, in September (5), October (85), November (50) and December (4) with monthly day-maxima of two on 19 September 2005, 13 on 17 October 2009, 31 on 5 November 2011 and three on 14 December 2009. Up to 60 were grounded at Pennington Marshes during 5–31 October 2003 and a solitary individual flew east at Normandy Farm on 1 April 2009.

Common Crossbill *Loxia curvirostra*
Scarce, an all-season passage migrant
'Occasional visitor. A large immigration of these birds commenced in July 1909 and continued over the following year, when many nests were found in many parts of England, including the New Forest district' (K&C).
During 1963–1992, a total of 37 individuals were recorded, in flight, in June (3), July (24), August (5), October (1), November (3) and January (1); the day-maximum of 12 flew east at Keyhaven on 17 July 1972.
Post-BoH, 122 occurred during 3 July (in 2005)–18 April (in 2007) in July (8), August (12), September (11), October (72), November (18) and April (1) and the day-maximum of 20 flew east at Keyhaven on 23 October 1997. An additional 27 individuals at Milford-on-Sea (four in July, 11 in September, six in October and six in December) were outside the recording area.

Bullfinch *Pyrrhula pyrrhula*
Common, a resident, spring and autumn passage-migrant and winter visitor
'Common resident' (K&C).
During the CBC, breeding was proved at Normandy Farm in 1976 (where it was also recorded during 1982–88 and 1995–97) and in most seasons at Salterns, where two to three pairs were the usual complement. During the Atlas Survey, breeding was confirmed at Keyhaven, Pennington Marshes, Waterford and Lisle Court and was considered likely at Sturt Pond, Lower Pennington and Pitts Deep.
Post-BoH, two or three territories were occupied annually at Oxey Marshes/Normandy Farm. The largest counts involved 13 at Lower Pennington on 1 November 1998 and ten at Normandy Farm/Oxey Marshes on 2 January 2006. Ten at Keyhaven Marshes on 28 August 2010 was described as 'a noticeable arrival', but as British Bullfinches are generally sedentary, it is unlikely that they had travelled from far afield. Others included singletons that flew high over Iley Point on 18 March 2003 and over Normandy Farm/Oxey Marshes on 25 March 2005 and doubletons that flew eastwards at Normandy Farm on 15th and 19 November 2010, were also most likely to refer to local, dispersing individuals.

Hawfinch *Coccothraustes coccothraustes*
Rare, an all-season visitor
'Resident, but generally overlooked on account of its secretive habits' (K&C).
As in K&C's day, this chunky but elusive finch probably remained largely undetected, with just five records that involved nine individuals and all since 2000, ie a pair in Normandy Lane on 18 June 2000, singletons that flew north-east at Normandy Farm on 1 November 2010, east at Normandy Farm on 27 August 2011 and off the sea at Hurst Spit on 6 May 2012 and four that flew east at the Spit on 25 October 2012.

Snow Bunting *Plectrophenax nivalis*

Scarce, a spring and autumn passage migrant and winter visitor; it breeds in northern Eurasia and northern N America and winters south to central Europe, central Asia and southern US

The first record for the NW Solent was one at Pennington Marshes on 22 December 1952. Between 1953 and 1992, a total of at least 99 were reported during 3 October (in 1975)–3 March (1971) in October (7), November (35), December (22), January (18), February (16) and March (1). They included a day-maximum of 15, of which 14 flew east and another was on the ground, at Sturt Pond on 23 February 1986 and five on Hurst Spit on 12 November 1960. At Pennington Marshes, up to three, present during 3 October–31 December 1975, decreased to two during 1 January–15 February 1976.

Post-BoH, a total of 51 were reported during 8 October (in 2006)–3 April (in 2000) in October (11), November (19), December (15), January (3), February (1), March (1) and April (1). One at Pennington Marshes on 5 November 2007 was observed to fly south towards the Isle of Wight, while a female wintered at Hurst Spit/Pennington Marshes during 31 October 1999–3 April 2000.

Snow Bunting

Lapland Bunting *Calcarius lapponicus*

Scarce, a spring and autumn passage migrant and winter visitor; it breeds in N Eurasia, and northern N America and winters south to central Europe, central Asia and southern US

Though unusual in Hampshire in March, one, together with five Wheatears, reported on the seawall near Lymington on 31st in 1949 (*Proc.*) was overlooked, ignored, or rejected by previous authors, but is listed here for completeness. The first fully authenticated records for the NW Solent occurred in 1961, when singletons were at Keyhaven on 24 September (the tenth county record) and on 12 October. During 1962–1992, 19 occurred during 9 September (in 1970)–14 March (in 1976) in September (5), October (3), November (2), December (4), January (4) and February (1) of which one apparently remained at Pennington Marshes during 13 December 1975–14 March 1976. Three reported at Pennington Marshes on 8 March 1969 (HBR) were considered to have been insufficiently documented so are excluded from this summary.

Post-BoH, c.76 were reported during 4 October (in 2006)– 27 March (in 2004) in October (7), November (60), December (1), January (4), February (3) and March (1); up to three were present during 17 November 2007–15 March 2008.

Arrivals in the Hebrides during early September 2010 heralded a major influx into Britain and two were reported in Hampshire on 12 September. The first on the NW Solent were two at Keyhaven on 19 September, but numbers rose to an unprecedented 34 by 24 November then to 56, a county record, by 29 November. Many remained into 2011 and 21 were reported on 1 January, but numbers then dwindled and the last were singletons in February, at New Lane on 20th and one that flew north at Keyhaven Marshes on 24th.

Yellowhammer *Emberiza citrinella*
Formerly common, now scarce, a resident, spring and autumn passage migrant and winter visitor
'Very common resident' (K&C).
Yellowhammers nested at Keyhaven in the mid-1960s. During the CBC, up to eight territories were occupied at Normandy Farm in 1980, but just two during 1997–2000. At Salterns, five occupied territories in 1989 fell to one in 1997. During the Atlas Survey, breeding was confirmed at Sturt Pond, Keyhaven, Lower Pennington and Woodside and was considered likely at Lisle Court.
Flocks usually contained fewer than 30 individuals, but at Keyhaven/Pennington Marshes, 60 were reported on 31 December 1966, 50 on 9 January 1971, 150 at on 20 November 1983 and 125 on 8 March 1986; also, 40 were on Normandy Farm on 29 December 1973.

Yellowhammer

Post-BoH, breeding territories were occupied at Keyhaven Marshes (one in 1996) Pennington Marshes (three in 2003) Oxey Marshes (one in 1999) Salterns (one in 1996 and 2007) and Normandy Farm (up to two during 1997–2000 and in 2006); none were proved to breed post-2007.
Only an additional 24 individuals were reported, ie in March, singletons flew east on 2nd in 2009 and 23rd in 2011, in April, one flew north on 8th in 2000, in September, singletons flew east on 1st in 2010 and west on 24th in 2011, in October, two flew north-east on 21st in 2003 and in November, one flew west on 13th in 2005. A flock of 14 was at Oxey Marshes on 3 December 2001 and two first-winters were at Hurst Spit on 22 October 2012, of which one remained during 23rd–28th.

Cirl Bunting *Emberiza cirlus*
Formerly common resident, now a rare visitor
'Common resident and one of the most characteristic birds of this coast' (K&C).
Judged by the number of references to this bunting during the mid-1930s–early 1950s, the status of the Cirl Bunting on the coastal strip between Milford-on-Sea/ and Colgrims apparently remained stable until the 1950s. At Keyhaven, birds were recorded in October 1935 and September 1936, males in late December 1947 and in April and June/July, in 1951, one on the shore at Pennington Marshes in late January 1937 and fledged young at Milford-on-Sea in late July 1946. They continued to breed at Milford-on-Sea, Keyhaven/Pennington Marshes, Lymington and Pitts Deep during 1953–1963; up to four were on the tide-line at Keyhaven on 1 April 1953. Other than monitoring by one or two pre-1940s 'nest-men' who were well acquainted with this bird, the Cirl Bunting was a prime example of those species (others included Corncrake and Wryneck) that disappeared, without adequate documentation, from under

the noses of post-Second World War Hampshire birdwatchers. It was very scarce on the NW Solent by the late 1950s and just single records in each of the following three decades came to light, ie a male at Keyhaven on 22 June 1966, one at Pennington Marshes on 30 October 1971 and two at Pennington Marshes on 23 September 1984.

Ortolan Bunting *Emberiza hortulana*
Rare, an autumn vagrant; it breeds in continental Europe, where it is in serious decline and east to Mongolia and winters in Europe, except the north, west-central Africa and Arabia

Small numbers of Ortolans occur annually as passage migrants to Britain, particularly in autumn. It is therefore, perhaps surprising that there was just one report for NW Solent, a singleton along the Ancient Highway at Keyhaven on 31 August 1992; it was the fifth county record.

The Hampshire total to 2015 was ten individuals.

Reed Bunting *Emberiza schoeniclus*
Common, a resident, spring and autumn passage migrant and winter visitor

'Resident and nesting in the marshes of Keyhaven. On Feb 9th 1912, Coles saw several flocks of these birds, feeding among the sea wrack along the harbour side of Hurst Beach' (K&C).

During the CBC, up to five territories (in 1985) were occupied at Normandy Farm and up to seven territories (in 1976) at Salterns; a combined maximum was ten territories in 1976 and 1985. During the Atlas Survey, breeding was confirmed at Sturt Pond, Keyhaven, Pennington Marshes, Waterford and Pitts Deep and was considered likely at Lower Pennington and Lisle Court.

Reed Buntings were often found among a mixed flock of finches and other buntings that frequented the Iley Point foreshore during the 1950s and 17 were there on 17 March 1985. Otherwise, 50 or more were on Keyhaven/ Pennington Marshes on 11 January 1967, though largest reported flocks were 60 at Keyhaven on 18 February 1976, 25 at Normandy Farm on 2 December 1975 and 26 at Keyhaven on 19 February 1991.

Post-BoH, one or two pairs continued to nest on the saltings west of Tanner's Lake and up to 15 occupied territories were on the Keyhaven/Normandy Farm grazing marshes in 2002.

Of a total of 59 logged in flight during 2001–2010, 44, of which 25 flew east, were reported during 14/15 October 2006, 12 (six at Keyhaven) flew south on 7 October 2005 and two flew west on 3 November 2009. Day-maxima included pre-roost gatherings of 69 in maize-stubble at Keyhaven on 28 November 2010 and 56 near Sturt Pond on 9 January 2006.

Corn Bunting *Emberiza calandra*
Formerly a common resident and possible migrant, now rare, all-season visitor

'Common resident, especially in the hedge-rows of cultivated land and in the furze-brakes' (K&C).

This bird remained a resident on the NW Solent and during 1966–1988 regularly nested on Milford-on-Sea cliff-top, Saltgrass Lane (Keyhaven), Vidle Van Farm, Manor Farm, Keyhaven/Oxey Marshes and Lower Pennington. The maximum annual NW Solent breeding population was estimated at 10–12 pairs/territories, three or four of those at Saltgrass Lane. During the CBC, occurrences were confined to singing males at Normandy Farm on single dates in May 1984 and March 1985 and at Salterns in May 1988. During the Atlas Survey, breeding was confirmed only at Keyhaven, but was considered likely at Sturt Pond and Lower Pennington. The Hampshire population declined considerably by the early 1990s and the only singing males on the NW Solent during that decade were at Pennington Marshes on 11 March 1990 (the sole record in south-west Hampshire in that year) and at Keyhaven on 3 May 1992. The largest reported groups were: 19 at Keyhaven on 29 December 1989, 16 at Keyhaven/Pennington Marshes on 27 September 1986 and 12 there a week later, 12 at Tanners Lane on 13 January 1963, ten on the Lower Woodside seawall on 14 February 1975 and ten at Keyhaven/Pennington Marshes on 25 September 1986. Occurrences that hinted at immigration included one at Hurst Castle on 10 April 1966, 21 that arrived at Keyhaven, from the direction of Hurst Castle, on 9 October 1977 and one that flew off the sea at Hurst Spit on 9 May 1988.

Post-BoH, it became a rare bird. Just eight records that involved 13 individuals in February (2), April (2), June (1), September (1, October (4) and December (3) included four at Keyhaven Marshes on 1 October 1994, two at Tanners Lane on 20 February 1994 and one on Hurst Spit on 3 December 2008. None were reported during 2009–2015.

Acknowledgements

My gratitude is due, not least for comradeship during a seventy-year ornithological adventure, to: Charlie Bury, George Clay, Barry Poate, Ron Ross, Maurice Townsend and Ken Willers, who were schoolboy companions of late-1940s bird-nesting forays; David and Rosemary Billett, John Bowers, Michael Burnop, Michael Bryant, George Clay (also see above), John Conchie, Cliff Henty, Peter LeBrocq, Graham Rees, Bryan Renyard, John Simons, Bill Truckle, Colin Tubbs and Alan Walker who were members of the Portsmouth Group, which I initially encountered in 1954; Roger Brown, Barry Duffin MBE, Pete Hobby, Len Mummery, Alan Searle, Jenni Tubbs, Diana Westerhoff, Gerald and Don Westerhoff, Jim Williams and Dave Wooldridge, all of whom I initially met during the 1950s/early 1960s and Pete and Mike Combridge, Chris Fox, Owen Haisell, Chris Hardy, Roger Harris, John (Fawley) Jones, Simon King, Royal Navy Captain Leslie Masters and Mrs Beryl (Jimmie) Masters, Captain John Nevitt MC (formerly of the Parachute Regt.) and Mrs Ruth Nevitt, David Peart, Bev Snellgrove, Mike Stewart, Phil Toye and Susan Wood, who all birdwatched at Keyhaven.

I offer my thanks to the following assistant wardens with whom I worked at Keyhaven: Graham Condell, Mike Riddy, Bill Rutherford, Des Sussex, Gordon LePard, Mark Langford and Adrian Clark. I also thank those Hampshire County Council employees who, from time to time, assisted with Lymington–Keyhaven estate-work, particularly Graham Baggs (the Lepe Ranger) as well as Jack McGrath and Dick Nunn who were footpath-maintenance men and among the most amiable and hardest-working individuals I ever encountered. Under the auspices of 1980s Government job-creation initiatives, several Lymington men who included Peter Coleby (the gang's foreman), Martin Cooper and Andy Rutter, also worked on the marshes. One task given the team was to form a low, water-retaining embankment around an area on Pennington Marshes. Together with measures to prevent drainage into the ancient salt-dock, the successful seasonal wetland feature immediately south of Lower Pennington Lane was created, hence my naming it 'Coleby's Pool'. I also valued the support of my Hampshire Wildlife Trust and Hampshire County Council immediate bosses, eg Jim White, Charles Cuthbert, John Davison, George Drye, Bob Chapman and John Maskrey. I am extremely grateful to my successor Pete Durnell and to Owen Haisell, Pete Hobby, Marc Moody, Tim Parminter and Marcus Ward, as well as local fishermen, Chris Cooke of Keyhaven and John Clarke and Roy Jenvey of Lymington, who all continued to share their observations with me and kept me abreast of local ornithological affairs, especially appreciated following my 'retirement' in 2001.

The work was particularly rewarding and due in no small measure to assistance and co-operation by Keyhaven and Milford-on-Sea marshmen and their families, especially Ray and Anne (née Cooke) Perrett and Chris and Celia (née Elford) Cooke, Norman Chambers, Bill Crane (a former Hurst Castle custodian) and his son Sean, also holder of that post and that of keeper of Hurst Light until having to relinquish both positions due to ill-health, Keith Perrett, Ray Pitt, Geoff and Tony Tate, Peter and Ron Wilkins, John (Wiggy) Woolgar and Lymington counterparts, John Clarke, Roy Jenvey, Dave Mitchell and Roy Freeman. Punts and outboard motors were placed at my disposal, much sound advice on local boating and marsh hazards was offered and they were always willing to impart their considerable and invaluable wildlife knowledge, particularly of the marshes' breeding birds and wintering wildfowl. It was always a pleasure to be with them on the marshes and to share their endless, good-natured banter, centred around such topics as local gossip, alleged inability to rise early in the morning, lack of 'proper' full-time employment or comrades' venerable, but much-loved punts and dinghies, one of which was often and irreverently referred to as 'Tar-barrel'. However, one had to be a very close friend to get away with such a gibe, as though a man might make light of derogatory remarks directed at his mother-in-law, woe-betide those who ridicule his boat.

I must also pay tribute to other Milford-on-Sea and Keyhaven residents I encountered during my working life on the west Solent. Though at risk of un-thoughtfully omitting those who warrant inclusion, for which I offer my sincerest apologies, I offer a big thank-you to the following, for their assistance, hospitality or for taking time-out to chat about the area, its wildlife and other sundries: John Berry, Mike and Margaret Busher, the Cecil-Wright family, Bill and Dolly Cooke, Mrs Diana (née Firth) Dickson, Tazeena Firth, Mrs Joan Easton, Christopher Hemmant, Joanna Lowis, Dennis and Audrey (née Prude, a Keyhaven fishing/wildfowling family) Macey, Jack & Nora Mitchell (proprietors of Keyhaven Stores & Post Office), Professor Gerald Smart OBE (Hampshire's Chief Planning Officer during 1963–1975) and Mrs Anne Smart, Mrs Deborah (née Nevitt) Swan, Ted Setchell, Eric and Madeline Snudden, Mark Snudden, Brian and Mary Trehearne, Ken Wreyford and Aubrey and Vidle Van Farms' staff. Recognition is also due to members of local organisations, eg Hurst Castle Sailing Club, Keyhaven Yacht Club, Milford-on-Sea & Keyhaven Sea Scouts and many individuals who, during their water-based activities, minimised disturbance to the saltmarsh breeding birds.

My thanks are due also to Lower Woodside, Waterford and Lymington residents with whom, when business or inclination took them onto the marshes, I also came into contact during long hours spent around the seawalls and shores: the Harvey brothers, Mrs Barbara Hill, Caroline Hill, David and Lisa Hill, Royal Navy Captain Mike Everett and Mrs Bronwyn Everett, Phil and Flo Wiseman (no relation), Frank and Mrs Webster, Mrs Jo Figgures, Geoff and Marylyn Holmes, Vernon Sainsbury, John and June Blake, John and Mandy Coles, Miss Williamson, Les Lane and Les Woodford, both of the former Hampshire River Authority, Norman Rickman, Mike Mapes, Mark Whitfield, sea-anglers Colin Hillman and Chris Clark, as well as Mrs Phillips and Mr and Mrs Van de Vorm, of Sowley.

Others who were also particularly helpful included John Clark of Hampshire Ornithological Society, who forwarded me Lymington–Keyhaven data from the Society's files and copies of Hampshire Bird Reports missing from my personal library and Barbara Wakeford of Lymington & District Naturalists' Society, who similarly made available immediate post-Second World War material from its archive. Input from Peter Hobby and Geoff Henman greatly improved an initial draft and Owen Haisell, Peter Hobby, Marc Moody and Bev Snellgrove addressed my many queries on the ornithology and other matters of the district. I am indebted to Clive Chatters who drew my attention to 1940s high-level west Solent conservation initiatives and provided the habitats section and a summary of the history of site designations, to my wife for contributing the account of the Lymington salt-industry and to Pete Combridge who assisted with the systematic species accounts and whose pertinent council on other matters was always available.

Thrift

On behalf of us all, I also recognise the efforts of Parish, New Forest District, Hampshire County Council members and officers and others, who worked tirelessly behind the scenes to protect the Lymington–Keyhaven marshes and their wildlife, particularly Mrs Flo Wiseman, Mrs Valerie Shepherd, Mrs Jean Vernon-Jackson, Alan Rice, Keith Metcalf, David Culver-Williams, David Pumfrett and Professor Gerald Smart, to name but some.

Sadly, many of those mentioned are no longer with us.

I thank Dennis Bill (our grandfathers were brothers) for information relating to our Ringwood (Hampshire) and Tollard Royal (Wiltshire) antecedents. Similarly afflicted with the ornithological bug, he is a Portsmouth Harbour watcher, a local historian and his research into our family trees is an ongoing project. I must also acknowledge the enormous debt I owe my dear family, particularly my mother, Eleanor Jane (née Smith) Wiseman, my grandfather James Walter (Jim) Smith, my grandmother Eleanor Jane (née Macey) Smith, my uncle Walter (Wally) Smith who, following his return from active Second World War service, lived with us until his marriage to Gwendoline Millen of North End (Portsmouth) and my two-in-a-million in-laws, George William (Ken) Lawson of Leeds and Violet (Vi) Edith Elizabeth (née Coleman) Lawson of Lane End, Buckinghamshire. All at some time must have despaired of my, seemingly, lack of interest in anything other than ornithology and my aversion to the mere thought of a 'good and proper' job. Finally, my wife Wendy has been a constant companion and a source of encouragement and assistance throughout more than forty years of my bird-watching life. At the same time she cared for our family, held down part and full-time employment and sought opportunity to pursue her passion for archaeology. I thank her particularly for her forbearance during preparation of this book. Not only did I neglect the many household and garden tasks to which I should have attended, but I commandeered our small bungalow's kitchen table and a couple of chairs, which for more than two years, were covered with books and other reference material.

References

Adams, M C 1966. Firecrests breeding in Hampshire. *British Birds* 59:240–246.

Anderson, K, Clarke, S & Lucken, R 2013. Nesting behaviour of the first breeding Great White Egrets in Britain. *British Birds* 106:258–263.

Asem, A 2008. Historical record on brine shrimp *Artemia* more than one thousand years ago from Urmia Lake, Iran. *Journal of Biological Research Thessaloniki* 9:113–114.

Austin, G, Collier, M, Calbrade, N A, Hall, C & Musgrove, A 2008. *Waterbirds in the UK 2006/07.* BTO/WWT/RSPB/JNCC, Thetford.

Austin, G E, Read, W J, Calbrade, N A, Mellan, H J, Musgrove, A J, Skellorn, W, Hearn, R D, Stroud, D A, Wotton, S R & Holt, C A 2014. *Waterbirds in the UK 2011/12: The Wetland Bird Survey.* BTO/RSPB and JNCC, in association with WWT. British Trust for Ornithology, Thetford.

Balmer, D E, Gillings, S, Caffrey, B J, Swann, R L, Downie, I S & Fuller, R J 2013. *Bird Atlas 2007–2011: The Breeding and Wintering Birds of Britain & Ireland.* BTO Books, Thetford.

Bamber, R N & Robbins, R S 2010 *Condition Monitoring of the Lymington to Keyhaven Coastal Saline Lagoons.* ARTOO Marine Biology Consultanats, Southampton.

Billett, D F 1965. Birds of Prey numbers in the Langstone Harbour, Farlington Marshes and Portsmouth area (P.G. observation area) 1953–1962. *Hampshire Bird Report 1965.*

Borrer, W 1891. *The Birds of Sussex.* Porter, London.

Boyd, H 1954. The "wreck" of Leach's Petrels in the autumn of 1952. *British Birds* 47:137–163.

Bright, D 2006. Norman William Orr 1918–2006. *Hampshire Bird Report 2006:6–7.*

British Ornithologists' Union 2013. The British List: A Checklist of Birds of Britain (8th edition) *Ibis* 155:635–676.

British Trust for Ornithology 2016 (online) www.birdfacts@bto.org

Burn, D M, & Mather, J R 1974. The White-billed Diver in Britain. *British Birds* 67:258–296.

Campbell, B 1979. *Birdwatcher at Large.* Dent, London.

Calbrade, N A, Holt, C A, Austin, G E, Mellan, H J, Hearn, R D, Stroud, D A, Wotton, S R & Musgrove, A J 2010. *Waterbirds in the UK 2008/09: The Wetland Bird Survey.* BTO/RSPB/JNCC in association with WWT, Thetford.

Carr, P 2003. The change in status and distribution of Little Egret in Hampshire 1993–2003. *Hampshire Bird Report 2003:200–204.*

Cerely, S 1955. *The Gyr Falcon Adventure.* Collins, London.

Chandler, R J 1981. Influxes into Britain and Ireland of Red-necked Grebes and other waterbirds during winter 1978/79. *British Birds* 74:55–81.

Clark, J M 1980. *Hampshire Bird Report 1980:56.*

Clark, J M & Eyre, J A (eds) 1993. *Birds of Hampshire.* Hampshire Ornithological Society.

Cohen, E 1955. Osprey in Hampshire in December. *British Birds* 48:454.

Cohen, E 1963. *Birds of Hampshire and the Isle of Wight.* Oliver & Boyd, Edinburgh & London.

Cohen, E & Taverner, J H 1972. *A Revised List of Hampshire and Isle of Wight Birds.* Oxford Illustrated Press, Oxford.

Combridge, P & Parr, C 1992. Influx of Little Egrets in Britain and Ireland in 1989. *British Birds* 85:16–21.

Combridge, P & Wiseman, E J 2009. The curious case of the disappearing storm-petrel. *British Birds* 102:213–214.

Cramp, S (ed) 1977. *The Handbook of the Birds of Europe, The Middle East and North Africa. The Birds of the Western Palearctic. Vol 1.* Oxford University Press, Oxford.

Cramp, S (ed) 1983. *The Handbook of the Birds of Europe, The Middle East and North Africa. The Birds of the Western Palearctic. Vol 11.* Oxford University Press, Oxford.

Cramp, S, Bourne, W R P & Saunders, D 1974. *The Seabirds of Britain and Ireland.* Collins, London

Curtis, W 1896. *A Short History and Description of the Town of Alton.* Warren & Son, Winchester.

Davies, E G 1941. Glaucous Gulls in Hampshire. *British Birds* 35:39.

Delacour, J & Scott, P 1954–64. *The Waterfowl of the World,* 4 volumes. Country Life, London.

Drummond, Maldwin 1975. *Conflicts in an Estuary.* Ilex Press.

Duffin, B S 1991. *The Birds of Titchfield Haven.* Pekkari Books, Hill Head.

Fisher, J 1951 (revised edition). *Watching Birds.* Penguin Books, Aylesbury and London.

Garr, J J 1994. White-billed Diver at Lymington. *Hampshire Bird Report 1993*:111–112.

Garrow, D W 1825. *The History of Lymington and its immediate vicinity in the County of Southampton.* C Baynes, London.

Gillham, E H & Homes, R C 1950. *The Birds of the North Kent Marshes.* Collins, London.

Gouletquer, P L 1974. The Development of Salt-making in Prehistoric Europe. *Essex Journal* 9:2–19.

Green, G 2004. *The Birds of Dorset.* Helm, London.

Harris, Dr V D 1914. Colonel Peter Hawker and his connection with Keyhaven. *Milford-on-Sea Record Soc.* 2:(1). May. Edwin W Hayter, Milford-on-Sea.

Harrop, A H J 2002. The Ruddy Shelduck in Britain. *British Birds* 95:123–128.

Holling, M & the rare Breeding Birds Panel 2014. Rare Breeding Birds in the United Kingdom in 2012. *British Birds* 107:504–560.

Hollom, P A D 1940. Report on the 1938 survey of Black-headed Gull colonies. *British Birds* 33:202–221, 230–244.

Holloway, S 1996. *The Historical Atlas of Breeding Birds in Britain and Ireland.* Poyser, London.

Holt, C A, Austin, G E, Calbrade, N A, Mellan, H J, Hearn, R D, Stroud, D A, Wotton, S R & Musgrove, A J 2009. *Waterbirds in the UK 2007/08: The Wetland Bird Survey.* BTO/RSPB/JNCC, Thetford.

Holt, C A, Austin, G E, Calbrade, N A, Mellan, H J, Mitchell, C, Stroud, D A, Wotton, S R & Musgrove, A J 2011. *Waterbirds in the UK 2009/10: The Wetland Bird Survey.* BTO/RSPB/JNCC, Thetford.

Holt, C A, Austin, G E, Calbrade, N A, Mellan, H J, Hearn, R D, Stroud, D A, Wotton, S R & Musgrove, A J 2012. *Waterbirds in the UK 2010/11: The Wetland Bird Survey.* BTO/RSPB/JNCC, Thetford.

Houseman, A E 1956. A Shropshire Lad XL. *Collected Poems.* Penguin Books, Middlesex.

Hume, R A, & Christie, D A 1989. Sabine's Gulls and other seabirds after the 1987 storm. *British Birds* 82:191–208.

Hurst Castle Sailing Club. Hurst Castle Sailing Club (online). June 2015. www.hcsc.org.uk

Hutchinson, C D & Neath, B 1978. Little Gulls in Britain and Ireland. *British Birds* 71:563–581.

James, J 1986. *Hurst Castle An Illustrated History.* St. Barbe Museum & Art Gallery, Lymington.

JNCC 2012. *Seabird Population Trends and Causes of change: 2012 Report.*

John, A W G & Roskell, J 1985. Jay movements in autumn 1983. *British Birds* 78:611–637.

Jones, C P 1930. *History of Lymington.* King, Lymington.

Kear, J 1990. *Man and Wildfowl.* Poyser, London.

Kelsall, J E & Coles, R E 1913. The Birds of Milford. *Milford-on-Sea Record Soc.* 1 (6): August. Edwin W Hayter, Milford-on-Sea.

Kelsall, J E & Munn, P W 1905. *The Birds of Hampshire and the Isle of Wight.* Witherby, London.

Kipling, Rudyard 1914–18. A Song in Storm.

Lack, P 1986. *The Atlas of Wintering Birds in Britain and Ireland.* Poyser, Calton.

Lloyd, C, Tasker, M L & Partridge, K 1991. *The Status of Seabirds in Britain and Ireland.* Poyser, London.

Love, J A 1983. *The Return of the Sea-Eagle.* Cambridge University Press, Cambridge.

Luckham, B 1947. *Proc. Hants Field Club,* 17:291.

Lyell, Sir C 1835. *Principals of Geology Vol 2.* London.

Mackintosh, I B 1984. *Breaching of Hurst Spit: A Desk Study.* New Forest District Council.

Marchant, J H, Hudson, R, Carter, S P & Whittington, P 1990. *Population Trends in British Breeding Birds.* British Trust for Ornithology, Tring.

Marchington, J 1980. *The History of Wildfowling.* A & C Black, London.

Marr, B A E 2003. From Pagham Harbour to Denzil Harber. *British Birds* 96:132–134.

Martin, B P 1992. *The Birds of Prey of the British Isles.* David and Charles, Newton Abbott.

Moore, R F 1969. *The Birds of Devon.* David and Charles, Newton Abbot.

Moreau, R E 1923. Migration of Kestrels on Hampshire coast. *British Birds* 16:191.

Munn, P W 1912. Madeiran Fork-tailed Petrel in Hampshire. *British Birds* 5:252–253.

Musgrove, A et al 2013. Population estimates of birds in Great Britain and the United Kingdom. *British Birds* 106: 64–100.

Nicholls, R J & Webber, N B 1987. The past, present and future evolution of Hurst Castle spit, Hampshire. *Progress in Oceanography* 18:119–37.

Nicholson, E M & Ferguson-Lees I J 1962. The Hastings Rarities. *British Birds* 55:299–384.

Owen, M, Atkinson-Willes, G & Salmon, D G 1986. *Wildfowl in Great Britain* (2nd edition). Cambridge University Press, Cambridge.

Payne-Gallwey, Sir R 1893. *The Diary of Colonel Peter Hawker.* Longmans, Green and Co., London.

Prater, A J 1981. *Estuary Birds of Britain and Ireland.* T & A D Poyser, Calton.

Ratcliffe, D 1980. *The Peregrine Falcon.* Poyser, Calton.

Rogers, M J 1982. Ruddy Shelducks in Britain 1965–79. *British Birds* 75:446–455.

Rogers, M J & the Rarities Committee 1988. Report on rare birds in Great Britain in 1987. *British Birds* 81: 554–555.

Saunders, H 1899. *An Illustrated Manual of British Birds* (2nd edition). Gurney & Jackson, London.

Sawyer, K F 1982. New Light on Milford's Salterns. *Milford-on-Sea Historical Record Society Occasional Magazine* 1:(2) 9–15. August.

Schlosser, D 1756. Extract d'une letter de Monsieur le Docteur

Scott, M S & Shaw, K D 2008. The status of White-billed Diver in north-west Scotland. *British Birds* 101:241–248.

Sedgwick, N et al (eds) 1970. *The New Wildfowler in the 1970's.* Barrie & Jenkins, London.

Sharrock, J T R (ed) 1976. *The Atlas of Breeding Birds of Britain and Ireland.* Poyser, Berkhamstead.

Spencer, R & The Rare Breeding Birds Panel 1993. Rare breeding birds in the United Kingdom in 1990. *British Birds* 86: 62–90.

Taverner, J H 1959. The spread of the Eider in Great Britain. *British Birds* 52:245–258.

Taverner, J H 1962. *Wildfowl in Hampshire.* Warren, Winchester.

Taverner, J H 1963. Further notes on the spread of the Eider in Great Britain. *British Birds* 56:273–285.

Ticehurst, N F, Witherby, H W & Hawke E L 1940. Report on the effect of the severe winter of 1939/40 on bird-life in the British Isles. *British Birds* 34:118–132, 142–155.

Trehearne, M 1988. *Keyhaven: An Odd Sort of Hamlet.* Keyhaven.

Troubridge, H C 1921. Records of Spoonbills in Hampshire. *British Birds* 15:20.

Tubbs, C R 1992. The diaries of William Mudge, Wildfowler. *Bull. Wader Study Group* 65:46–54.

Tubbs, C R 1999. *The Ecology, Conservation and History of The Solent.* Packard Publishing, Chichester.

Tubbs, C R & Wiseman, E J 1992. Severe weather wader kill in The Solent, Southern England during February 1991. *Bull. Wader Study Group* 66:61–62.

Vesey-Fitzgerald, B 1946. *British Game.* Collins, London.

Vinicombe, K E & Harrop, A H J 1999. Ruddy Shelducks in Britain and Ireland 1986–1994. *British Birds* 92:225–255.

Weidmann, U 1956. Observations and experiments on egg-laying in the Black-headed Gull (*Larus ridibundus*). *British J. Anim. Behavior* 4:150–161.

Wernham, C V, Thoms, M P, Marchant, J H, Clark, J A, Siriwadena G M & Baillie, S R (eds) 2002. *The Migration Atlas: Movements of the birds of Britain and Ireland.* T & A D Poyser, London.

West, I M 1980. Geology of The Solent estuarine system. In *The Solent Estuarine System: An Assessment of Present Knowledge* (ed. M. Burton) Natural Environment Research Council Publications Series C, No 22, NERC, Swindon, 6–18.

Winstanley, D, Spencer, R & Williamson, K 1974. Where have all the Whitethroats gone? *Bird Study* 21:1–14.

Wise, J R 1895. *The New Forest: Its History and Scenery* (5th edition). Southeran, London.

Wiseman, E J et al. Squadron-Leader Norman William Orr (1918–2006). *British Birds* 100:568–569.

Wiseman, E J 2014. *A Checklist of the Birds of Keyhaven–Lymington and Milford-on-Sea.* Hampshire Ornithological Society.

Wiseman, W J 2001. *The Lymington Salt Industry, Hampshire: An Appraisal.* Unpublished dissertation for a degree of Batchelor of Arts (Archaeology and History) King Alfred's College, Winchester.

Wright, J 1849. Bitterns near Lymington. *The Zoologist* 7: 2392.

Wynn, R B 2012. An exceptional inshore movement of Great and Arctic Skuas off south-east England in spring 2012. *British Birds* 105:626–628.

Yalden, D W 2007. The older history of White-tailed Eagle in Britain. *British Birds* 100:471–480.

Sea Campion

Observers

Contributors to the Lymington-Keyhaven ornithological record during 1993–2012:

Abbott S D
Adams M C
Agombar D
Alexander G
Allen C A
Allen Col.
Allnutt D
Andrews J K
Annell G R
Applebee J
Arber K A
Armitage M C
Ash S
Attwood B
Baker B
Baker M J
Baldwin J R
Ball D
Ball K
Ball T G
Ballam I D
Barbagallo P
Barnes E
Barnes T
Barrass C
Barrett D L
Barrett GC
Barrett M
Bartlett C
Bass D
Bassett S
Bates C
Bates O H
Beckett T
Bell M O
Bennett M
Berryman A
Bertenshaw J A
Bespolka C
Betton K F
Birkett J
Birt S G
Bishop D R
Bishop M
Bissell L
Bissett M
Blackburn K
Blakeley A F
Blandford D
Bloss J
Blumsom W
Blunden A
Bonsor R
Boras W
Borwick R M
Boswell M
Boswell S R
Boult P
Bowman R P
Bown C
Boyce T

Bradley S D
Brain C
Bray A
Brett E C
Brickwood M
Broad R
Broadley D
Broadway R
Brunton S
Bryant M J
Bryant P
Budd P A
Burch C
Burr I J
Burry B
Butcher J
Butler A J
Butler T J
Butterworth A M B
Calderwood I
Campbell M R
Cannings M
Carey S
Carpenter T F
Carr P
Carrington-Cotton A
Carruthers D
Casalis de Pury R J
Casson J
Chapleo C
Chapman C
Chapman J W
Chapman R A
Chappell L
Charlton D C
Chawner J
Cheese T E
Chislett G
Christopher R
Clark A
Clark F C
Clark J M
Clark R T
Clark W J
Clarke D W J
Claxton A J
Cleave A J
Clements J
Clemons S
Clifford A
Cloyne J M
Coates B
Codlin T D
Cole L
Coles L
Coles M
Collins A R
Collins M
Collman J R
Combridge M C
Combridge P
Cook R
Cooke R E
Coomber R
Cooper A
Cooper L
Cooper M
Cooper M C

Cooper Mtn
Cooper P F
Copsey S
Cornford H
Cornford R
Coward T
Cowley T P
Cox A
Cox A F & P R
Cox A P
Cox I N
Cozens B R
Craig M
Crane S
Crawford H
Crespin D B
Cresswell M
Crisp K
Cronan S C
Crook C
Crowley P J
Crump D
Crutch M
Curtis C R
Curzon S
Cuthbert C R
Cutts M
Dalgleish J
Darvill B
Darvill G
Davenport M
Davidson A
Davis A M
Dedman J
De Vries P
Dicker D
Dicker G
Dicks D E J
Dimond S
Doherty M E
Doran T M J
Douglas E
Dow C
Downey B
Duckworth N
Duffin B S
Duffy M D
Dunn R
Durkin E
Durnell P R
Easom L
Edgeller M L
Ellery T
Elliott N & M
Etheridge L
Evans G C
Evans H W
Evans L G R
Evans M
Ewers B J
Eyre J A
Facer R D
Facer R L L
Faichnie I J J
Faithful J
Farmer E
Farmer S
Farwell G

Fawkes P F
Field, G
Fisher S L
Floyd P
Flynn P
Foad P
Foote B
Foote S
Ford R E
Ford S
Fordham W
Forster M
Frampton O
Franklin P
Freeman S J
French A
Fry D
Fuller L
Gaites S
Gambrill D
Gammage P A
Garr J J
Gibb A
Gibbons C
Gibbons M J
Giddens G S A
Gifford D
Gilham R
Gillingham J
Glue D E
Goater B
Goodridge J
Greaves A N
Green A
Green G
Green G P
Greenfield C
Greensmith A
Greensmith J D
Group K
Gutteridge A C
Guy D
Guymer P
Gwynn B
Hack P J
Hackett J
Haisell O
Hale A P S
Hallett R
Halligan M
Hardinge D
Hargrave S
Harker B
Harley R
Harley S
Harmer A
Harris A
Harris C J
Harris R A
Harthill S
Harvey S C
Hawtree J
Hay M J W
Hayward R
Heath D
Hedgecock J
Hedgecock T
Hedley B

Hewson T
Hibbert R
Hicks R K
Hill M J
Hilton J I
Hoare D J
Hobby P
Hogan P
Holland D
Hollands B J
Hollins J R
Holloway D
Holmes P J
Horacek-Davis G
Horner N
Horton R
Houghton D
Howard R
Howe A
Howell R
Hubble D S
Hughes D
Hughes D J
Hull J D
Hull N J
Hume R A
Hutchins P E
Huxley G H
Ilsley K
Ingram C
Ingram J
Ingram S
Irvine B
Irvine J
Ivon-Jones B
Ivon-Jones M A
Jackson S
Jacobs R J K
James R
James R M R
James W
Jardine A
Jardine M A
Jarvis K
Jayne F
Jennings C
Jennings F
Jepson G
Jepson P
Jeske E
Johnson A C
Jones B
Jones C
Jones J M
Jones M
Jones N R
Jones P D
Jordon T
Jump E
Keedy A
Keen S G
Keen S S
Kelson D
Kemm H
Kemp N
King A
King M
King R A

189

King S S
Kitching I
Lacey M
Lakin I
Lankester S & S
Larter M
Last A J
Laughton A W
Lavin J C
Lawman T A
Lawrence E S
Lawrence J
Layton S
LeBrocq P F
Lee R D
Leeke-Bennett L
Legge W G D
Lester A J B
Lever A
Levett R K
Lewis A
Lewis A P
Lewis M
Liley M J S
Lilley H A
Lintott B
Litjens M
Locke A
Lockton, D
Lord P
Lowings V A
Lowther J
Luke D J
Lushington R
Lyle R
Lynch D M
Maasz T
McNair D F
McVeigh A
Mann L
Mansfield S
Marchant R
Marks D
Marriott B
Marshall L
Marston P C
Martin A
Martin A P
Maskell K
Matthews N
Matthews P
May G
Maycock K W
Mayhead C
Mead B
Mead D
Metcalf K
Middlecote B
Middleton J
Miles S
Miller D G
Miller L
Milligan R F
Montegriffo N
Moody M P
Moon J & J
Moore A P
Moore S

Morgan J
Morris E
Morris N G
Morris S
Morrison D M
Morrison P
Morrison S
Mortimore J
Mortimore K
Moseley J C
Mould-Ryan R B
Mountford A
Munday C
Munday D
Mung B
Munts D
Nash P & P
Naylor (Dr) E G
Neal S
Nelson R
New K
Newell M A
Newman M A H
Nicholson D
Nicholson J B
Nieuwkerk A
Nobbs J
Norris P R
Norton J A
Nurse M W
Oakes S
Offer D
Olden A
Olliff-Cooper J
Oram M A
Orr N W
Osborne G
Owen A
Painter M G
Painton J L
Palmer K W
Palmer M J
Papsa N
Parfitt A
Parminter T J
Parr C
Pascal R W
Payne I D
Payne PC
Peace N D
Pearce D F
Pearce K
Pearce R K
Pearson D J
Peck R
Peters S P
Philpott D J
Piggott S P
Pinchen B J
Pink B J
Pink M A
Piper D
Pitman J A C
Pitt M J
Pleasance J
Poland J
Polley A J
Powell A

Pratt E M
Preston R
Pritchard D M
Prophet I
Proyer J
Pullen A
Purkiss A E
Raby P N
Radden D
Rafter M
Ralphs I L
Ransom D
Raymond C J
Raynor A P
Raynor E M
Raynor P
Reedman R
Reeve J
Reeves D
Reeves J
Renyard B W
Reynolds A
Rhodes A
Rhodes A S
Rich G
Rickwood B
Rix J B
Roberts B
Roberts B J
Roberts H
Roberts J
Robinson P
Robinson R
Robinson S
Rolfe M D
Rooke A
Rose C
Rosenvinge H P
Ross J G
Ross R
Rothwell R G
Rowbottom M D
Rowe J
Russell R W
Rutter P M
Rylands K
Ryves D
Saunders J
Saunders R
Savage C
Sawyer R
Sayer K
Scaife D
Schmedlin R
Schubert J
Scorey P S
Scott M A
Scott R E
Scott R W
Sharkey B
Sharp G
Shepley P R
Shillitoe J R D
Ship R
Shrubsole R
Sibsey I
Simcox W F
Simmonds M

Sluman N
Small R G
Smallwood J
Smart A
Smart A D G
Smart G & G
Smith A
Smith B E
Smith M
Smith N
Smith P
Smith P J S
Smith P M
Smith T C
Snook A M
Snudden E
Snudden M
Souter R
Sporke H
Sporne K
Sporne L
Sporne S H
Spring-Smyth J
Stalker B
Stancliffe D
Stancliffe P
Stephenson G C
Stephenson N
Stevens T
Stevenson D
Stiff M G
Stockwell J
Stone S
Strangeman P J
Summerhayes J L V
Sutton P
Swann M
Talbot K L
Taylor C
Taylor D H
Taylor S
Teesdale R
Terry M G W
Terry M H
Thelwell D A
Theobald H
Theobald P
Theobald R
Thirwell I
Thomas C
Thornton D
Thorpe C J
Tindale A D
Toft R
Tompsett A J
Toye P
Toynton P
Treacher D
Tremain A
Trew M E
Truckle W H
Trundle R
Tubb K I
Tubbs C R
Tubbs J M
Tucker I
Twigg R
Twyman A P

Tyler J
Unsworth D
Uphill N
Upton P
Urry N
van Beusekom R
Venables H
Vickerman J
Vokes M
Waddington J I
Walford M
Walker S
Walker T H
Wall M J
Wallace D
Wallace R J
Walmsley A P
Walmsley W
Ward M & Z
Wardley M
Warren M
Waterman J R
Waters W E
Watson I R
Watson R F
Watts I R
Watts R
Wearing M F
Weaver R
Webb R M
Webley J J
Welch A J
Wells J N
Wells T J
Wheatcroft A
Whitbread J
Whitbread M
White D & D
Wiggins M
Wildish M
Wilkinson D
Williams C T
Williams J
Williamson D A G
Williamson I
Wills K B
Wilson C
Wilson D C
Wilton I J
Wines J
Winter P A
Winter P D
Wiseman E J
Wiseman W J
Witherick M E
Wood S
Woodley B
Woods A E L
Woodward G
Wooldridge D B
Wooley S K
Wright A
Wynn R B
Yorke-Norris A
Young K

190

Index

Birds species with main
entries in systematic list.

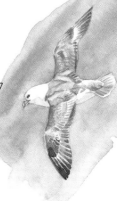

Fulmar

Barn Owl